Date Due

MECHANICS OF AUTOMOBILES

MECHANICS OF AUTOMOBILES

H. E. BARNACLE
B.Sc.(Eng.) London, A.M.I.Mech.E.

PERGAMON PRESS
OXFORD · LONDON · EDINBURGH · NEW YORK
PARIS · FRANKFURT
1964

PERGAMON PRESS LTD.
Headington Hill Hall, Oxford
4 & 5 Fitzroy Square, London W.1

PERGAMON PRESS (SCOTLAND) LTD.
2 & 3 Teviot Place, Edinburgh 1

PERGAMON PRESS INC.
122 East 55th Street, New York 22, N.Y.

GAUTHIER-VILLARS ED.
55 Quai des Grands-Augustins, Paris 6

PERGAMON PRESS G.m.b.H.
Kaiserstrasse 75, Frankfurt am Main

Distributed in the Western Hemisphere by
THE MACMILLAN COMPANY · NEW YORK
pursuant to a special arrangement with
Pergamon Press Limited

Library of Congress Card No. 63–18930

Set in 10 on 12 pt. Times and printed in Great Britain by
PITMAN PRESS, BATH

CONTENTS

PREFACE

THIS book deals with the application of the basic theory of mechanics to certain problems arising from the motion of an automobile.

Whilst many books have been written on the construction, functioning, maintenance etc., of vehicles and some topics in this book appear in books on Theory or Mechanics of Machines, few have been published dealing specifically with dynamics applied to automobiles. Development of research in vehicle ride and stability points to the need of such a book for engineering students, and particularly those attending Technical Colleges. It is hoped that the present book will help to satisfy this need.

The material and method of presentation, which is based on teaching the subject to full time National Diploma Courses at Higher and Advanced level, should be of direct value to students preparing for the examination of the Institution of Mechanical Engineers and those at Technical Colleges studying Automobile Engineering, in H.N.D. or Dip. Tech. Courses. It has been the custom for examination papers in Theory or Mechanics of Machines for B.Sc. London External Engineering Degrees to include questions on vehicle dynamics and vibrations, and students preparing for parts I, II and III should find the appropriate chapters adequate for these examinations. The book should also be of value to many junior research engineers, designers and draughtsmen employed in the automobile industry.

Throughout, many worked examples are included as experience shows that students derive most benefit from these. The examples form an integral and necessary part of the book and they have been carefully selected and graded. Almost all are taken from Examinations of the University of London and the Institution of Mechanical Engineers, and the author wishes to thank these bodies for permission to use the examples. Neither body is, however, committed to approve the solutions given in this book.

In order to keep the book to a reasonable size consistent with coverage of topics, some problems have had to be excluded. A detailed study of vehicle stability is one of these. However, the basic material for such a study is contained in Chapters 9 and 11. Knowledge of vehicle stability is increasing at a fast rate and treatment of it is, in the author's opinion, more suited to research papers than to a text book at the present time.

H. E. BARNACLE

CHAPTER ONE

VEHICLE PERFORMANCE

Linear Inertia

ONE of the essential preliminaries to automobile design is prediction of performance. Essentially, power from the engine is made available at the wheels and a tractive effort is exerted on the vehicle due to the interaction between the tyres and the road surface. Certain "losses" occur within the vehicle and there are resistances to the motion of the vehicle. Thus knowledge of these resistances is important if a reasonable estimate of the effective tractive effort is to be made. In addition, knowledge of the forces acting between the tyres and the road is required since, no matter how large the engine output may be, the tyre forces limit the eventual performance.

1.1. Acceleration and Inertia

The tractive effort (P) between tyres and road give rise to the vehicle acceleration (f) and in the absence of any resistances to motion, the full tractive effort would be available to accelerate the vehicle. The acceleration is then given by,

$$P = \frac{W}{g} . f \tag{1.1}$$

where, W/g is the vehicle mass in slugs.

If the vehicle is accelerated by the forces from the road, the vehicle itself, due to its inertia, will react with equal and opposite forces on the road. A state of "dynamic" equilibrium is assumed to exist when the resultant of the external forces on the vehicle is equal and opposite to the inertia force.

WORKED EXAMPLE

1.1. A motor car weighs 3000 lb and the engine develops 50 b.h.p. at 4000 r.p.m. The transmission efficiency is 85% when the gear ratio of engine to road wheels is 5·4 to 1. The effective diameter of the road wheels is 26 in. Ignoring resistances to motion, determine the acceleration of the car on a level road when the engine speed is 4000 r.p.m.

Solution

$$\text{Power at wheels (transmission efficiency } 100\%) = 50$$

$$\text{Power at wheels (transmission efficiency } 85\%) = 50 \times 0{\cdot}85 = 42{\cdot}5 \text{ h.p.}$$

$$\text{Speed of wheels} = \frac{4000}{5{\cdot}4} \text{ r.p.m.}$$

$$\text{hence total torque at wheels} = \frac{42{\cdot}5 \times 33{,}000}{2\pi \times 4000/5{\cdot}4} = 301 \text{ lb ft.}$$

$$\text{Total tractive effort on car} = \frac{\text{torque}}{\text{wheel rad.}} = \frac{301}{13/12} = 277 \text{ lb.}$$

$$\text{Inertia force of car} = \frac{W}{g} \cdot f = \frac{3000}{32{\cdot}2} \cdot f \text{ lb} = \text{total external force.}$$

$$= 277 \text{ lb.}$$

$$\text{Hence, } f = \frac{277 \times 32{\cdot}2}{3000} = 2{\cdot}97 \text{ ft/sec}^2.$$

1.2. Resistances to Motion

Resistances to motion, ignoring transmission losses between the power unit and the wheels, are usually considered to be (*a*) air resistance; (*b*) rolling resistance; (*c*) gradient effect.

(a) AIR RESISTANCE (R_a)

The air offers a resistance to the movement of a vehicle and can have an influence on the performance, ride and stability of the vehicle. So far as performance is concerned, the air force is found to depend upon several factors including the shape, size and surface of the frontal part of the vehicle, and its speed relative to the air. The air resistance is given in the form

$$R_a = C_D \,.\, A \,.\, v^n \tag{1.2}$$

where C_D is a drag coefficient, A the projected frontal area, v the relative velocity through the air, and n some index. n is normally taken as 2, C_D can vary over a wide range, but for a given vehicle the air resistance can be expressed in the form,

$$R_a = k \,.\, v^2 \tag{1.3}$$

acting in a direction opposing the car relative velocity.

(b) ROLLING RESISTANCE (R_r)

This arises from the interaction of the tyres and the road surface and in the case of cars operating on hard surfaces, the interaction manifests itself primarily in the deformation of the tyres. The deformation and recovery of shape is not completely elastic and as a result energy is released. In addition, the relative drag between the tyre and the road causes wear of the tyre tread. The energy dissipated as heat etc. from these causes, together with other losses such as bearing friction, can be represented as the work done against a resistance to rolling.

The value of the rolling resistance depends upon several factors such as, vehicle speed, tyre inflation pressure, vertical load on the tyre, tyre diameter, road surface, and there are many others particularly concerned with the tyre construction. Prediction of rolling resistance is still uncertain, particularly in view of the experimental difficulties in its measurement, but there seems to be general acceptance that

$$R_r = W(a + b \,.\, v^n) \tag{1.4}$$

The index, n, is assigned values between 1 and 3 but $n = 1$ is common, and the values of a and b, can vary considerably, having, if v is in m.p.h., mean values of $a = 0{\cdot}015$, $b = 0{\cdot}0001$.

(c) GRADIENT (R_g)

If a vehicle moving along a level road at constant speed, under the action of a fixed engine output, starts to climb a gradient,

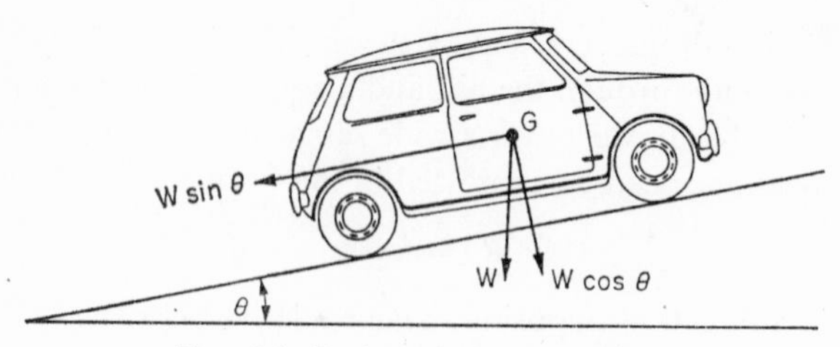

FIG. 1.1. Resistance due to gradient

energy is required to provide for the change in potential energy. The effect is the same as though the vehicle were acted on by a resistance to its motion. The value of the resistance is given by

$$R_g = W \,.\, \sin \theta \tag{1.5}$$

as shown in Fig. 1.1.

Provided θ is small, as in most practical gradients, then if the gradient is specified as 1 in x, then

$$R_g = \frac{W}{x} \text{ (approximately).} \tag{1.6}$$

WORKED EXAMPLE (A.M.I.Mech.E., 1950)

1.2. For a typical motor car the rolling resistance is given by the expression $35 + 0{\cdot}25V$ and the air resistance by the expression $0{\cdot}048V^2$, the resistance being in lb and V, the speed in m.p.h. in each case. If the transmission efficiency is 88%, calculate the b.h.p. required for a top speed of 90 m.p.h. Assuming that the engine torque at 30 m.p.h. in top gear is 25% more than at 90 m.p.h. and that the vehicle inertia corresponds to a weight of 4500 lb, calculate the acceleration in ft/sec² at 30 m.p.h.

Solution

For a speed of 90 m.p.h., the total resistance

$$= 35 + 0{\cdot}25 \times 90 + 0{\cdot}048 \times 90^2 \text{ lb} = 35 + 22{\cdot}5 + 389 \text{ lb}$$
$$= 446{\cdot}5 \text{ lb.}$$

Rate of working against this resistance = resistance × velocity

$$= 446{\cdot}5 \times 90 \times \frac{44}{30} \text{ ft lb/sec.}$$

Therefore horsepower

$$= 446{\cdot}5 \times \frac{90 \times 44}{30 \times 550} = 107 \text{ h.p.}$$

Hence engine b.h.p. $= 107 \times \dfrac{1}{0{\cdot}88} = 122$ h.p.

Tractive effort at 30 m.p.h. $= 446{\cdot}5 \times 1{\cdot}25 = 557$ lb.

Resistance at 30 m.p.h. $= 35 + 0{\cdot}25 \times 30 + 0{\cdot}048 \times 900$
$$= 85{\cdot}7 \text{ lb.}$$

Resultant force (available for acceleration)

$$= 557 - 85{\cdot}7$$
$$= 471{\cdot}3 \text{ lb}$$

$$471{\cdot}3 = \frac{4500}{32{\cdot}3} \cdot f$$

$$f = 3{\cdot}38 \text{ ft/sec}^2$$

WORKED EXAMPLE (U.L.1 Ext. 1954)

1.3. A car weighing 3000 lb has when running on the level a resistance to motion of $a + bV^2$ lb, where a is 60 lb, b is a constant and V the speed in m.p.h. It is also found that the car maintains a speed of 80 m.p.h. with an effective horsepower of 50 when running on the level. Find

(i) the value of b,

(ii) how far the car will run up a slope of 1 in 10 before the speed drops to 40 m.p.h. assuming it starts at 80 m.p.h. and that a constant torque is maintained.

Solution

(i) Resistance at V m.p.h. $= 60 + bV^2$ lb.

Horsepower on level road = rate of work in ft-lb/sec/550

$$= \underset{\text{lb}}{(60 + b\,.\,80^2)}\ \underset{\text{ft/sec}}{V\left(\frac{44}{30}\right)}\frac{1}{550} = 50.$$

$$60 + 6400b = 234,$$

$$b = \frac{174}{6400} = 0{\cdot}0272$$

(ii) When the car ascends the slope, its speed drops and so the motion will not be at constant retardation as the resistances will vary.

Resistance to motion $= (60 + 0{\cdot}0272\,V^2)$ if V is in m.p.h.

$$= \left(60 + 0{\cdot}0272 \times \left(\frac{30}{44}\right)^2 v^2\right)$$

lb if v in ft/sec

$$= 60 + 0{\cdot}01265v^2 \text{ lb.}$$

The car is slowing down hence the inertia force helps the tractive effort,

$$234 + \frac{3000}{32{\cdot}2}f = 60 + 0{\cdot}01265v^2 + \frac{3000}{10}.$$

Acceleration f can be expressed as $f = \frac{dv}{dt}$ or $f = v \, . \frac{dv}{ds}$ and either used. Here $f = v \, . \frac{dv}{ds}$ is used since the distance covered is required.

$$93{\cdot}3 \, v \, . \frac{dv}{ds} = 126 + 0{\cdot}01265 v^2,$$

giving

$$ds = \frac{7370 v \, . \, dv}{9960 + v^2}$$

which is a standard differential equation having the variables separable. The solution is

$$s = \frac{7370}{2} \Big[\log_e (9960 + v^2) \Big]_{58{\cdot}6}^{117{\cdot}3}$$

where the limits are the two speeds in ft/sec. Evaluation using limits gives

$$s = 3685 \log_e \left[\frac{23730}{13408} \right] = 3685 \log_e 1{\cdot}768 \text{ ft}$$

$$= 3685 \times 0{\cdot}57 = 2100 \text{ ft.}$$

Examples

1.4. A motor car, all up weight 2900 lb, is fitted with an engine developing 38 b.h.p. at 2000 r.p.m. The top gear ratio is 4·8 to 1 with an effective wheel diameter of 26 in. and a transmission efficiency of 88% at 2000 r.p.m. The rolling resistance is 30 lb/ton weight and the resistance due to windage is equal to $0{\cdot}05 V^2$ lb where V is the forward speed in m.p.h. The inertia of the car including that of engine, transmission and road wheels may be assumed as equal to that of a weight of 4000 lb. From this data calculate:

(*a*) The forward speed of the car at 2000 r.p.m.
(*b*) The horsepower available for hill climbing at this speed.
(*c*) The maximum acceleration possible at this speed.

(A.M.I.Mech.E., 1948)

Answers. (*a*) 32·2 m.p.h.; (*b*) 25·7 b.h.p.; (*c*) 2·41 ft/sec².

1.5. A motor car, of total weight 2500 lb, has wheels with an effective tyre diameter of 28 in. and attains a maximum speed, on level ground, of 75 m.p.h. at an engine speed of 3600 r.p.m. The rolling resistance is 42 lb/ton, and the air resistance is $0{\cdot}05V^2$ lb where V is the speed in m.p.h. Calculate the top-gear ratio and assuming a transmission efficiency of 90%, the b.h.p. developed by the engine. If the engine develops a maximum torque of 130 lb ft at 1800 r.p.m., find the maximum gradient that the vehicle should climb, at this engine speed, in top gear. (A.M.I.Mech.E., 1959)

Answers: 4·0; 74 b.h.p.; $\theta = 6° 36'$.

1.6. A motor car weighs 2800 lb and has an engine developing 52 b.h.p. at 4200 r.p.m. The transmission efficiency is 92% in the top gear of 4·7 to 1 and 85% in the second gear of 7·7 to 1. The performance characteristics are such that it will just reach 70 m.p.h. at 4200 r.p.m. at full throttle when running on the level in still air and at the same engine speed in second gear it will just climb a gradient of 1 in 12. The total resistance to motion in lb is given by a formula of the form $R = A + BV^2$. Calculate the values of A and B when R is in lb and V in m.p.h., and hence deduce the engine power required for top gear cruising on the level at 30 m.p.h. (A.M.I.Mech.E., 1949)

Answers: $A = 93{\cdot}7$; $B = 0{\cdot}331$; 10·7 horsepower.

1.7. For a typical motor car the rolling resistance is given by the expression $40 + 0{\cdot}22V$, and the air resistance by $0{\cdot}06V^2$, the resistance being in lb and V the speed in m.p.h. in each case. Assuming that the power output at engine speed corresponding to 30 m.p.h. is 34 b.h.p. with a transmission efficiency of 84%, and that the inertia of the vehicle corresponds to a weight of 2800 lb, calculate the maximum possible acceleration in ft/sec when running on the level under these conditions. (A.M.I.Mech.E., 1955)

Answer: 2·95 ft/sec^2.

1.8. A motor vehicle, weight 2800 lb, with the engine at full throttle can travel at a speed of 100 m.p.h. on a level road with the engine developing 100 b.h.p. The resistance to windage and road drag varies as the square of the road speed. Determine the time taken for the speed of the vehicle to rise from 45 m.p.h. to 75 m.p.h. at full throttle on an upgrade of 1 in 20, assuming that the engine torque remains constant. (U.L.2 Ext., 1952)

Answer: 50 sec.

CHAPTER TWO

VEHICLE PERFORMANCE

Linear and Angular Inertia

IN THE preceding chapter the performance of an automobile acted on by various resistances was considered without regard to any rotational motion. Obviously, there are parts, such as engine, transmission and wheels, that rotate whilst the vehicle has linear motion and consequently power will be required to accelerate these parts. In this chapter, the performance of an automobile will be considered allowing for the inertia of the main rotating parts.

2.1. Torque to Angularly Accelerate a Body

A simple relationship exists between the torque applied to a body and its resulting angular acceleration. This relationship is

$$T = I \, . \, \alpha \tag{2.1}$$

where T is the applied torque, α the angular acceleration and I the moment of inertia of the body about the axis of rotation.

2.2. Moment of Inertia

When a body is, or tends to be, angularly accelerated, its inertia is such as to oppose this acceleration, i.e., there is a moment of inertia. Clearly all particles of a body will not have the same inertia effect about the axis of rotation since their linear accelerations and distances from the axis of rotation will be different. The total moment of inertia is defined by the equation

$$I = \Sigma m \, . \, x^2 \tag{2.2}$$

where m is the mass of a particle of the body and x the distance from the axis of rotation. If the total mass of the body is imagined to be placed at a constant distance k from the axis, then

$$I = \Sigma m \, . \, k^2 = M \, . \, k^2 = \frac{W \, . \, k^2}{g} \tag{2.3}$$

where M or W/g is the total mass of the body, W its weight and k its radius of gyration about the axis of rotation.

The units for equation 2.1 and 2.3 are

Torque	= Moment of Inertia	×	Angular Acceleration
(force × distance)	(mass × distance²)	×	Angular Acceleration
lb ft	slugs . ft²	×	rad/sec²
	(W/g × ft²)		

2.3. Inertia of a Simple Gear Train

The main rotational inertias that have to be considered are generally those of an engine and parts rotating at engine speed and,

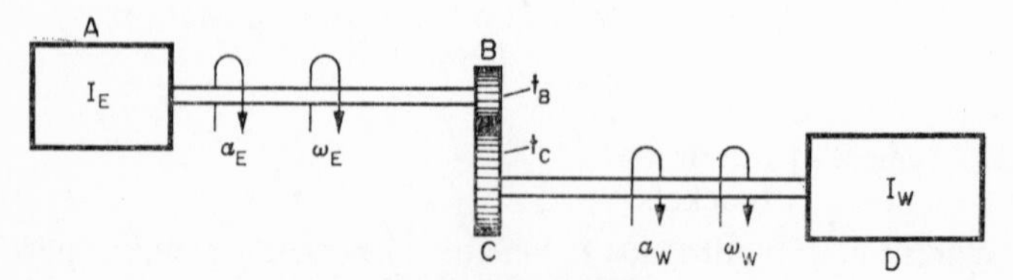

FIG. 2.1. Simplified automobile system

through a gear system, the wheels and parts rotating at wheel speed. A simplified system such as this is shown in Fig. 2.1.

The moments of inertia of parts rotating at engine speed are I_E and those at wheel speed are I_W. The gear ratio, engine speed to wheel speed, is the ratio of the numbers of teeth, t_C/t_B, on the gears at B and $C = G = \alpha_E/\alpha_W$, the ratio of the angular accelerations of engine and wheels.

Torque on AB to accelerate engine $T_E = I_E \, . \, \alpha_E$.

Angular acceleration of wheels $= \alpha_W = \alpha_E \, . \, t_B/t_C = \alpha_E/G$.

Torque on CD to accelerate wheels

$$= T_W = I_W \, . \, \alpha_W = I_W \, . \, \alpha_E/G.$$

Assuming a transmission efficiency of 100%, the torque on AB to accelerate the wheels $= I_W \, . \, \alpha_E/G \, . \, t_B/t_C = I_W \, . \, \alpha_E/G^2$.

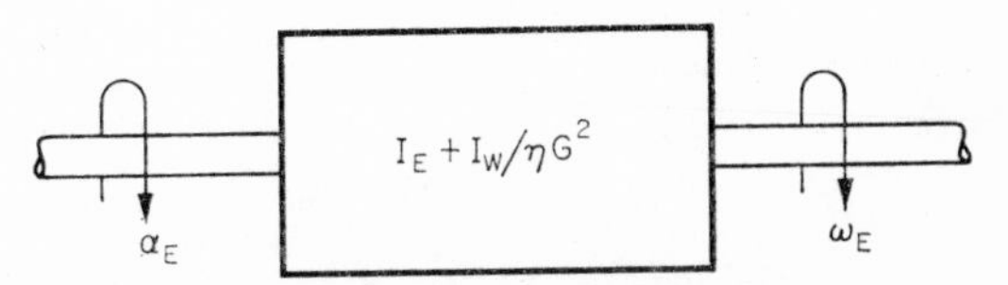

FIG. 2.2. Equivalent automobile system

If the transmission efficiency is η (fraction) then torque on AB is

$$I_W \, . \, \alpha_E/\eta \, . \, G^2.$$

Total torque on AB to accelerate engine and wheels is thus

$$= I_E \, . \, \alpha_E + \frac{I_W \, . \, \alpha_E}{\eta \, . \, G^2}$$

$$= \alpha_E \left[I_E + \frac{I_W}{\eta \, . \, G^2} \right]. \tag{2.4}$$

The quantity in brackets is the equivalent inertia of the rotating system, i.e., the inertia of a system all rotating at the engine speed, as shown in Fig. 2.2.

WORKED EXAMPLE (U.L.1 Ext., 1948)

2.1. The engine of a motor car runs at 3420 r.p.m. when the road speed is 60 m.p.h. The weight of the car is 2400 lb. The inertia of the rotating parts of the engine corresponds to 24 lb. at a radius of gyration of 0·48 ft and that of the road wheels to 240 lb at 0·8 ft. The efficiency of the transmission is 0·9 and the wind resistance is 200 lb. The road wheel diameter is 2·5 ft. Estimate the horsepower developed by the engine when the car travels on a level road at 60 m.p.h. with an acceleration of 3 ft/sec².

Solution

Angular velocity of wheels at 60 m.p.h.

$$= 60 \times \frac{44}{30} \times \frac{1}{1{\cdot}25} = 70{\cdot}3 \text{ rad/sec.}$$

Angular velocity of engine

$$= \frac{3420 \times 2\pi}{60} = 358 \text{ rad/sec.}$$

Hence gear ratio

$$= \frac{358}{70{\cdot}3} = 5{\cdot}08.$$

Angular acceleration of wheels

$$= f/r = \frac{3}{1{\cdot}25} = 2{\cdot}4 \text{ rad/sec}^2.$$

Hence angular acceleration of engine

$$= 2{\cdot}4 \times 5{\cdot}08 = 12{\cdot}2 \text{ rad/sec}^2.$$

Force at wheels to give the car its linear acceleration

$$= \frac{2400}{32{\cdot}2} \times 3 = 223{\cdot}5 \text{ lb.}$$

Force for linear acceleration and air resistance

$$= 223{\cdot}5 + 200$$
$$= 423{\cdot}5 \text{ lb.}$$

Torque on wheels for this

$$= 423{\cdot}5 \times 1{\cdot}25 = 530 \text{ lb ft.}$$

Torque from engine for this

$$= \frac{530}{5{\cdot}08} \times \frac{1}{0{\cdot}9} = 115{\cdot}5 \text{ lb ft.}$$

Torque from engine for rotating parts

$$= 12{\cdot}2 \left[\frac{24 \times 0{\cdot}48^2}{32{\cdot}2} + \frac{240 \times 0{\cdot}8^2}{32{\cdot}2} \times \frac{1}{5.08^2 \times 0{\cdot}9}\right] \text{ lb ft.}$$

$$= 12{\cdot}2(0{\cdot}171 + 0{\cdot}205) \text{ lb ft.}$$
$$= 4{\cdot}58 \text{ lb ft.}$$

Total engine torque

$$= 115{\cdot}5 + 4{\cdot}58 = 120{\cdot}1 \text{ lb ft (approx).}$$

Engine power

$$= \frac{2\pi \times 3420 \times 120{\cdot}1}{33{,}000} = 78{\cdot}4 \text{ h.p.}$$

WORKED EXAMPLE (A.M.I.Mech.E. Automobile Engineering, 1959)

2.2. The engine of a motor car develops a maximum torque of 180 lb ft with a transmission efficiency of 85%. The total weight of the vehicle is 2600 lb and each road wheel weighs 80 lb with a radius of gyration of 10 in. and an effective tyre diameter of 26 in. The rotating parts of the engine and transmission have an equivalent total inertia of 24 lb ft^2 at engine speed.

Assuming that the road and air resistance is 70 lb at all speeds calculate the maximum acceleration possible when climbing a gradient of 1 in 10 with a gear ratio of 16 to 1.

Solution

Air resistance + gradient resistance

$$= 70 + \frac{2600}{10} = 330 \text{ lb.}$$

Let acceleration be f ft/sec², then the inertia force

$$= \frac{2600 \times f}{32{\cdot}2} = 80{\cdot}8f \text{ lb.}$$

Torque on wheels, for linear forces, $= (330 + 80{\cdot}9f)\,\frac{13}{12}$ lb ft

$$= 357 + 87{\cdot}5f \text{ lb ft.}$$

Torque on engine for this

$$= \frac{357 + 87{\cdot}5f}{16 \times 0{\cdot}85} = 26{\cdot}3 + 6{\cdot}44f \text{ lb ft.}$$

Angular acceleration of engine

$$= \frac{f \times 12 \times 16}{13} = 14{\cdot}75f \text{ rad/sec}^2$$

Torque on engine for the rotating parts

$$= 14{\cdot}75f\left[\frac{24}{32{\cdot}2} + \frac{4 \times 80}{32{\cdot}2} \times \left(\frac{10}{12}\right)^2 \times \frac{1}{16^2 \times 0{\cdot}85}\right] \text{ lb ft}$$

$$= 14{\cdot}75f(0{\cdot}746 + 0{\cdot}0317) \text{ lb ft}$$

$$= 11{\cdot}45f \text{ lb ft.}$$

Hence, $180 = 26{\cdot}3 + 6{\cdot}44f + 11{\cdot}45f$

$$f = \frac{153{\cdot}7}{17{\cdot}89} = 8{\cdot}6 \text{ ft/sec}^2.$$

Note: Students sitting examinations are advised not to rely on their memory of equation (2.4) to solve questions, but to solve them from first principles as in the next worked example.

WORKED EXAMPLE (U.L.2 Ext., 1950)

2.3. A motor car of total mass 2500 lb has wheels 30 in. diameter and total moment of inertia 215 lb ft². The engine shaft is geared to the back axle through a 6 to 1 worm drive and its moment of inertia is 12·3 lb ft². The engine exerts a torque of 125 lb ft. The frictional torque on the engine shaft is 23 lb ft. The total frictional torque on the front and rear axles is 15·2 lb ft. Windage and other resistances are equivalent to a force of 94 lb on the car itself. The car is on a level road. Find its acceleration.

Solution

Let the linear acceleration of car be f ft/sec².
Then angular acceleration of wheels

$$= f/r = f \times \frac{24}{30} = 0{\cdot}8f \text{ rad/sec}^2.$$

Hence angular acceleration of engine

$$= 6 \times 0{\cdot}8f \text{ rad/sec}^2 = 4{\cdot}8f \text{ rad/sec}^2.$$

Torque required to be supplied to wheels
= (inertia force + windage) radius + frictional + wheel inertia

$$= \left[\left(\frac{2500 \times f}{32{\cdot}2} + 94\right)\frac{5}{4} + 15{\cdot}2 + \frac{215}{32{\cdot}2} \times 0{\cdot}8f\right] \text{ lb ft}$$

$$= 97{\cdot}2f + 117{\cdot}5 + 15{\cdot}2 + 5{\cdot}34f \text{ lb ft}$$

$$= 102{\cdot}54f + 132{\cdot}7 \text{ lb ft}$$

Torque from engine for this

$$= \frac{102{\cdot}54f + 132{\cdot}7}{6} = 17{\cdot}1\,f + 22{\cdot}1 \text{ lb ft}.$$

Torque available from engine

$$= 125 - \text{friction} - \text{engine inertia}$$

$$= 125 - 23 - \frac{12{\cdot}3 \times 4{\cdot}8f}{32{\cdot}2} \text{ lb ft} = 102 - 1{\cdot}84f \text{ lb ft.}$$

Hence, $102 - 1{\cdot}84f = 17{\cdot}1f + 22{\cdot}1$

$$f = \frac{79{\cdot}9}{18{\cdot}94} = 4{\cdot}23 \text{ ft/sec}^2.$$

2.4. Gear Ratio for Maximum Acceleration

The magnitude of the equivalent inertia of a gear train depends upon the value of the gear ratio. The torque available for acceleration must therefore depend upon the gear ratio and it is of interest to know the gear ratio giving the maximum forward acceleration. Considering the vehicle system of Fig. 2.1, and using the symbols of paragraph 2.3.

Torque at the wheels allowing for the inertia of the rotating parts (engine speed)

$$= (T_E - I_E \,.\, \alpha_E)\eta \,.\, G.$$

Torque at the wheels allowing for the inertia of the wheels

$$= (T_E - I_E \,.\, \alpha_E) \,.\, \eta \,.\, G - I_W \,.\, \alpha_W$$

Tractive force available at wheels

$$= \frac{(T_E - I_E \,.\, \alpha_E) \,.\, \eta \,.\, G - I_W \,.\, \alpha_W}{r}.$$

Assuming constant resistance to motion of R, then

$$\frac{W \,.\, f}{g} = \frac{(T_E - I_E \,.\, \alpha_E) \,.\, \eta G - I_W \,.\, \alpha_W}{r} - R$$

or $$\frac{W \,.\, r \,.\, f}{g} = T_E \,.\, \eta \,.\, G - I_E \,.\, \alpha_E \,.\, \eta \,.\, G - I_W \,.\, \alpha_W - R \,.\, r$$

but $$\alpha_E = G \,.\, \alpha_W = \frac{G \,.\, f}{r},$$

hence $$\frac{W \,.\, r \,.\, f}{g} = T_E \,.\, \eta \,.\, G - \frac{I_E \,.\, \eta \,.\, f \,.\, G^2}{r} - \frac{I_W \,.\, f}{r} - R \,.\, r$$

thus

$$f = \frac{T_E \,.\, \eta \,.\, G - R \,.\, r}{\dfrac{W \,.\, r}{g} + \dfrac{I_W}{r} + \dfrac{I_E \,.\, \eta \,.\, G^2}{r}} \tag{2.5}$$

For convenience, let $a = T_E \,.\, \eta$; $b = R \,.\, r$; $c = \dfrac{W \,.\, r}{g} + \dfrac{I_W}{r}$

and $d = \dfrac{I_E \,.\, \eta}{r}$,

then

$$f = \frac{a \,.\, G - b}{c + d \,.\, G^2} \tag{2.6}$$

and the curve of acceleration plotted against gear ratio is of the form shown on Fig. 2.3. The maximum value of f will be given when $\mathrm{d}f/\mathrm{d}G = 0$, hence,

$$\mathrm{d}f/\mathrm{d}G = 0 = \frac{(c + d \,.\, G^2)a - (a \,.\, G - b)2 \,.\, d \,.\, G}{(c + d \,.\, G^2)^2},$$

and so

$$ac + adG^2 - 2adG^2 + 2dbG = 0$$
$$adG^2 - 2dbG - ac = 0$$

or

$$G^2 - \frac{2b \,.\, G}{a} - \frac{c}{d} = 0$$

and solution of this quadratic in G is

$$G = \frac{\frac{2b}{a} \pm \sqrt{\frac{4b^2}{a^2} + \frac{4c}{d}}}{2} = \frac{b}{a} \pm \sqrt{\left(\frac{b}{a}\right)^2 + \frac{c}{d}}$$

Substitution of the values for a, b, c and d give

$$G_{\text{max}} = \frac{R \,.\, r}{T_E} \pm \sqrt{\frac{R \,.\, r^2}{T_E} + \frac{\frac{W \,.\, r^2}{g} + \frac{I_W}{r}}{I_E}}. \qquad (2.7)$$

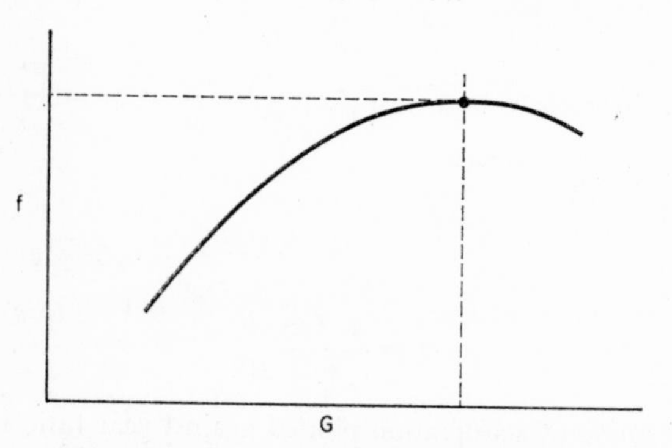

FIG. 2.3. Gear ratio for maximum acceleration

Students sitting examinations are advised not to try to remember equation (2.6) to solve questions but, to work from first principles as shown in the following worked example.

WORKED EXAMPLE (U.L.2 Ext., 1951)

2.4. A motor vehicle weighs 2000 lb and has road wheels of 24 in. rolling diameter. The total moment of inertia of all four road wheels together with the half shafts is 200 lb ft², while that of the engine and clutch is 20 lb ft². The engine torque is 100 lb ft;

the transmission efficiency is 90%; the tractive resistance is constant at 100 lb. Determine (a) the gear ratio between engine and road wheels to give maximum acceleration on an upgrade of 1 in 20 and (b) this acceleration in ft/sec².

Solution

(a) Let the required gear ratio be G and acceleration f ft/sec². Tractive force required from wheels

$$= 100 + \frac{2000}{20} + \frac{2000}{32 \cdot 2} . f \text{ lb.}$$

Torque from wheels for this

$$= (200 + 62 \cdot 2f)\frac{12}{12} = 200 + 62 \cdot 2 \text{ lb ft.}$$

Inertia torque of wheels

$$= \frac{200}{32 \cdot 2} \cdot \frac{12}{12} . f = 6 \cdot 2f \text{ lb ft.}$$

Hence, torque to wheels (total) $= 200 + 68 \cdot 4f$ lb ft.
Torque from engine (transmits)

$$= \left[\frac{200 + 68 \cdot 4f}{G}\right] \frac{100}{90} \text{ lb ft.}$$

Inertia torque for engine inertia

$$= \frac{20}{32 \cdot 2} . G . \frac{12f}{12} = 0 \cdot 62Gf \text{ lb ft.}$$

Hence, torque needed to be developed by engine

$$= 100 = \left[\frac{200 + 68 \cdot 4f}{G}\right] \frac{100}{90} + 0 \cdot 62Gf,$$

giving

$$f = \frac{900G - 2000}{5 \cdot 58G^2 + 684} \text{ ft/sec}^2$$

and for f to be maximum,

$$df/dG = 0 = \frac{900(5{\cdot}58G^2 + 684) - 11{\cdot}16G(900G - 2000)}{(5{\cdot}58G^2 + 684)^2}$$

$$900(5{\cdot}58G^2 + 684) = 11{\cdot}16G(900G - 2000)$$

or

$$5{\cdot}58G^2 + 684 = 11{\cdot}16G^2 - 24{\cdot}8G$$

$$G^2 - 4{\cdot}44G - 122 = 0$$

whence the positive root is $G = 13{\cdot}5$

(b) $$f = \frac{900 \times 13{\cdot}5 - 2000}{5{\cdot}58 \times 13{\cdot}5^2 + 684} = \frac{10{,}150}{1704} = 5{\cdot}97 \text{ ft/sec}^2.$$

2.5. Measurement of Rolling and Air Resistance

Owing to the number of factors that appear to influence the values of the rolling and air resistances of a moving vehicle, some difficulty is experienced in obtaining reliable measurements showing the variations due to the separate parameters. Difficulty is also experienced in separating from some total resistance, the parts due to either rolling or air resistance.

Generally, the total resistance is calculated from measurements of a vehicle's retardation when allowed to coast in neutral or, by measurements using a dynamometer trailer. The retardation may be measured in a variety of ways including the following,

(a) timing the progress of the vehicle past markers placed at known distances apart;

(b) using markers made by firing pellets on to the road surface at known intervals of time;

(c) towing a fifth wheel and noting the indicated number of revolutions or speed of the wheel at given time intervals;

(d) using an accelerometer;

(e) using a method of photo-electric pulse measurements.

It is not possible to review all of these methods which have all been the subject of research and reports of the Motor Industry Research Association, but some mention can be made of methods (d) and (e), with a very brief comment on method (c).

Whenever a vehicle is retarded, the rolling radius will vary with the retardation and the speedometer of the car may not be adequate to provide an accurate value of the speed. This is undoubtedly the case in braking and to a limited extent during free coasting. If however a light wheel can be towed behind the vehicle, the revolutions and angular velocity of the wheel can be indicated and this will give a more reliable value of the vehicle speed than that shown by the speedometer. The rolling radius of the fifth wheel will, owing to its low inertia, not vary much when the vehicle is retarded. Care must be taken in the design of the fifth wheel so that there is no loss of motion between it and the road due to bounce over bumps.

"Accelerometers" utilize the inertia forces set up during retardation. The inertia force of a concentrated mass will be proportional to the vehicle retardation and indication of the value of this retardation can be the movement of the mass relative to its casing. The means of indication may be in a variety of ways for example,

(a) the inertia force sets up a pressure head in a fluid, the head being calibrated to indicate acceleration;

(b) the mass is part of a pendulum which is positioned by the resultant action of the inertia force and the dead weight of the pendulum;

(c) the inertia force causes a material to be strained and by using a strain gauge, an unbalanced current is made to flow in an electric circuit. The magnitude of the current is then a measure of the acceleration. This principle is also used in certain piezo-type ceramic pick ups;

(d) the motion of the inertia mass may cause a change in the inductance or capacitance of an electrical circuit. The resulting unbalanced current can then be a measure of the acceleration.

In the photo-electric method, a disc with evenly spaced holes around its periphery is inserted between the propeller shaft and the rear axle and the passage of these holes past a photo-electric cell attached to the rear axle housing is recorded. When played back into a dekatron counter, the distances covered in successive seconds can be obtained and thus the speed and acceleration, or retardation, measured. Changes in rolling radius of the tyres are reported not to have been significant.

The air resistance is given by the total measured resistance minus that due to rolling, inertia effects and frictional resistances. These can be estimated as follows. The rear and front axle losses can be obtained by taking free retardation readings with the axles jacked up. Tyre losses can be measured by driving large diameter rotating drums and measuring the power consumption for this. Alternatively, the vehicle driving wheels can be made, whilst coasting, to drive round a large diameter dynamometer wheel. The retardation of the dynamometer wheel, after an allowance for its own inertia and friction etc., is a measure of the rolling resistance and transmission losses. Similarly, the vehicle may tow a trailer dynamometer but in this case, air resistance of the trailer must be allowed for.

Fuller details of resistance measurements can be obtained by reading recent research articles and the information given here is not intended to be a full survey.

Examples

2.5. A motor car weighs 3000 lb. The wheels, axles, etc., running at road wheel speed weigh 540 lb with a radius of gyration of 8 in. The engine and gear parts running at engine speed weigh 192 lb with a radius of gyration of 3 in. The effective wheel diameter is 27 in. the engine torque is 90 lb ft, the transmission efficiency is 84% and the road resistance is 80 lb. Under these conditions calculate the acceleration of the car in ft/sec^2,

(*a*) in top gear ratio, engine speed/wheel speed = 5;

(*b*) in bottom gear, engine speed/wheel speed = 16.

(A.M.I.Mech.E., 1950)

Answers: (*a*) 2·44 ft/sec^2; (*b*) 6·12 ft/sec^2.

2.6. A motor car weighs 1·5 tons and when travelling up a slope of 1 in 8 at a speed of 15 m.p.h. the engine develops 40 h.p. at 2100 r.p.m. The moment of inertia of the wheels and rotating parts of the transmission taken as rotating at wheel speed is 200 lb ft^2. The moment of inertia of the parts rotating at engine speed is 12 lb ft^2. The wheel diameter is 29 in. and the mechanical efficiency of the drive is 85%. The air resistance at 15 m.p.h. is 55 lb and varies directly with the square of the speed. Assuming constant engine torque, determine (*a*) the acceleration at 15 m.p.h., (*b*) the maximum speed up the slope. (U.L.2 Ext., 1954)

Answers: (*a*) 2.68 ft/sec^2; (*b*) 42 m.p.h.

2.7. A motor car weighs 5000 lb including the four wheels, each of which has an effective diameter of 28 in., a radius of gyration of 12 in. and a weight of 72 lb. The engine develops 90 b.h.p. at 2200 r.p.m. and the parts rotating at engine speed weigh 240 lb with a radius of gyration of 4·5 in. The transmission efficiency is 88% and the total road and air resistance at this engine speed in top gear of 4·1 to 1 is 220 lb on the flat. Calculate the acceleration in ft/sec^2 under these conditions and (assuming the acceleration to remain uniform) the time taken to increase the speed by 20 m.p.h.

(A.M.I.Mech.E., 1954)

Answers: 2·56 ft/sec^2; 11·5 sec.

2.8. A motor car weighs 2000 lb. The moment of inertia of the rotating parts of the engine is 7·7 lb ft^2. The gear ratio between the engine and back axle is 5·7. The wheels are 26 in. diameter and the total moment of inertia of the four wheels is 80 lb ft^2. When the car is moving with a speed of v ft/sec^2 the torque developed by the engine is $(60 - 0{\cdot}004v^2)$ lb ft and the linear resistance to the motion of the car is $(50 + 0{\cdot}025v^2)$ lb. Calculate the acceleration of the car at 45 ft/sec on a level road and the time required for the car to accelerate from 45 to 70 ft/sec. (Neglect transmission losses.)

$$\text{Note:} \quad \int \frac{dx}{(a^2 - x^2)} = \frac{1}{2a} \log_e \frac{(a + x)}{(a - x)}.$$

(U.L.2 Ext., 1952)

Answers: 2·4 ft/sec^2; 18·5 sec.

2.8. A motor vehicle total weight 3000 lb has road wheels of 24 in. diameter. The effective moment of inertia of the four road wheels and rear axle together is 160 lb ft^2, while that of the engine and flywheel is 20 lb ft^2. The transmission efficiency is 85% and the tractive resistance at a speed of 15 m.p.h. is 60 lb. The total torque available is 150 lb ft.

(*a*) Determine the gear ratio, engine to back axle, to provide maximum acceleration on an upgrade whose sin is 0·25 when travelling at 15 m.p.h.

(*b*) What is this maximum acceleration?

(*c*) Determine the engine r.p.m. and horsepower under these conditions.

(U.L.2 Ext., 1953)

Answers: (*a*) 21·3; (*b*) 5·66 ft/sec^2; (*c*) 4500 r.p.m.; (*d*) 128 h.p.

2.9. A car travelling down an incline of 1 in 13 at 20 m.p.h. experiences a frictional resistance to motion of 70 lb in addition to a frictional torque on the engine of 0·0012N lb ft, where N is the engine speed in r.p.m. The total weight of the car is 3000 lb. The wheels are 26 in. diameter and have a total moment of inertia of 75 lb ft^2. The engine torque is 50 lb ft. The rotating parts of the engine and flywheel have a moment of inertia of 10 lb ft^2. There is a four-speed gearbox, giving ratios of 20, 13, 8 and 5 between the engine speed and axle speed. What gear should be selected for maximum acceleration? How much will the acceleration be? (U.L.2 Ext., 1946)

Answers: 13; 5·12 ft/sec^2.

CHAPTER THREE

VEHICLE BRAKING AND BRAKES

.1. Vehicle Braking

The forces that eventually are responsible for the performance, positive as in acceleration or negative as in braking, of a vehicle are those developed between the tyres and the road. In the preceding chapters it has been assumed that whatever tractive effort was required for a certain performance then such demand could be met by the tyres. It is apparent, however, that there are limits to the tractive effort and that the transmission of more power than is necessary to develop this effort can result in wheel spin. Similarly there is a limit to the braking effort.

The forces generated by the road and tyre interaction, depend upon many characteristics of both the road and tyres and these will be considered in detail in later chapters. However a simple consideration shows that the maximum tractive, or braking, effort depends upon the normal thrust between the tyres and the road. The ratio of the total maximum tractive, or braking, effort (F) to the normal thrust (R) is taken as a constant and called the coefficient of friction or coefficient of adhesion (μ).
Thus

$$F_{max} = \mu \cdot R \tag{3.1}$$

The value of the tractive effort (F) applied to the wheels can, theoretically, vary from zero to its maximum, but any attempt to increase the value will result in wheel spin, or a locked skidding wheel, and then, in either case, the frictional force will be less than the limiting value with consequent loss of braking efficiency.

Development is now towards devices that will automatically release a braked skidding wheel. Nevertheless calculations of the required braking force, or coefficient of friction, are in the first instance based on an assumption of limiting frictional conditions as shown by equation 3.1.

3.2. Braking (or Performance) of a Vehicle: Straight Motion

Problems on vehicle braking are similar to those on performance, and both are as outlined in chapters 1 and 2, except that the frictional tractive, or braking, effort on the wheels is related to the load carried by the wheels and such thrust between the wheels and road has to be considered. It is again convenient to consider the "dynamic equilibrium" of the vehicle. Many varieties of problems can be met according to the circumstances, e.g., whether motion is on level road or, up or down a hill, or whether braking is applied to the front or rear wheels, or to both. The following worked examples should cover most of the possible problems.

WORKED EXAMPLE (A.M.I.Mech.E., 1949)

3.1. The wheel base of a car is 100 in. and the centre of gravity is 42 in. behind the front axle and 31 in. above the ground level. The coefficient of friction between the tyre and the road is 0·35. Calculate the maximum possible acceleration as determined by wheel spin, when:

(a) the front wheels are driven;

(b) the rear wheels are driven;

(c) both front and rear axles are driven (i) with no third differential and (ii) with a third differential.

Solution

(a) The forces acting on the vehicle and giving rise to the dynamic equilibrium are shown in Fig. 3.1a. These are: weight of

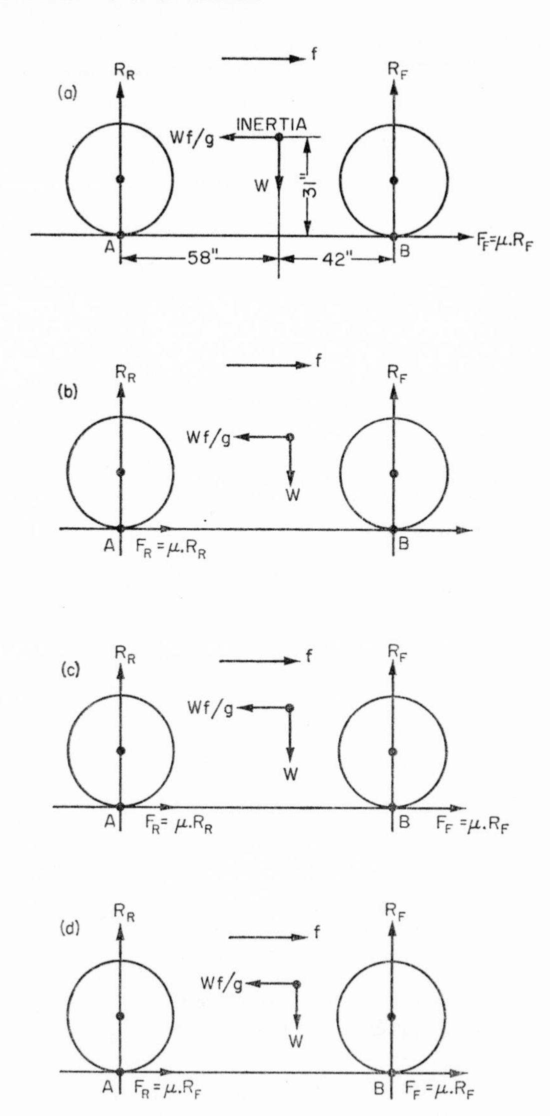

FIG. 3.1. Forces acting on the vehicle of example 3.1

the car acting through the centre of gravity, reactions of the road on the wheels perpendicular to the road and in the case of the front and rear wheels are shown as total front reaction R_F and total rear reaction R_R, tractive frictional effort on front wheels at point of contact with road (force for both wheels is combined) F_F. Finally the inertia force acting through the centre of gravity and in a direction opposite to the vehicle acceleration. For maximum tractive effort $F_F = \mu . R_F$ and this force in the horizontal direction gives the car its acceleration or is balanced by the inertia force, thus

$$F_F = \mu . R_F = \frac{W . f}{g} \tag{3.2}$$

To determine f, the value of R_F is required and can be found by taking moments of the forces about point A. A is selected so that the moment of R_R is zero.

$$R_F . 100 + \frac{W . f}{g} . 31 = W . 58 \tag{3.3}$$

Hence, from equations (3.2) and (3.3),

$$100 . \frac{W . f}{\mu . g} + 31 . \frac{W . f}{g} = 58 . W$$

(note that the weight of car is not required)

$$f(100/\mu + 31) = 58 \times 32{\cdot}2$$

$$f = \frac{58 \times 32{\cdot}2}{317} = 5{\cdot}9 \text{ ft/sec}^2.$$

(b) The forces acting on the car are shown in Fig. 3.1b. The maximum braking force on the rear wheels is $F_R = \mu . R_R$ and

$$\mu . R_R = \frac{W . f}{g}$$

Moments of the forces are in this case taken about point B

$$R_R \,.\, 100 = W \,.\, 42 + 31 \,.\, \frac{W \,.\, f}{g}$$

hence

$$100 \times \frac{W \,.\, f}{\mu \,.\, g} - 31 \times \frac{W \,.\, f}{g} = 42\, W$$

$$f = \frac{42 \times 32{\cdot}2}{255} = 5{\cdot}3 \text{ ft/sec}^2$$

(c) i. With no third differential it is assumed that limiting friction occurs on all four wheels simultaneously. The forces acting are then shown in Fig. 3.1c.

On rear wheels $F_R = \mu \,.\, R_R$ and on front wheels $F_F = \mu \,.\, R_F$ Then

$$F_R + F_F = \mu(R_R + R_F) = \frac{W \,.\, f}{g}$$

Considering vertical forces, $R_R + R_F = W$ and so

$$\mu \,.\, W = \frac{W \,.\, f}{g} \text{ or } f = \mu \,.\, g = 0{\cdot}35 \times 32{\cdot}2 = 11{\cdot}25 \text{ ft/sec}^2.$$

(d) ii. The third differential will provide an equal torque to the front and rear wheels. Tractive effort will then be limited by slip occurring first at rear or front wheels, and this will be at the wheels having the smaller of the two normal thrusts. If the centre of gravity was mid-way between wheels, slip would be first at the front wheels since the inertia effect would be to reduce the static reaction. In this problem it will be assumed that slip is first at the front wheels. The forces will be as shown in Fig. 3.1d. Note that tractive effort on both wheels is the same.

Total tractive effort

$$= \mu \,.\, R_F + F_R = 2 \,.\, \mu \,.\, R_F = \frac{W \,.\, f}{g}$$

Moments of forces about point A give

$$31 \,.\, \frac{W \,.\, f}{g} + 100 \,.\, R_F = 58 \,.\, W$$

$$31 \,.\, \frac{W \,.\, f}{g} + \frac{100}{2 \,.\, \mu} \cdot \frac{W \,.\, f}{g} = 58 \,.\, W$$

$$f = \frac{58 \times 32 \cdot 2}{31 + 143} = 10 \cdot 7 \text{ ft/sec}^2$$

Check on reaction,

$$R_F = \frac{W \times 10 \cdot 7}{32 \cdot 2} \times \frac{1}{0 \cdot 7} = \text{to less than half } W$$

and so R_F is less than R_R and slip will be first at the front wheels.

WORKED EXAMPLE (U.L.2 Ext., 1955)

3.2. A vehicle having a wheel base of 11 ft is driven along a horizontal road by a torque applied to the rear wheels. The centre of gravity is 2·5 ft above the ground and 4·5 ft behind the front axle. The coefficient of friction between the wheels and the ground is 0·3. Determine:

(a) the maximum acceleration of the vehicle if the wheels are not to slip:

(b) the maximum retardation of the vehicle when a braking torque is applied to the rear wheels.

Solution

(a) Figure 3.2a shows the forces acting.

Horizontal forces give $F_R = \mu \,.\, R_R = \dfrac{W \,.\, f}{g}$.

Moments of forces about point of contact of front wheels and road

$$R_R \times 11 = \frac{W.f}{g} \times 2{\cdot}5 + W \times 4{\cdot}5$$

$$R_R = \frac{W.f}{g} \times \frac{2{\cdot}5}{11} + W \times \frac{4{\cdot}5}{11}.$$

Hence, $$\frac{W.f}{g} \times \frac{2{\cdot}5 \times 0{\cdot}3}{11} + W \times \frac{4{\cdot}5 \times 0{\cdot}3}{11} = \frac{W.f}{g}$$

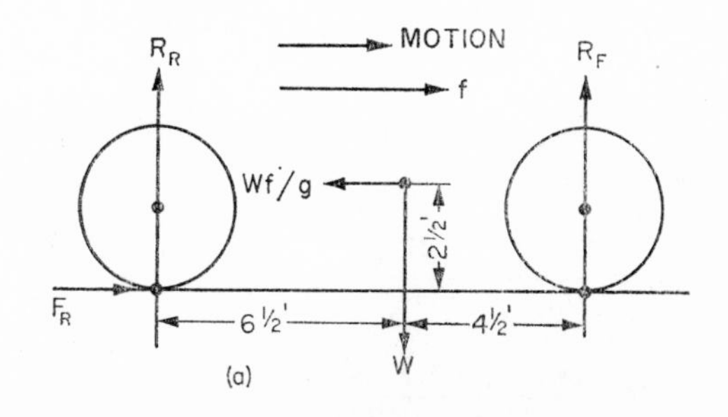

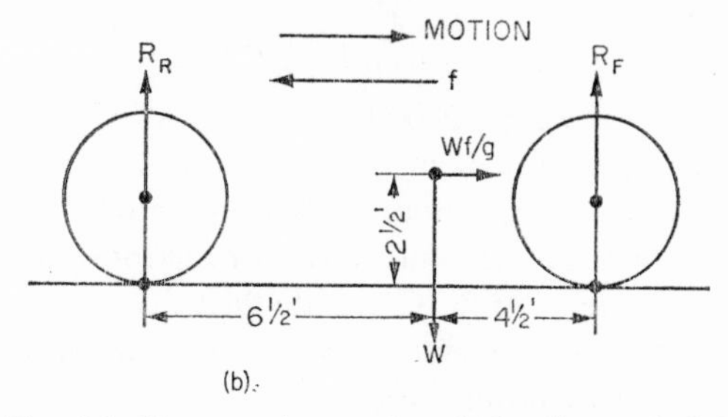

FIG. 3.2. Forces acting on the vehicle of example 3.2

and

$$f(1 - 0{\cdot}0682) = \frac{4{\cdot}5 \times 0{\cdot}3 \times 32{\cdot}2}{11};$$

$$f = \frac{4{\cdot}5 \times 0{\cdot}3 \times 32{\cdot}2}{11 \times 0{\cdot}9318} = 4{\cdot}24 \text{ ft/sec}^2$$

(b) Figure 3.2b shows the forces acting. Note with braking, the frictional force opposes the motion and inertia force is in the same direction as motion.

Horizontal forces give $F_R = \mu \, . \, R_R = \dfrac{W.f}{g}$

Moments about point of contact of front wheel with road

$$\frac{W.f}{g} \times 2{\cdot}5 + R_R \times 11 = W \times 4{\cdot}5$$

$$R_R = W \times \frac{4{\cdot}5}{11} - \frac{W.f}{g} \times \frac{2{\cdot}5}{11}$$

thus,

$$W \times \frac{4{\cdot}5 \times 0{\cdot}3}{11} - \frac{W.f}{g} \times \frac{2{\cdot}5 \times 0{\cdot}3}{11} = \frac{W.f}{g},$$

$$f = \frac{4{\cdot}5 \times 0{\cdot}3 \times 32{\cdot}2}{11 \times 1{\cdot}0682} = 3{\cdot}7 \text{ ft/sec}^2.$$

WORKED EXAMPLE (A.M.I.Mech.E., 1953)

3.3. A motor car weighs 2800 lb and has a wheel base of 100 in. The centre of gravity is 42 in. behind the front axle and 31 in. above ground level. Maximum braking on four wheels on level ground will bring the car uniformly to rest from a speed of 45 m.p.h. in a distance of 85 ft. Calculate the value of the coefficient of friction between tyre and road for this condition and the distance required to bring the car to rest from 30 m.p.h. when descending a hill of gradient 1 in 6 and when it is braked on the front wheels only.

Solution

Equating total horizontal forces to inertia force as in Fig. 3.3a

$$F_R + F_F = \frac{W.f}{g} = \mu \, . \, R_R + \mu \, . \, R_F \text{ for maximum braking.}$$

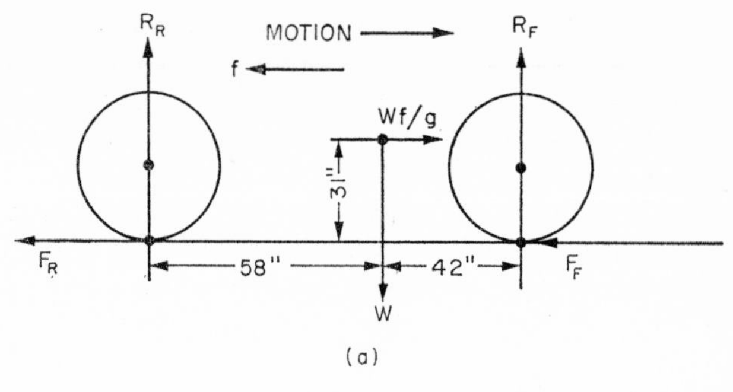

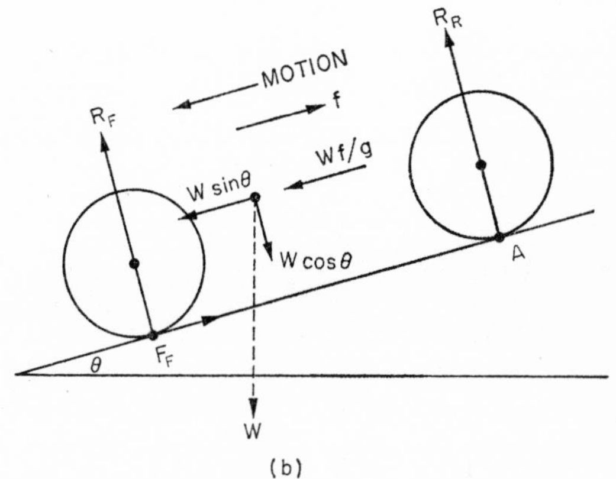

FIG. 3.3. Forces acting on the car of example 3.3

Vertically, $R_R + R_F = W$, and so

$$\frac{W \cdot f}{g} = \mu \cdot W$$

For uniform retardation, $v^2 = 2 \cdot f \cdot s$, hence

$$f = \frac{66 \times 66}{2 \times 85} = 25{\cdot}6 \text{ ft/sec}^2,$$

$$\mu = f/g = \frac{25{\cdot}6}{32{\cdot}2} = 0{\cdot}795$$

When the vehicle is on a hill the weight no longer acts in a direction perpendicular to the road, i.e., parallel to the wheel reactions and problems are generally most easily solved by considering the weight W to consist of two components $W \, . \sin \theta$ acting parallel to and down the slope and $W \, . \cos \theta$ acting perpendicular to the plane as shown in Fig. 3.3b. The slope of 1 in 6 is taken as the sine of θ, so that $\theta = 9° \, 33'$ and $\cos \theta = 0{\cdot}9863$.
Considering forces parallel to the road give

$$\frac{W \, . f}{g} + W \, . \sin \theta = F_F = \mu \, . R_F$$

Moments about point of contact of rear wheel with road (point A)

$$\left(\frac{W \, . f}{g} + W \, . \sin \theta\right) 31 = R_F \times 100 - W \, . \cos \theta \times 58$$

$$\mu \, . R_F \times 31 = R_F \times 100 - W \, . \cos \theta \times 58,$$

$$R_F = \frac{2800 \times 58 \times 0{\cdot}9863}{100 - 0{\cdot}795 \times 31} = 2125 \text{ lb.}$$

Hence $$\frac{W \, . f}{g} + \frac{W}{6} = 0{\cdot}795 \times 2125,$$

$$f = (0{\cdot}795 \times 2125 - 467) \frac{32{\cdot}2}{2800} \text{ ft/sec}^2$$

$$f = 14{\cdot}1 \text{ ft/sec}^2.$$

Then $$v^2 = 2f \, . s \quad \text{or} \quad s = \frac{44 \times 44}{28{\cdot}2} = 68{\cdot}7 \text{ ft.}$$

3.3. Braking of a Vehicle: Motion in a Curve

When a vehicle moving round a curve is braked, the frictional forces between the tyres and road become more complex than in straight line motion. This is because of the necessary side forces acting on the wheels. The nature of the tyre forces that arise when a driven rolling wheel is acted on by a side thrust will be considered in detail in later chapters, but a simple consideration may be used here.

All parts of the vehicle are assumed to have the same forward velocity (v) and to turn in a circular path of large radius (r) compared with the vehicle dimensions. The vehicle may then be

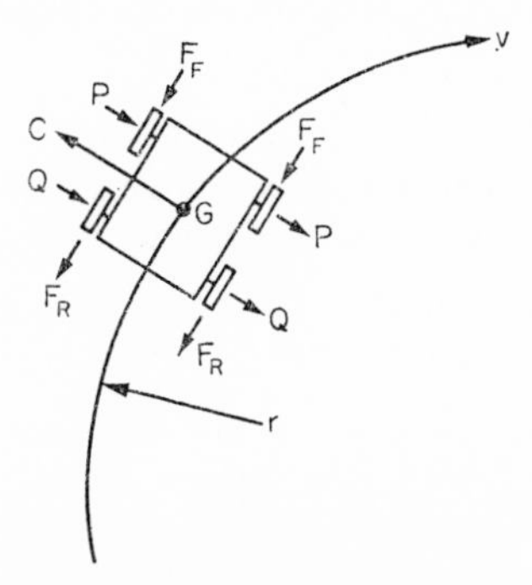

FIG. 3.4. Forces acting on a braked vehicle moving in a curved path

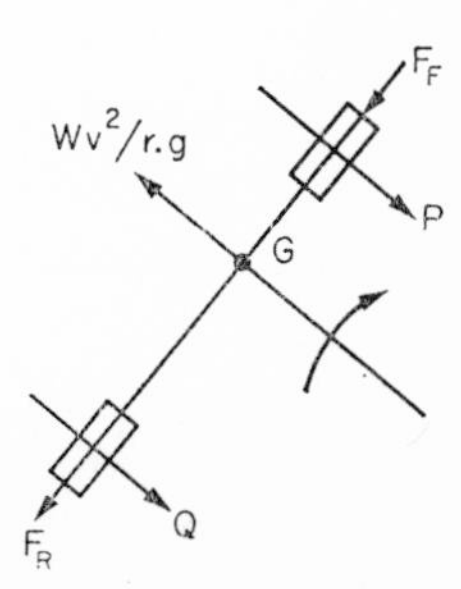

FIG. 3.5. Simplified system of Fig. 3.4

considered acted on by a single centrifugal force, of magnitude $\frac{Wv^2}{r \cdot g} = C$, through the centre of mass (G), and this centrifugal force resisted, to prevent side slip, by side forces P and Q at the tyres. All the side tyre forces will be parallel and opposite to the centrifugal force. In addition, the braking forces at the tyres are all assumed to act in a fore and aft direction. These forces are shown in plan view in Fig. 3.4. If the rolling effects on the wheel reactions due to the centrifugal force, and the yawing effects of braking due to unequal forces at inner and outer wheels are neglected, then the vehicle wheel forces can be assumed "compressed" into a single plane through the centre of gravity, i.e., as though the four wheeled automobile behaves as a two-wheeled cycle as shown in Fig. 3.5.

At each wheel the maximum frictional force is the product of the coefficient of adhesion and the vertical load (R) on the wheel, and part of this frictional force is used to resist the side slip. Only part of the frictional force is therefore available for braking, as shown in Fig. 3.6.

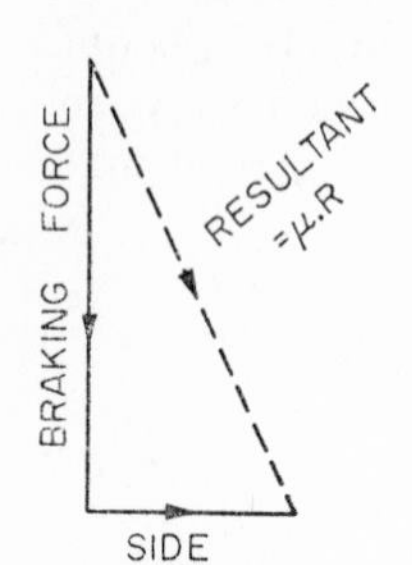

FIG. 3.6. Frictional forces acting at a wheel

The braking capacity of a vehicle is thus reduced when moving in a flat turn.

Finally, if the coefficient of adhesion is sufficiently high, the vehicle may, above a certain speed, overturn before sliding sideways.

WORKED EXAMPLE (U.L.2 Ext., 1953)

3.4. The centre of gravity of a motor cycle with rider is 2 ft behind the front axle and 2 ft above ground level. The distance between the axles is 54 in. The coefficient of friction between the tyres and the road is 0·4. The total weight of rider and machine is 600 lb. Determine the greatest possible retardation when using the front brake only on a level road

(a) when travelling in a straight path,
(b) when travelling in a curve of 300 ft radius at 30 m.p.h.,
(c) when travelling in a curve of 300 ft radius at 42·5 m.p.h.

Neglect the effects of air and mechanical resistance and assume the clutch is disengaged.

Solution

(a) Figure 3.7a shows the forces acting.

Horizontal forces give, $F_F = \mu \,.\, R_F = \dfrac{W.f}{g}$ and moments of forces about point of contact of rear wheel with ground gives

$$R_F \times 4{\cdot}5 = W \times 2{\cdot}5 + \frac{W.f}{g} \times 2,$$

hence

$$\frac{W.f \times 4{\cdot}5}{g \times 0{\cdot}4} = W \times 2{\cdot}5 + \frac{W.f}{g} \times 2$$

$$f = \frac{32{\cdot}2 \times 2{\cdot}5}{11{\cdot}25 - 2} = \frac{32{\cdot}2 \times 2{\cdot}5}{9{\cdot}25} \text{ ft/sec}^2$$

$$f = 8{\cdot}72 \text{ ft/sec}^2.$$

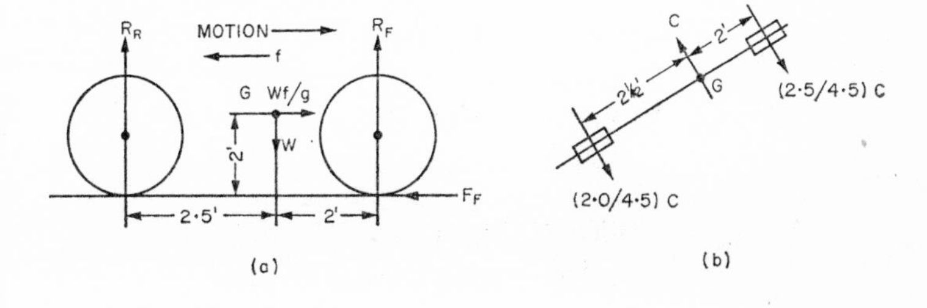

FIG. 3.7. Forces acting on the motor cycle of example 3.4

(b) Centrifugal force through $G = \frac{Wv^2}{r.g} = \frac{600 \times 44^2}{300 \times 32{\cdot}2} = 120$ lb.

The centrifugal force is shared by the front and rear wheels in the proportion shown in Fig. 3.7b.

Side force at front wheel $= \frac{2{\cdot}5}{4{\cdot}5} \times 120 = 66{\cdot}6$ lb.

The frictional forces at the front wheel are as shown in Fig. 3.7c. Maximum frictional force at front wheel $= \mu \,.\, R_F$ and part of this available for braking in direction of motion

$$= F_F = \sqrt{(\mu \,.\, R_F)^2 - 66{\cdot}6^2} = \frac{W\,.\,f}{g}$$

$$\frac{W^2f^2}{g^2} = \sqrt{(\mu R_F)^2 - 66{\cdot}6^2}.$$

Moments of forces about rear wheel contact with ground gives

$$4{\cdot}5 \times R_F = W \times 2{\cdot}5 + 2 \times \frac{W\,.\,f}{g}$$

thus squaring gives

$$20{\cdot}25\, R_F{}^2 = (1500 + 37{\cdot}3f)^2$$

and

$$R_F{}^2 = \frac{(1500 + 37{\cdot}3f)^2}{20{\cdot}25} = \frac{W^2f^2}{\mu^2\,.\,g^2} + \frac{66{\cdot}6^2}{\mu^2}$$

$$110{,}000 + 4030f + 69{\cdot}4f^2 = 2170f^2 + 27{,}700$$

$$f^2 - 1{\cdot}91f - 39{\cdot}2 = 0$$

and so

$$f = 7{\cdot}85 \text{ ft/sec}^2.$$

(c) Centrifugal force $= 120 \times \left(\frac{42{\cdot}5}{30}\right)^2 = 241$ lb.

Side force at front wheel $= \frac{2{\cdot}5}{4{\cdot}5} \times 241 = 134$ lb.

Frictional forces are shown in Fig. 3.7d.

Hence, $$F_F = \sqrt{(\mu \,.\, R_F)^2 - 134^2} = \frac{600}{32{\cdot}2}f$$

giving

$$R_F{}^2 = 2170f^2 + 112{,}500$$

and moments as in (b) give

$$4{\cdot}5 \times R_F = 2{\cdot}5\,W + 2 \times \frac{W\,.\,f}{g}$$

whence, as in (b),

$$f^2 - 1{\cdot}95f + 0{\cdot}707 = 0$$

and

$$f = 1{\cdot}47 \text{ ft/sec}^2.$$

3.4. Internal Expanding Shoe Brakes

These brakes, used extensively on motor vehicles, essentially consist of curved shoes to which a lining of friction material is rigidly attached. The shoes are generally pivoted at one end, or allowed to rest against a fixed abutment, and an actuating plunger at the "free" end forces the shoes apart so that the friction lining is thrust against the inside surface of a rotating brake drum. The frictional drag of the linings on the drum thus provides a braking torque. There are many varieties, but two simple types only are shown in Fig. 3.8 as these represent the basic mechanics of operation.

The determination of the braking torque, actuating and pivot forces etc., for a given shoe depends largely on assumptions made concerning either the pressure between the brake lining and the drum or the position of the resultant thrust of the drum on the shoe. When the variation of pressure is known, or assumed, the braking torque can be calculated although, in the case of fixed abutments, the analysis becomes somewhat tedious. Graphical methods have been evolved which whilst appearing to be suitable

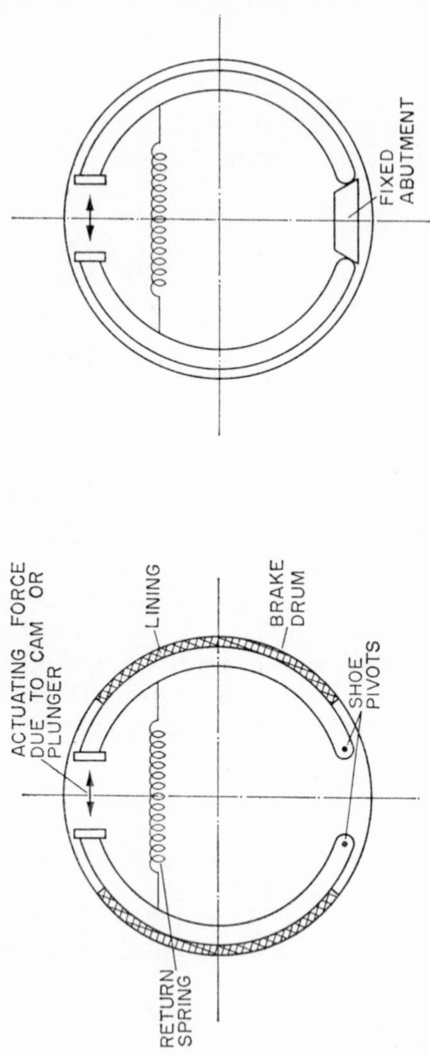

FIG. 3.8. Simple internal expanding shoe brakes

for abutment shoes, do not seem to offer advantages over the analytical methods for pivoted shoes.

3.5. Pressure Between Lining and Drum

The intensity of pressure between the shoe lining and the brake drum at any position on the lining depends upon numerous factors

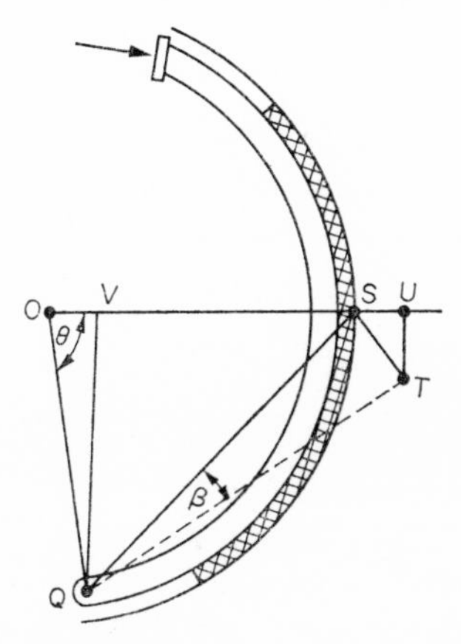

FIG. 3.9. Geometry of shoe assuming the lining elastic

and as it is unlikely that the value can be predicted with certainty, assumptions have to be made. For the purposes of calculation two assumptions appear to have been considered,

(a) that the intensity of pressure is constant over the surface of the lining and,

(b) that the shoe is rigid and the deformed lining is elastic in compression.

(i) The implications of assumption (a) are obvious and it is unlikely that the assumption is valid since the mode of operation of the brake does not enter into the calculation.

(ii) The implications of assumption (b) are as follows:

Figure 3.9 shows a shoe and lining pivoted at Q and a brake drum whose centre is at point O. S is a point on the lining. If the shoe turns through a small angle β (exaggerated in the Figure), point S would move, if unrestricted by the drum, to point T. The deformation of the lining at S is approximately the length ST and this is considered to consist of a part $SU = \delta x$ radial to the drum and a part UT tangential to the drum. If the lining thickness is (x), then the strain (e) in a radial direction is given approximately by

$$e = \frac{\delta x}{x}$$

and if the lining material is elastic, the intensity of pressure (p) is given by

$$p \propto \delta x/x$$

and if the lining thickness is constant,

$$p \propto \delta x.$$

If QV is drawn perpendicular to OS, then

$$SU = \delta x = QV \,.\, \beta = OQ \,.\, \sin \theta \,.\, \beta$$

and

$$p \propto OQ \,.\, \beta \,.\, \sin \theta$$

or

$$p \propto \sin \theta \tag{3.4}$$

3.6. Calculation of Brake Torque with Pivoted Shoes

Figure 3.10 shows an arrangement of a pivoted shoe type brake with the brake drum rotating in a clockwise direction. Shoe (1) is called a leading shoe because the frictional drag on it tends to increase the radial thrust between it and the drum, whilst shoe (2), called a trailing shoe, has its radial thrust reduced.

Consider, on each shoe, an element of lining subtending an angle $\delta\theta$ at the drum centre and located by angle θ to the line joining the pivot and drum centres. Let the intensities of pressure

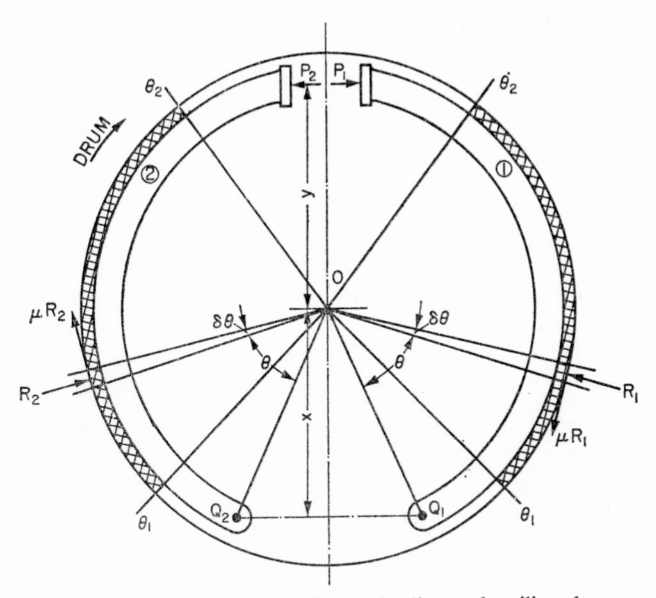

FIG. 3.10. Braking forces acting on leading and trailing shoes

on these elements be p_1 and p_2, the width of the lining be t, and the drum radius be r. The forces acting on the elements are:

radial thrust on leading shoe element

$$= R_1 = p_1 \times \text{area} = p_1 r\delta\theta t,$$

radial thrust on trailing shoe element

$$= R_2 = p_2 \,.\, r\delta\theta \,.\, t$$

and so, frictional drag of drum on shoe (1)

$$= \mu \,.\, R_1 = \mu \,.\, p_1 \,.\, r\delta\theta \,.\, t$$

and on shoe (2)

$$= \mu R_2 = \mu \, . \, p_2 \, . \, r\delta\theta \, . \, t.$$

The frictional torque on drum due to elements $= \mu \, . \, R_1 \, . \, r + \mu \, . \, R_2 \, . \, r$. Hence total braking torque

$$= \int_{\theta_1}^{\theta_2} \mu \, . \, p_1 \, . \, r^2 \, . \, t \, . \, d\theta + \int_{\theta_1}^{\theta_2} \mu \, . \, p_2 \, . \, r^2 \, . \, t \, . \, d\theta \qquad (3.5)$$

For equilibrium of the shoes, moments of forces about Q_1 and Q_2 give, if $OQ_1 = OQ_2 = L$,

$$P_1(x + y)$$

$$= \int_{\theta_1}^{\theta_2} p_1 \, . \, r \, . \, t \, . \, L \, . \, \sin \theta d\theta - \int_{\theta_1}^{\theta_2} \mu \, . \, p_1 \, . \, r \, . \, t(r - L \, . \, \cos \theta) d\theta \quad (3.6)$$

$$P_2(x + y)$$

$$= \int_{\theta_1}^{\theta_2} p_2 \, . \, r \, . \, t \, . \, L \, . \, \sin \theta d\theta + \int_{\theta_1}^{\theta_2} \mu \, . \, p_2 \, . \, r \, . \, t(r - L \, . \, \cos \theta) d\theta \quad (3.7)$$

Equations (3.5), (3.6), (3.7) may be evaluated for a given brake provided an assumption is made concerning the variation of p_1 and p_2 with θ, and usually these are assumed to be either constant or proportional to $\sin \theta$. The equations are not developed any further in general terms and examination candidates are advised not to try to remember them, but to work from first principles as shown in the following worked example. However some information may be deduced from equations (3.5)–(3.7) which show the following.

(i) If the actuating mechanism at the shoe tip provides forces $P_1 = P_2$, then the braking torque on the leading shoe is greater than that on the trailing shoe.

(ii) If there are to be equal braking torques on the shoes, then the actuating forces cannot be equal.

(iii) The magnitude of the frictional torque on the drum depends upon the value of μ, but there is a practical limit to the value of μ. The limit is reached on the leading shoe when the moment of the frictional drag on the lining together with that of the actuating force, about Q becomes greater than that due to the radial thrust. The shoe then locks to the drum and is then said to "sprag."

WORKED EXAMPLE (U.L.2 Ext., 1957)

3.5. Figure 3.11 shows part of a brake drum and shoe rotating clockwise and the shoe being pivoted at B. A force of 200 lb is

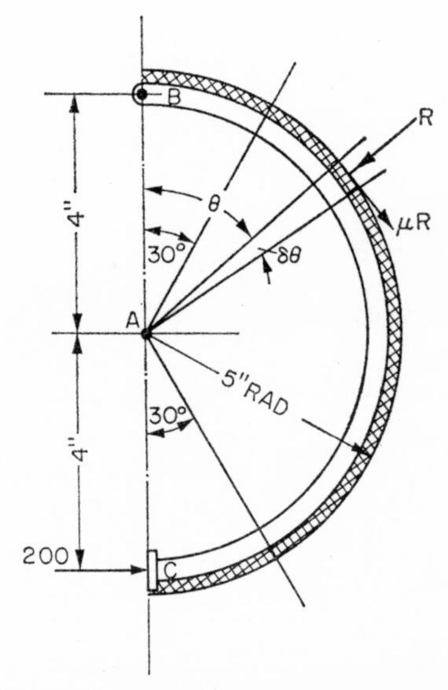

FIG. 3.11. Forces acting on the shoe of example 3.5

applied at C. The lining width is 1 in. and the coefficient of friction between lining and drum is 0·2. (a) Determine the braking torque for one shoe assuming constant radial pressure. (b) If the radial pressure $p = K \,.\, \sin\theta$, where θ is measured from AB and K is constant, evaluate K and calculate the braking torque.

Solution

Consider an element as shown in Fig. 3.11.

(a) Radial thrust on element

$$= R = p \times 5\delta\theta \times 1 = 5p\delta\theta \text{ lb.}$$

Frictional drag $= \mu \,.\, R = 0{\cdot}2 \times 5p \times \delta\theta = p \,.\, \delta\theta$ lb.

Frictional torque $= 5p\delta\theta$ lb in.

and thus,

Total torque on lining

$$= \int_{30}^{150} 5 \,.\, p \,.\, \mathrm{d}\theta = (5 \,.\, p \,.\, \theta)_{30}^{150} = 5p \times \frac{120\pi}{180} \text{ lb in.}$$

Moments about B give

$$200 \times 8 = \int_{30}^{150} 5p \,.\, \mathrm{d}\theta \,.\, 4 \,.\, \sin\theta + \int_{30}^{150} p \,.\, \mathrm{d}\theta(5 - 4 \,.\, \cos\theta)$$

$$= \int_{30}^{150} (20 \,.\, p \,.\, \sin\theta + 5 \,.\, p - 4 \,.\, p \,.\, \cos\theta)\mathrm{d}\theta$$

$$= (-20 \,.\, p \,.\, \cos\theta + 5 \,.\, p \,.\, \theta - 4 \,.\, p \,.\, \sin\theta)_{30}^{150}$$

$$\frac{200 \times 8}{p} = (20 \times 0{\cdot}866 + 20 \times 0{\cdot}866) + \left(5 \times \frac{120\pi}{180}\right) - (4 \times 0{\cdot}5 - 4 \times 0{\cdot}5)$$

$$= 34{\cdot}64 + 10{\cdot}45$$

Hence, $$p = \frac{200 \times 8}{45{\cdot}09} = 35{\cdot}6 \text{ lb/in}^2.$$

$$\text{Therefore torque} = 5 \times 35{\cdot}06 \times \frac{120\pi}{180} = 373 \text{ lb in.}$$

(b) Radial pressure $= K \,.\, \sin\theta$ and radial thrust on element

$$= 5K \,.\, \sin\theta \,.\, \delta\theta$$

and thus frictional drag

$$= 0{\cdot}2 \times 5 \,.\, K \sin\theta \,.\, \delta\theta$$

$$\text{Total torque} = \int_{30}^{150} 5K \,.\, \sin\theta \,.\, d\theta.$$

Moments about B give

$$200 \times 8 = \int_{30}^{150} 20K \,.\, \sin\theta^2 \,.\, d\theta + \int_{30}^{150} K \,.\, \sin\theta(5 - 4 \,.\, \cos\theta)d\theta$$

$$\frac{200 \times 8}{K} = \int_{30}^{150} (10 - 10 \,.\, \cos 2\,\theta + 5 \,.\, \sin\theta - 2 \,.\, \sin 2\theta)d\theta$$

$$\frac{200 \times 8}{K} = (10\theta - 5 \,.\, \sin 2\theta - 5 \,.\, \cos\theta + \cos 2\theta)_{30}^{150}$$

$$= \left(\frac{10 \times 120\pi}{180}\right) - (-5 \times 0{\cdot}866 - 5 \times 0{\cdot}866)$$

$$= 38{\cdot}32$$

$$K = \frac{200 \times 8}{38{\cdot}32} = 41{\cdot}7$$

and hence,

$$\text{torque} = \int_{30}^{150} 208{\cdot}5 \,.\, \sin\theta \,.\, d\theta \text{ lb in.}$$

$$= 208{\cdot}5(-\cos\theta)_{30}^{150}$$

$$= 208{\cdot}5 \times 1{\cdot}732 \text{ lb in.} = 360 \text{ lb in.}$$

3.7. Graphical Determination of Braking Torque

Several attempts have been made to determine the braking torque, thrust on shoes, forces at pivots or abutments, etc., using graphical methods based on the results of analysis. Most consist of considering the equilibrium of a shoe when acted on by three forces, the shoe tip actuating force (P), the resultant reaction of

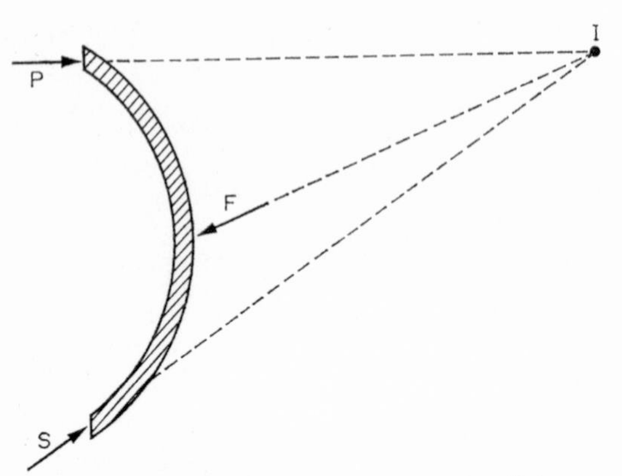

FIG. 3.12. Main forces acting on a shoe lining

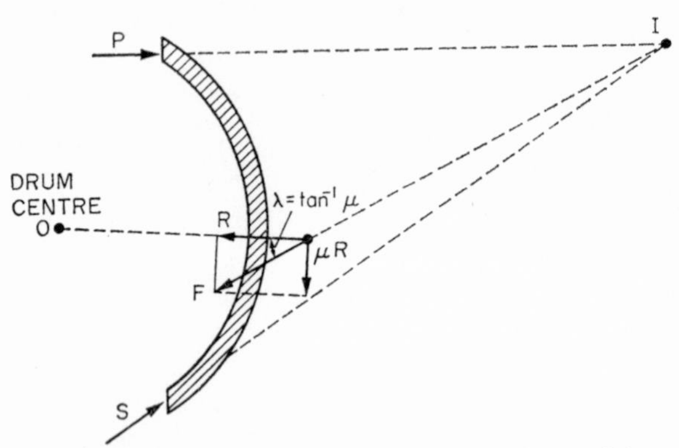

FIG. 3.13. Position of the resultant force on a shoe lining

the drum on the shoe (F) and the force at the pivot or abutment (S). For equlibrium of the shoe, the lines of action of these forces must pass through a point, (I), as shown in Figure 3.12.

The direction of the shoe tip force is generally known and so also, in the case of an abutment type shoe, is the force at the abutment. With a pivoted shoe, the direction of the pivot force is not known. It is assumed that the various thrusts and frictional drags on small elements of the lining can be combined into a single resultant reaction on the shoe, and most controversy lies in deciding the position and direction of this force. If the resultant force (F) is considered the same as a resultant normal thrust (R), together with a resultant frictional drag ($\mu \cdot R$) both acting at the same point as shown in Fig. 3.13, then all that remains to be decided is the location of the point of intersection of force R and $\mu \cdot R$.

To show this type of determination of braking torque, the following example is worked out. Other graphical methods follow.

WORKED EXAMPLE (A.M.I.Mech.E., 1952)

3.6. A motor vehicle of 3500 lb all up weight is fitted with brakes on all four wheels and is slowed uniformly from 60 m.p.h. to 30 m.p.h. in a distance of 2000 ft while running down an incline of 1 in 12. Assuming uniform distribution of braking forces calculate the mean lining pressure in lb/in.^{2} from the following data:

Effective wheel diameter	28 in.
Brake drum diameter	12·5 in.
Brake lining width	2 in.
Lining contact angle in each drum	210°
Coefficient of friction	0·3

Calculate the amount of heat generated at each wheel during this brake operation and describe how adequate means of heat dissipation can be provided with modern wheel construction and body form.

Solution

$$\text{Retardation of vehicle} = \frac{v^2 - u^2}{2 . s} = \frac{88^2 - 44^2}{2 \times 2000} = 1.452 \text{ ft/sec}^2.$$

Tractive force for this

$$= P = \frac{W}{12} + \frac{W . f}{g} = W(0{\cdot}0833 + 0{\cdot}045)$$

$$= 3500 \times 0{\cdot}1283 = 450 \text{ lb.}$$

Hence braking torque on each wheel

$$= \frac{450}{4} \times 14 = 1575 \text{ lb in.}$$

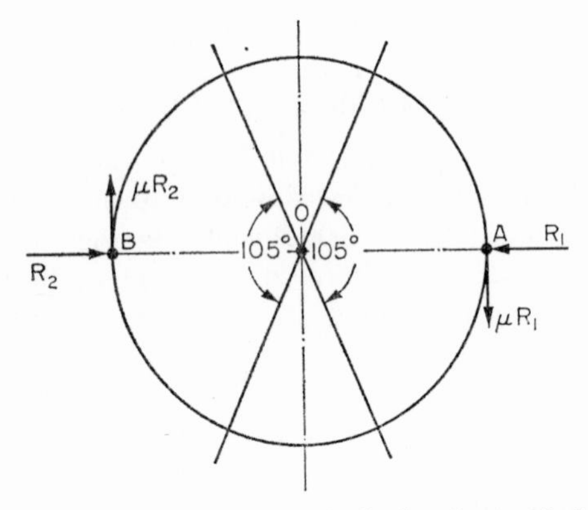

FIG. 3.14. Forces acting on the brake of example 3.6

The forces are as shown in Fig. 3.14 and for this brake, many assumptions have to be made,

(i) linings are symmetrical.
(ii) Force R_1 and $\mu . R_1$ act at point A, the lining contact centre.
(iii) Similarly for forces R_2 and $\mu . R_2$ which intersect at point

B. Braking torque on drum $= (\mu \, . \, R_1 + \mu \, . \, R_2)r$ and if it is assumed that $R_1 = R_2$, then

$$\text{torque} = 2 \, . \, \mu \, . \, r \, . \, R_1 = 1575$$

$$R_1 = \frac{1575}{2 \times 0{\cdot}3 \times 6{\cdot}25} = 420 \text{ lb}$$

Area of lining = width × radius × arc subtended at *O*

$$= 2 \times 6{\cdot}25 \times \frac{105 \times \pi}{180} = 22{\cdot}9 \text{ in}^2.$$

$$\text{Average lining pressure} = \frac{420}{22{\cdot}9} = 18{\cdot}3 \text{ lb/in}^2.$$

Work done in braking per wheel

= tractive force at wheel × distance covered

$$= \frac{450 \times 2000}{4} = 225{,}000 \text{ ft lb}$$

$$\text{Heat equivalent of this work} = \frac{225{,}000}{778} = 289 \text{ B.t.u.}$$

3.8. Other Constructions

These constructions for determining the position of the resultant drum reaction are based on the work of Acres,[1] Waller[2] and Robinson[3] and are given for the case of an abutment and pivoted shoe. The mathematical justification of the construction is beyond the scope of this book but references to other work are given at the end of the chapter.

(a) Shoe With Abutment

In this construction, a line *OV* is set off at the friction angle (λ) to the line *OW*. Note $\tan \lambda = \mu = \tan \widehat{WOV}$. A construction

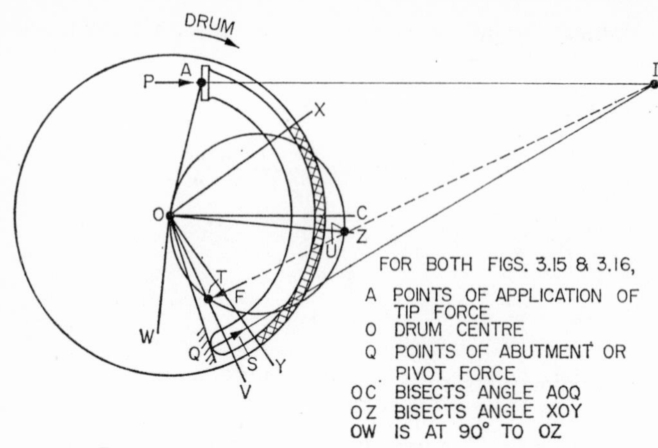

FIG. 3.15. Graphical determination of resultant force on a shoe with abutment

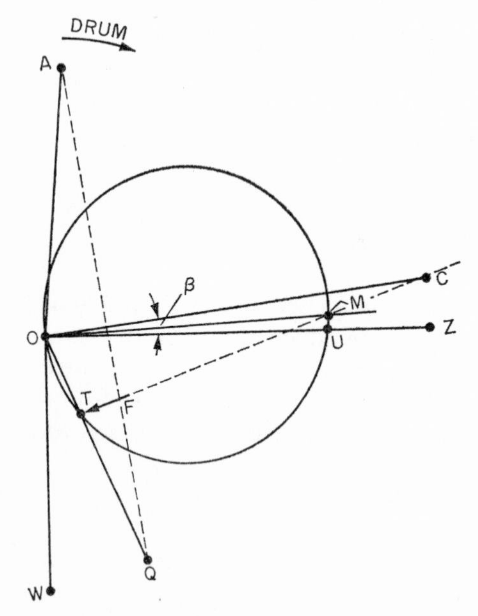

FIG. 3.16. Graphical determination of resultant force on a pivoted shoe

circle is drawn whose diameter OU lies on the line OZ. Where this circle cuts OV gives the second point T on the line of action of the resultant drum reaction. The diameter of the construction circle is given by, angle $XOZ = \alpha$,

$$d = \frac{2 . r . \sin \alpha}{\alpha + 0{\cdot}5 . \sin 2}. \qquad (3.8)$$

(b) PIVOTED SHOE

In this construction, two points T and M on the line of action of the resultant drum reaction are needed since the location of point I is not known. Point T is located as in the previous construction. The angle ZOM is set off from ZO to cut the construction circle at M. If angle $ZOC = \beta$ and angle $XOZ = \alpha$, as before, then

$$\tan \widehat{ZOM} = \left[\frac{\alpha - 0{\cdot}5 \sin 2}{\alpha + 0{\cdot}5 \sin 2}\right] . \tan \beta. \qquad (3.9)$$

3.9. Disc Brakes

The mechanics of these brakes, which are rapidly superseding the expanding shoe type, is simple since the basic principle of operation is to push friction pads against a rotating disc as shown in Fig. 3.17. The pads usually have a small area compared with the area of the disc and the friction torque is given by

$$T = \mu . P . r, \qquad (3.10)$$

where P is the thrust normal to a pad and r the mean radius of the pad from the disc centre. To equalize the thrust on the disc in an axial direction, a second pad is usually placed on the other side of the disc, a caliper action being then applied by the pads to the disc. The torque resulting from the two pads is then

$$T = 2 . \mu . P . r \qquad (3.11)$$

Some degree of "self actuation" is often incorporated whereby two discs are forced apart against friction pads. The relative turning of the discs forces balls to move in radial grooves, and by so doing, force the discs further apart. This increase of normal thrust of one disc on the contacting friction pad gives an increased frictional drag and so an increased braking torque.

Whilst the determination of the frictional torque is theoretically simple, and these brakes have advantages of good anti-fade

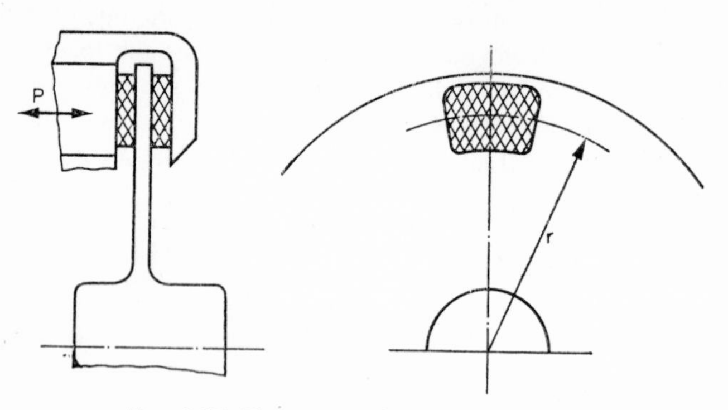

FIG. 3.17. Thrust on a simple disc brake pad

properties, their development has not been equally simple and many factors have yet to be evaluated. Some of these include, basic arrangements of axial floating disc with fixed calipers, fixed disc and axially floating calipers, both disc and calipers fixed, the choice of suitable shape and number of pads to give optimum wear, the dissipation of heat and rigidity of the brake, to name a few. All of these parameters have been the subject of research and readers are referred to recent publications of this work for information which is beyond the scope of this book.

Examples

3.7. A motor car weighing 2500 lb has axles 8 ft apart. When standing on a level road, the centre of gravity of the car is 2 ft above ground level and 3 ft in front of the rear axle. Calculate the normal reaction on each wheel when the car is moving down a gradient of 1 in 20 against a wind pressure of 40 lb acting parallel to the road and 2 ft 6 in. from it, with the engine switched off and the rear wheel brakes applied so as to give a deceleration of 2 ft/sec^2. What must the coefficient of friction between the rear wheels and the road be if the rear wheels are not to skid under these conditions?

(U.L.1 Ext., 1950)

Answers: 752·5 lb each rear wheel; 497·5 lb each front wheel; 0·157.

3.8. A motor car running down a hill of gradient 1 in 5 is brought to rest uniformly from a speed of 35 m.p.h. in a distance of 80 ft when braked on the front wheels only. The wheel base of the car is 9 ft and the centre of gravity 5 ft behind the front axle and 2 ft 6 in. above the ground. Calculate the value of the coefficient of friction between road and tyre, and the stopping distance when climbing the hill at the same speed and braked on the rear wheels only.

(A.M.I.Mech.E., 1950)

Answers: 1·12, 61 ft.

3.9. A motor vehicle has a wheel base of 8 ft and centre of gravity 3 ft behind the front axle and 2 ft above the ground. The vehicle is allowed to run freely down an incline whose sine is 1/6, until a speed of 30 m.p.h. is attained. The hand brake is then fully applied so as to provide the maximum possible braking effect on the rear wheels only. If μ between tyres and road surface is 0·4, calculate the speed of the vehicle after a distance of 200 ft from rest has been covered. Comment on your answer. (U.L.1 Ext., 1956)

Answer: 30·3 m.p.h. Although brakes are applied, the vehicle is still accelerating.

3.10. A motor car has a total weight of 2500 lb with a wheel base of 100 in. and the centre of gravity 45 in. behind the front axle and 30 in. above the ground. The brakes are applied when the car is running down a hill of gradient 1 in 10 at 45 m.p.h. so that all the wheels are skidding, and it is brought to rest with uniform deceleration in a distance of 220 ft. Calculate:

(*a*) the value of the coefficient of friction between tyre and road;

(*b*) the stopping distance and normal load on the front wheels for the same running conditions when the car is braked to skid the front wheels only with the rear brakes inoperative. (A.M.I.Mech.E., 1960)

Answers: (*a*) 0·41; (*b*) 457 ft; 778 lb.

3.11. A motor cycle has wheels 4 ft 9 in. apart. The centre of gravity of the cycle and rider is 2 ft 6 in. above ground level and 2 ft in front of the rear axle.

The coefficient of friction between the tyres and the road is 0·75. If the rear wheel is braked, find the greatest deceleration that can be obtained

(*a*) if the cycle is moving in a straight path,

(*b*) if it is going round a curve of 150 ft radius at 30 m.p.h. Assume a level road and neglect air resistance. Neglect rotational inertia and obliquity when turning. (U.L.2 Ext., 1951)

Answers: (*a*) 10 ft/sec^2; (*b*) 7·7 ft/sec^2.

3.12. Figure 3.18 shows a brake drum 11 in. diameter, acted on by two brake shoes which are mounted on a pin *A*, and pushed apart by two hydraulically operated pistons at *B*, each exerting a force of *P* lb on each shoe on which

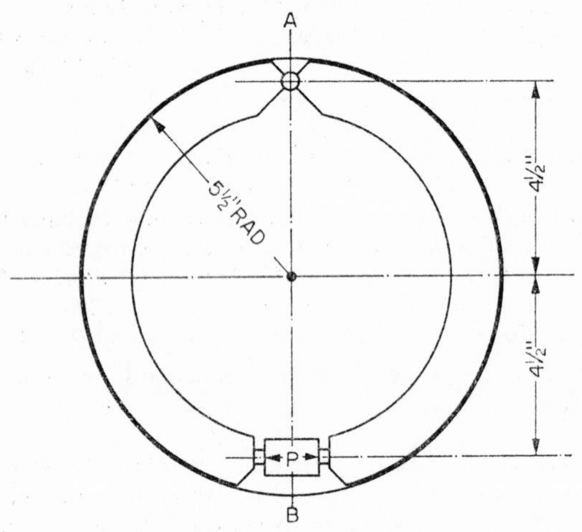

FIG. 3.18. Brake arrangement for example 3.12

it makes contact. The brake lining on each shoe extends 60° above to 60° below the horizontal centre line. The coefficient of friction is 0·2 and the lining width is 1 in. The radial pressure between the lining and the drum is proportional to the rate of wear of the lining. Find graphically, or otherwise, the value of *P* to produce a braking torque of 100 lb ft.

(U.L.2 Ext., 1951)

Answer: 214 lb (assuming $p \propto \sin\theta$).

3.13. In Figure 3.19 particulars are given of two brake shoes which act on the internal surface of a cylindrical brake drum; the lining forces F_1 and F_2 are applied as shown and are equal in magnitude (each being the reaction of the other) and each shoe pivots on its fixed fulcrums P_1 and P_2. The width of the lining is 1·5 in. and the intensity of pressure at any point X is 65 sin θ lb/in² where θ is measured as shown from either pivot. The coefficient of

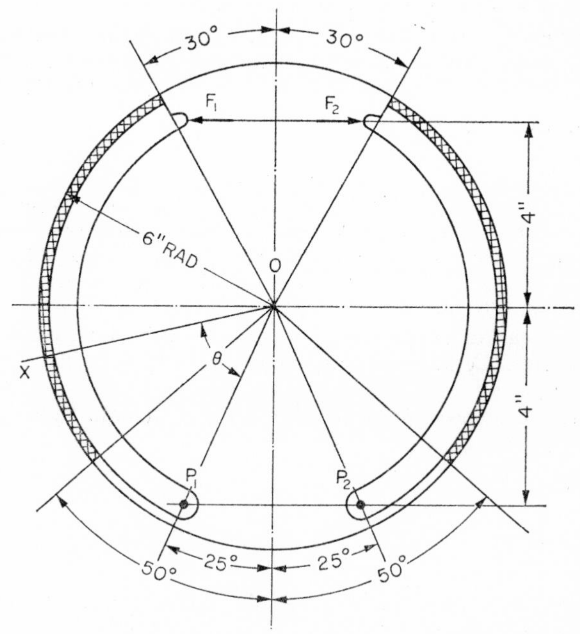

FIG. 3.19. Brake arrangement for example 3.13

riction is 0·35. Determine the braking torque and magnitude of forces F_1 and F_2. (U.L.2 Ext., 1955)

Answers: (If pressure as stated then F_1 cannot equal F_2.) $F_1 = 620$ lb; $F_2 = 220$ lb.

3.14. A motor vehicle of 3000 lb all up weight is fitted with brakes on all four wheels and is slowed down uniformly from 60 m.p.h. to 30 m.p.h. in a distance of 500 ft while running down an incline of 1 in 15. Assuming that the front wheels share 55 per cent of the braking forces, calculate the mean lining pressure in lb/in^2 on the front wheel brakes from the following data:

Effective wheel diameter	28 in.
Brake drum diameter	12·5 in.
Brake lining width	2·5 in.
Lining contact in each drum	210°
Coefficient of friction	0·35

Calculate the amount of heat generated in B.t.u. during this operation and discuss methods of improving the heat transfer from the brake drum to the air.

(A.M.I.Mech.E., 1955)

Answers: 23 lb/in^2; 475 B.t.u.

3.15. Describe, with the aid of sketches, the actions of leading and trailing shoes of internal-expanding brakes and discuss the effects of using a floating-cam mechanism for operating the shoes. A brake drum is 10 in. diameter. The pivots for the brake shoes and the points of application of the forces separating the shoes are each at 4 in. from the axis of rotation. Assuming that the pressure distribution over the brake-lining is such that the resultant normal pressure is equal to a single force acting radially, and that the coefficient of friction is 0·25, calculate the braking torque exerted by an operating force of 200 lb on:

(*a*) the leading shoe; (*b*) the trailing shoe. (A.M.I.Mech.E., 1958)

Answers: (*a*) 728 lb in.; (*b*) 428 lb in.

References

1. Acres, F. S., Some problems in the design of braking systems, *Proc. Inst. Automobile Eng.* **41** 405 (1946).
2. Waller, I. M., Internal expanding shoe brakes for road vehicles, *Proc. Inst. Automobile Eng.* **41** (1949–1950).
3. Robinson, J. G., Brake design considerations, *Automobile Engineer*, Sept. 1959, pp. 340–348.

CHAPTER FOUR

DRY FRICTION CLUTCHES

DRY friction clutches which are, or have been, used on automobiles consist broadly of conical and single or multiple plate types. In this chapter only the plate type clutches will be considered

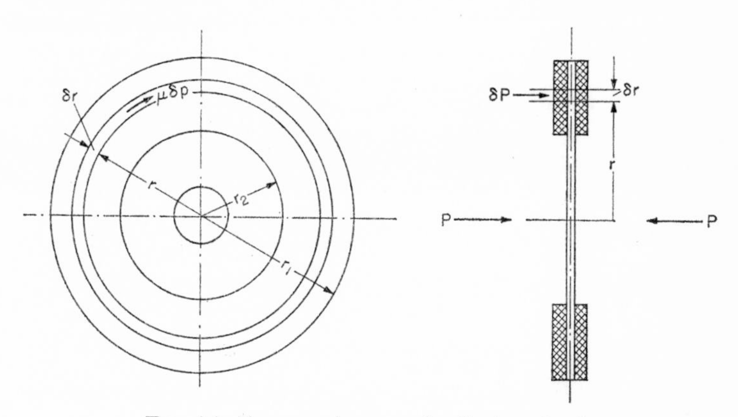

FIG. 4.1. Forces acting on a simple plate clutch

since the conical type are nowadays little used and the method of calculating the power transmitted is, in any case, applicable to both types. The mechanics of plate clutches is usually concerned with the determination of the thrust on the disc, the torque transmitted, withdrawal forces, etc.

4.1. Single Plate Clutch

Figure 4.1 shows a plate clutch having linings whose internal and external radii are r_2 and r_1 respectively. Consider an elementary ring of the lining of radius r and width δr, so that no matter how the pressure normal to the lining may vary over the lining, on the element it can be considered constant having a value p.

Thrust δP on element of lining $= p \times \text{area} = p \,.\, 2\pi r \,.\, \delta r$, and so the total thrust in an axial direction is

$$P = \int_{r_2}^{r_1} 2\pi p \,.\, r \,.\, \mathrm{d}r. \tag{4.1}$$

The frictional drag δF on the element

$$= \text{coefficient of friction} \times \text{normal thrust}$$

$$\delta F = \mu \times \delta p = \mu \,.\, p \,.\, 2\pi r \,.\, \delta r$$

and so the frictional torque due to this

$$= r \,.\, \delta F$$

$$= \mu \,.\, p \,.\, 2\pi r^2 \,.\, \delta r$$

Hence total torque (for one set of contacting surfaces)

$$= \int_{r_2}^{r_1} 2\pi \,.\, \mu \,.\, p \,.\, r^2 \mathrm{d}r$$

and in the case of a single disc with two operating surfaces, i.e., the disc has friction material on both sides, driven by contact with a pressure plate and flywheel, then

$$\text{effective torque, } T = 2\int_{r_2}^{r_1} 2\pi \,.\, \mu \,.\, p \,.\, r^2 \mathrm{d}r \tag{4.2}$$

Equations (4.1) and (4.2) cannot be developed further without some knowledge, or assumptions, of the variation of μ and p, with r. It is customary to assume that μ is constant over the whole contact surface, but the variation of p is by no means fully known or, for a given surface, can be predicted. With a pair of new, carefully produced surfaces the intensity of normal pressure when axially loaded can be assumed reasonably constant. However, when slid relative to each other, the surfaces will not wear uniformly over the full extent of their contact and so, when wear takes place, the distribution of pressure will alter. Some doubt therefore must exist as to the precise condition of the surfaces and their normal pressure when in use. Calculations are generally made on a basis of either:

(i) uniform normal intensity of pressure, or
(ii) constant rate of wear.

(i) Assuming uniform pressure (p),

$$\text{Axial thrust } P = 2\pi \,.\, p\int_{r_2}^{r_1} r \,.\, \mathrm{d}r = 2\pi \,.\, p[r^2/2]_{r_2}^{r_1}$$

$$P = \pi \,.\, p(r_1^2 - r_2^2) \tag{4.3}$$

Total torque (two sides)

$$T = 2\pi \,.\, \mu \,.\, p\int_{r_2}^{r_1} r^2\mathrm{d}r = \frac{2\pi}{3} \,.\, \mu \,.\, p[r^3]_{r_2}^{r_1}$$

$$T = \frac{2\pi \,.\, \mu p}{3}(r_1^3 - r_2^3) \tag{4.4}$$

(ii) The implication of constant rate of wear is that material is abrased at a constant rate which will be proportional to the volume of material worn away. The frictional rate of work = frictional force × velocity of rubbing. Hence, equating the rates of working,

volume removed $\propto \mu \,.\, p \,.\, v$, where v is the rubbing velocity.

Thus $p \,.\, v$ = constant, and since in a flat disc, $v = r \,.\, \omega$, where ω is the relative angular velocity between surfaces,

$$p \,.\, r = \text{constant for uniform wear rate} \tag{4.5}$$

Note that on this assumption p is largest when r is smallest, i.e., at the internal radius.

Thus for constant wear,

$$\text{axial thrust} \quad P = 2\pi(p \,.\, r)\int_{r_2}^{r_1} \mathrm{d}r = 2\pi(p \,.\, r)(r_1 - r_2) \tag{4.6}$$

and

$$\text{torque (for two sides)} \; T = 2 \,.\, 2\pi \,.\, \mu \,.\, (p \,.\, r)\int_{r_2}^{r_1} r \,.\, \mathrm{d}r$$

$$T = 2\pi \,.\, \mu \,.\, (p \,.\, r)(r_1^2 - r_2^2) \tag{4.7}$$

In general for a given axial load, p or $(p \,.\, r)$ may be determined using equations (4.3) or (4.6) and then substitution for p or $(p \,.\, r)$ in equation (4.4) or (4.7), as applicable, will give the torque transmitted.

Regarding which assumption to use, it should be noted that equation (4.4) always gives a larger value for T than does equation (4.7) and so if the clutch is designed on the basis of the smaller power transmitted, then equation (4.7) should be used. There is however no fixed rule. Examination candidates are advised to answer questions from first principles as shown in the following worked example, and it is hoped that examiners will indicate the required assumption to make. In the absence of any indication, it is common practice to use constant wear assumption for clutches and constant pressure assumption for bearings.

WORKED EXAMPLE (A.M.I.Mech.E., 1960)

4.1. A motor car is fitted with a single-plate, dry disc type of clutch with lining dimensions; external diameter 9 in., internal diameter 6 in. The clutch is engaged by six springs of free length 2·5 in. and stiffness 160 lb/in. Assuming a coefficient of friction of 0·4 calculate the length to which the springs must be compressed for the clutch to transmit 80 h.p. at 2000 r.p.m. Describe, with the aid of sketches, the construction of the friction plate hub including any features designed to reduce noise and vibration.

Solution

Referring to Fig. 4.1, assuming constant wear, $(p\,.\,r) =$ constant.

Total axial thrust

$$= P = 2\pi\,.\,(p\,.\,r)\int_{3}^{4\cdot 5} dr = 2\pi\,.\,(p\,.\,r)(4\cdot 5 - 3\cdot 0) = 3\pi\,.\,(p\,.\,r)\text{ lb}$$

Frictional torque

$$= 2 \times 2\pi\,.\,\mu\,.\,(p\,.\,r)\int_{3}^{4\cdot 5} r\,.\,dr = 4\pi\,.\,\mu\,.\,(p\,.\,r)(4\cdot 5^2 - 3^2)/2.$$

But torque $= \dfrac{80 \times 33{,}000}{2\pi \times 2000} \times 12 = 2520$ lb in.

$$2520 = 2\pi \times 0\cdot 4 \times 7\cdot 5 \times 1\cdot 5\,(p\,.\,r)$$

and so

$$(p\,.\,r) = \frac{2520}{2\pi \times 0\cdot 4 \times 7\cdot 5 \times 1\cdot 5} = 89\cdot 3$$

Therefore axial thrust $= 3\pi \times 89\cdot 3$ lb $= 840$ lb.

Load supplied by each spring $= \dfrac{840}{6} = 140$ lb.

Compression of spring

$$= \frac{140}{160} = 0\cdot 875\text{ in.}$$

and so length of compressed springs

$$= 2\cdot 5 - 0\cdot 875 = 1\cdot 625\text{ in.}$$

WORKED EXAMPLE (U.L.1 Ext., 1956)

4.2. A plate clutch having a single driving plate with contact surfaces on each side is required to transmit 150 horsepower at 1250 r.p.m. The outer diameter of the contact surfaces is to be 12 in. The coefficient of friction is 0·4.

(a) Assuming a uniform pressure of 25 lb/in², determine the inner diameter of the friction surfaces.

(b) Assuming the same dimensions and the same total axial thrust, determine the maximum torque that can be transmitted and the maximum intensity of pressure when "uniform wear" conditions have been reached. Work from first principles throughout.

Solution

Refer to Fig. 4.1 and using symbols defined in paragraph 4.1,

$$\text{(a) torque on plate} = T = \frac{150 \times 33{,}000}{2 \times 1250} \,.\, 12 = 7560 \text{ lb in.}$$

Hence

$$7560 = 2 \times 2\pi \times 0{\cdot}4 \times p \int_{r_2}^{6} r^2 dr = \frac{4\pi \times 0{\cdot}4 \times 25}{3}(6^3 - r_2^3)$$

$$6 - r_2^3 = \frac{7560 \times 3}{4\pi \times 0{\cdot}4 \times 25} = 180$$

$$r_2^3 = 216 - 180 = 36$$

$$r_2 = 3{\cdot}3 \text{ in. and internal diameter} = 6{\cdot}6 \text{ in.}$$

(b) $(p \,.\, r) =$ constant.

Axial thrust $(p \,.\, r)$ constant

$$= 2\pi \,.\, (p \,.\, r) \int_{3\cdot3}^{6} dr = 2\pi \,.\, (p \,.\, r) \times 2{\cdot}7$$

Axial thrust (p) constant

$$= 2\pi \times 25 \int_{3\cdot3}^{6} r dr = \frac{2\pi \times 25 \times 9{\cdot}3 \times 2{\cdot}7}{2},$$

therefore $$(p \, . \, r) = \frac{25 \times 9{\cdot}3}{2} = 116{\cdot}2.$$

Maximum intensity of pressure is when $r = 3{\cdot}3$ and so

$$p = \frac{116{\cdot}2}{3{\cdot}3} = 35{\cdot}3 \text{ lb/in}^2.$$

Torque, $$T = 2 \times 2\pi \times 0{\cdot}4 \times 116{\cdot}2 \int_{3\cdot3}^{6} r dr$$

$$= 2\pi \times 0{\cdot}4 \times 116{\cdot}2(6^2 - 3{\cdot}3^2) \text{ lb in.}$$

$$= 2\pi \times 0{\cdot}4 \times 116{\cdot}2 \times 9{\cdot}3 \times 2{\cdot}7 = 7330 \text{ lb in.}$$

The time taken to accelerate a system through a clutch is of interest particularly when clutch slip occurs. The following worked example illustrates this aspect for a friction drive suddenly applied and then with normal slip.

WORKED EXAMPLE (U.L.2 Ext., 1949 (Modified))

4.3. An engine drives a co-axial rotor through a single plate clutch which has two pairs of driving surfaces each of 11 in. external and 8 in. internal diameter; the total spring load pressing the plate together is 125 lb. The weight of the engine flywheel and shaft is 1750 lb and its radius of gyration 10·5 in.; the rotor weighs 3000 lb and its radius of gyration is 9 in. The engine is brought up to a speed of 1250 r.p.m., the ignition switched off and the clutch suddenly engaged. Determine the final speed of the engine and rotor, and find the time taken to reach that speed and the kinetic energy lost during the period of slipping. How long would slipping continue if a constant engine torque of 40 lb ft were maintained on the engine shaft. Coefficient of friction = 0·35 and assume constant wear conditions.

Solution

The sudden engagement of the clutch results in an impulsive torque of engine on rotor and vice versa. As there is no external applied torque (engine ignition off), there will be no change in the total angular momentum of the engine and rotor. Thus,

$$I_E \cdot \omega_E + 0 \text{ (rotor at rest)} = (I_E + I_R) \cdot \omega$$

where ω is the common speed.

$$\omega = \frac{I_E}{I_E + I_R} \times \omega_E$$

$$I_E = \frac{1740}{32{\cdot}2}\left(\frac{10{\cdot}5}{12}\right)^2 = 41{\cdot}6 \text{ slugs ft}^2;$$

$$I_R = \frac{3000}{32{\cdot}2}\left(\frac{9}{12}\right)^2 = 52{\cdot}4 \text{ slugs ft}^2$$

Thus $N = \dfrac{41{\cdot}6}{94} \times 1250 = 553$ r.p.m. or 58 rad/sec.

$$\text{Frictional torque} = 2 \times 2\pi \times 0{\cdot}35 \times (p \,.\, r)\int_4^{5{\cdot}5} r \,.\, dr \text{ lb in.}$$

Axial thrust

$$= 125 = 2\pi \times (p \,.\, r)\int_4^{5{\cdot}5} dr = 2\pi(p \,.\, r) \,.\, (5{\cdot}5 - 4{\cdot}0)$$

and

$$2\pi(p \,.\, r) = \frac{125}{1{\cdot}5}$$

hence, torque

$$= \frac{125 \times 0{\cdot}35 \times 9{\cdot}5 \times 1{\cdot}5}{1{\cdot}5} = 416 \text{ lb in.} = 34{\cdot}7 \text{ lb ft.}$$

Acceleration of rotor under this torque

$$= \frac{34{\cdot}7}{52{\cdot}4} = 0{\cdot}662 \text{ rad/sec}^2$$

Time to reach speed $= \dfrac{58}{0{\cdot}662} = 87{\cdot}6$ sec.

Angular K.E. before clutch is engaged

$$= 0{\cdot}5 \times 41{\cdot}6 \times \left(\frac{1250 \times 2}{60}\right)^2 = 356{,}000 \text{ ft lb.}$$

Angular K.E. at common speed

$$= 0{\cdot}5(41{\cdot}6 + 52{\cdot}4) \times 58^2 = 158{,}000 \text{ ft lb.}$$

Loss of K.E. = 198,000 ft lb.

When the clutch is engaged with the engine torque applied, torque on engine shaft

$$= 40 - \text{frictional torque} = 40 - 34{\cdot}7 = 5{\cdot}3 \text{ lb ft}$$

which accelerates the engine shaft from 1250 r.p.m. to the common speed, acceleration

$$= \frac{5{\cdot}3}{41{\cdot}6} = 0{\cdot}1275 \text{ rad/sec}^2$$

and thus

$$\frac{\omega - 131}{t} = 0{\cdot}1275.$$

Torque on rotor shaft = frictional torque = 34·7 and so acceleration

$$= \frac{34{\cdot}7}{52{\cdot}4} = 0{\cdot}663 \text{ rad/sec}^2$$

and thus

$$\frac{\omega}{t} = 0{\cdot}663,$$

giving

$$0{\cdot}663t - 131 = 0{\cdot}1275t$$

and $$t = \frac{131}{0{\cdot}5355} = 245 \text{ sec.}$$

4.2. Multi-Disc Clutches

The mechanics of the friction of these is similar to that of a single disc. The full load in the axial direction is carried by each disc. The torque transmitted will be the sum of the torque for each contacting pair of surfaces that drive.

Examples

4.4. A plate clutch consists of a flat driven plate gripped between a driving plate and a pressure plate so that there are two active driving surfaces each having a diameter of 8 in. and 14 in. The working pressure is limited to 25 lb/in^2 and the coefficient of friction is 0·4. Assume uniform pressure and calculate the h.p. transmitted at 1000 r.p.m. If due to wear, the intensity of pressure becomes inversely proportional to the radius the total axial force on the pressure plate remaining unaltered, calculate the h.p. and the greatest intensity of pressure on the friction surfaces. (U.L.1 Ext., 1944)

Answers: 184 h.p.; 181 h.p.; 34·2 lb/in^2.

4.5. A clutch for a motor vehicle is required to transmit 60 h.p. at 2500 r.p.m. It is to be of the single plate type (using both sides), the inner diameter being 3/4 of the outer. Allowing for a maximum intensity of pressure of 12·5 lb/in^2 and a coefficient of friction of 0·2 determine, from first principles, the external diameter of the plate. State clearly any assumptions made. Make a diagrammatic sketch showing the way in which the pressure is applied, and the means for relieving that pressure. (U.L.1 Ext., 1954)

Answer: 13·3 in.

4.6. A friction clutch is required to transmit 45 horsepower at 2000 r.p.m. It is to be of single-plate disc type with both sides of the plate effective, the pressure being applied by means of springs and limited to 10 lb/in^2. If the outer diameter of the plate is to be 12 in., find the required inner diameter of the clutch ring and the total force exerted by the springs. Assume wear to be uniform and a coefficient of friction of 0·3. (U.L.1 Ext., 1949)

Answers: 5·14 in. or 8·68 in.; 553 lb or 453 lb. Hint. Solve cubic equation by graph.

4.7. A power shaft running at a steady speed of 175 r.p.m. drives a countershaft through a single plate friction clutch of external and internal diameters 15 in. and 9 in. respectively. The masses on the countershaft have a radius of gyration of 10 in. and a total weight of 750 lb. The axial spring load operating the clutch is 100 lb and the limiting coefficient of friction for the surfaces is 0·3. Assuming uniform acceleration, determine the time required to reach full speed from rest and the work dissipated due to clutch slip during that time. Any formula used for the clutch torque should be established. Assume uniform wear and two pairs of active surfaces. (U.L.1 Ext., 1941)

Answers: 9·9 sec; 2723 ft lb.

4.8. A rotor A on a shaft X is connected through light gearing G with a shaft Y carrying a rotor B; the moments of inertia of the two rotors are 120 [illegible] respectively. Between A and G is a single plate clutch with two pairs of friction surfaces, of inner and outer diameters 6 in. and 10 in.; the total thrust of the springs is 150 lb. The coefficient of friction on the friction surfaces is 0·35 and the speed ratio from X to Y is 1·4 when slipping has ceased. The rotor A is given a speed of 2500 r.p.m., with the clutch disengaged; if the clutch is then engaged determine the final speeds of the two rotors, stating clearly any assumptions made. The inertia of clutch, the shafts and gearing may be neglected. (U.L.1 Ext., 1956)

Answers: $A = 326$ r.p.m., $B = 1304$ r.p.m. (Note, Very simple by momentum.)

CHAPTER FIVE

GEAR BOX

CONVENTIONAL gearing in automobiles has for many years been of the compound synchromesh type owing mainly to the advantage of low initial cost, simplicity and low cost of maintenance. The epicyclic type of gear box has been known for many years but has been used very little prior to the advent of automatic transmissions. The Wilson gear box is a notable exception which has been used in fighting vehicles and the heavier commercial vehicles. Nowadays, automatic transmission is the vogue and whether semi or full, epicyclic gearing is conveniently and extensively used. The composition of the gear box to give a predetermined velocity ratio and the torque carried by the gears when power is transmitted are factors of interest. The conventional type of gear box has received ample treatment in elementary books and in this chapter therefore, most attention will be given to epicyclic trains.

5.1. Simple Epicyclic Gear. Velocity Ratios

A simple epicyclic train, shown in Fig. 5.1, consists of a sun wheel S meshing with planet wheels P. The planet wheels can rotate about pins carried on an arm M, sometimes called a spider, whilst being carried bodily by the arm around the sun. The planet wheels also mesh with an internal gear wheel called an annulus A. Usually the input and output shafts are connected to the arm and sun gear whilst the annulus is generally held stationary. The epicyclic train is clearly more complex than a simple or compound train since whilst in the latter all gears rotate about fixed axes, in the epicyclic gear the planet gears rotate about axes that can themselves move in circular paths. Since the planet gear has a motion which is the combination of two other motions, the basic problem is therefore one of relative angular velocities. It is convenient to consider the velocities of gears relative to that of the

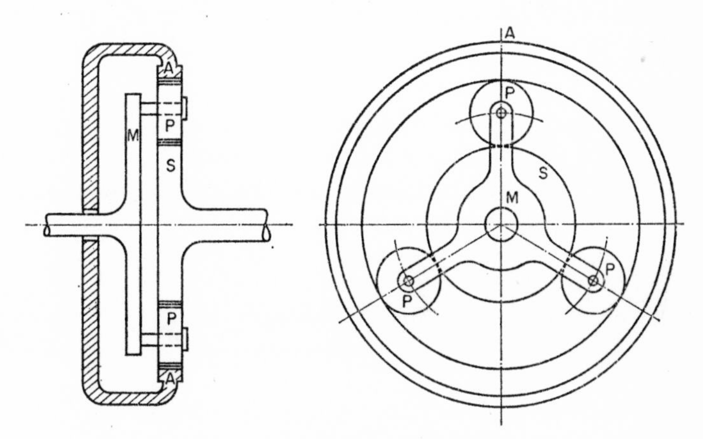

FIG. 5.1. Simple epicyclic gear train

arm M, since by so doing, the arm can be imagined "fixed" and then the speeds of the gears are related to the numbers of teeth on the gear wheels. Thus

$$\frac{\text{Speed of planet wheel relative to arm}}{\text{Speed of sun relative to the arm}} = -\frac{\text{number of teeth on } S}{\text{number of teeth on } P}$$

(the minus sign indicates that there is a reversal of rotation between the externally meshing sun and planet gears when each is considered relative to the motion of the arm. See Fig. 5.2a).

But the speed of the planet gear relative to the arm is a direct subtraction, or addition, of speeds since only rotations are possible and so, if N denotes gear speed, and t teeth,

$$\frac{N_P - N_M}{N_S - N_M} = -\frac{t_S}{t_P} \qquad (5.1)$$

Similarly for motion of annulus and planet

$$\frac{N_A - N_M}{N_P - N_M} = +\frac{t_P}{t_A} \qquad (5.2)$$

(Note positive sign for internal meshing of planet and annulus. See Fig. 5.2b.)

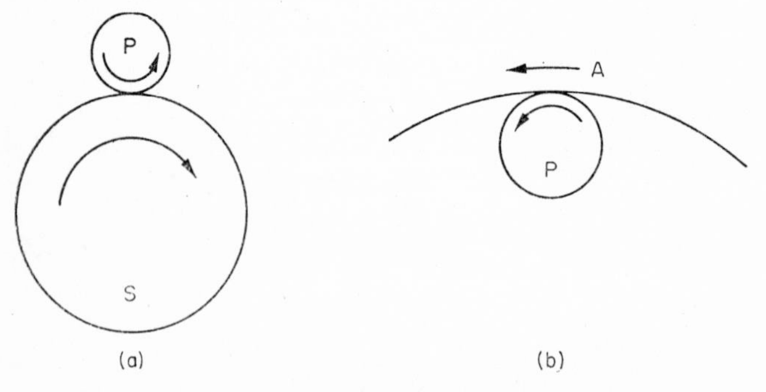

FIG. 5.2. External and internal meshing of the planet gear

This method known as the velocity ratio method, will apply to any pairs of gears in the epicyclic train provided their speeds are compared both relative to the arm and so, for example, for the simple train considered

$$\frac{N_A - N_M}{N_S - N_M} = \left(-\frac{t_S}{t_P}\right) \times \left(+\frac{t_P}{t_A}\right) = -\frac{t_S}{t_A}. \qquad (5.3)$$

Solution of these equations to suit given requirements enables the speeds of the gears to be determined. This method has full application and is recommended. Other methods are all derived from velocity ratio considerations and are either limited in their application or are cumbersome in application, this is particularly so in compound epicyclic gear trains used in automatic transmission.

WORKED EXAMPLE

5.1. A simple epicyclic gear consists of a sun wheel having 60 teeth, planet wheels having 20 teeth carried on a spider and an internally geared annulus. Determine:

(a) the number of teeth on the annulus,

(b) the speed of the arm when the sun wheel rotates at 100 r.p.m. and the annulus is held stationary,

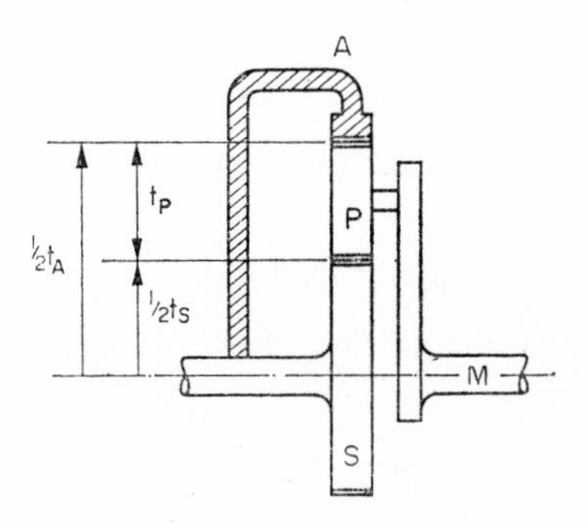

FIG. 5.3. Epicyclic gear of example 5.1

(c) the speed of the arm when the sun wheel rotates at 100 r.p.m. and the annulus is driven at a speed of 20 r.p.m. in the same direction as the sun wheel.

Solution

(a) The teeth must have the same diametral pitch and so the numbers of teeth are proportional to the gear diameters. But, rad. of A = rad. of S + dia. of P

$$\tfrac{1}{2}t_A = \tfrac{1}{2}t_S + t_P = 30 + 20$$

$$t_A = 100.$$

(b) Choice of equation is determined by information that speed S, speed A are known, and arm M must be included, hence

$$\frac{N_A - N_M}{N_S - N_M} = \left(-\frac{t_S}{t_P}\right) \times \left(+\frac{t_P}{t_A}\right) = -\frac{60}{100} = \frac{-3}{5}.$$

Substituting values of $N_A = 0$ and $N_S = 100$,

$$\frac{0 - N_M}{100 - N_M} = \frac{-3}{5}$$

hence

$$-300 + 3N_M = -5N_M$$

and so

$$N_M = \frac{300}{8} = 25 \text{ r.p.m.}$$

and since value is +ve the arm rotates in same direction as S.

(c) Equation as before but now $N_A = 20$ and $N_S = 100$, giving

$$\frac{20 - N_M}{100 - N_M} = \frac{-3}{5}$$

and

$$N_M = 50 \text{ r.p.m.},$$

i.e., in same direction as sun.

WORKED EXAMPLE

5.2. In the epicyclic gear train shown in Fig. 5.4, the wheel A and wheel E (30t) are fixed to a sleeve Y which is free to rotate on spindle X. B (24t) and C (22t) are keyed to a shaft which is free to rotate in a bearing on arm F. D has 70 teeth. H has 15 teeth and is mounted on a shaft V rotating at 100 r.p.m. Spindle X

makes 300 r.p.m. in the same direction as V. All teeth are of the same pitch. Find the speed and direction of rotation of Z. (U.L.1 Ext., 1951).

Solution

$$\tfrac{1}{2}t_A + \tfrac{1}{2}t_B = \tfrac{1}{2}t_C + \tfrac{1}{2}t_D$$

and so

$$t_A = 70 + 22 - 24 = 68.$$

When using the velocity ratio method, apply it ONLY to the epicyclic part, which here is: $D(CB)F(AE)$

$$\frac{N_D - N_F}{N_A - N_F} = \left(\frac{-22}{70}\right) \times \left(\frac{-68}{24}\right).$$

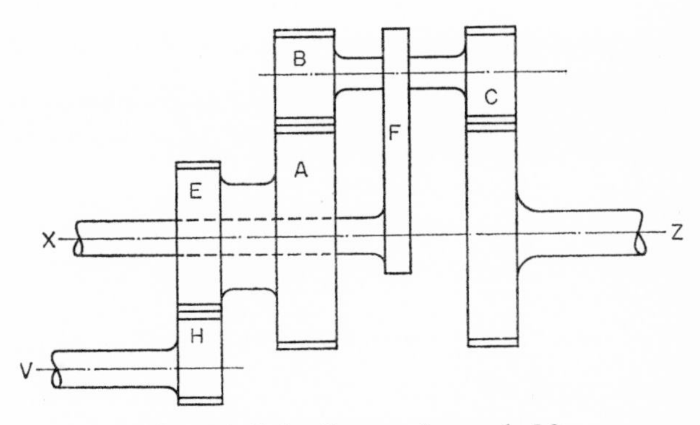

FIG. 5.4. Epicyclic gear of example 5.2

Hint. Let gear in denominator turn once and express turns of gear that meshes with it. This number of turns will be either increased or diminished by the next pair meshing and so on, putting in the appropriate sign at each meshing pair. Take care over this particularly, as in this problem, when the planet is compound.

Note also planet meshes with double sun and not with annulus.

$$\frac{N_D - 300}{N_A - 300} = \frac{22 \times 68}{70 \times 24} = \frac{187}{210} = \frac{N_Z - 300}{N_E - 300}$$

But

$$N_E = -\frac{15}{30} \cdot N_H = -\frac{15 \times 100}{30} = -50 \text{ r.p.m.}$$

Therefore

$$\frac{N_Z - 300}{-50 - 300} = \frac{187}{210},$$

and giving

$$N_Z - 300 = -311\tfrac{2}{3} \text{ r.p.m.}$$

$$N_Z = -11\tfrac{2}{3} \text{ r.p.m.},$$

i.e., opposite to spindle X.

5.2. Compound Epicyclic Gear: Velocity Ratios

Simple epicyclic gears are not of much value in gear boxes since they cannot give adequate velocity ratios. In order therefore to give higher velocity ratios and to allow several ratios to be obtained from one gear box, simple epicyclic trains are coupled together giving a compound epicyclic train. A common way of doing this is to join together all the arms of the separate simple trains, but a variety of means of coupling can be made. Examination of some automatic transmission gear boxes will show the variety possible. However no matter how complex the train may be, the velocity ratio method outlined in paragraph 5.1 can be applied, and it is only the algebra that becomes more complex. The following worked examples will show the value of the velocity ratio method.

WORKED EXAMPLE (U.L.2 Ext., 1950)

5.3. Figure 5.5, shows a compound epicyclic gear train, gears S_1 and S_2 being rigidly attached to the shaft Q. If the shaft P rotates at 1000 r.p.m. clockwise, while the annulus A_2 is driven in the opposite direction at 500 r.p.m., determine the speed and direction of rotation of the shaft Q.

The numbers of teeth in the wheels are: $S_1 = 25$, $S_2 = 40$, $A_1 = 100$, $A_2 = 120$.

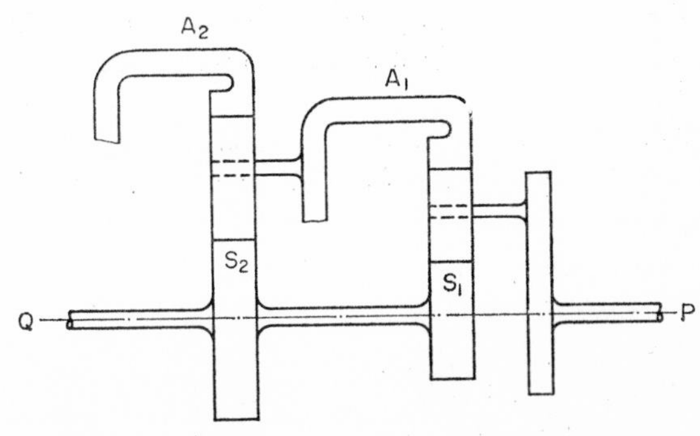

FIG. 5.5. Compound epicyclic gear of example 5.3

Solution

Refer to Fig. 5.5 and consider train P, S_1, A_1

$$\frac{N_{S1} - N_P}{N_{A1} - N_P} = \frac{-100}{25} = -4,$$

giving

$$N_{S1} + 4N_{A1} = 5000 \quad \text{or} \quad N_Q + 4N_{A1} = 5000. \qquad (1)$$

Consider train S_2, A_2 and arm A_1

$$\frac{N_{S2} - N_{A1}}{N_{A2} - N_{A1}} = \frac{-120}{40} = -3,$$

giving

$$N_{S2} - 4N_{A1} = -3N_{A2}, \quad \text{or} \quad N_Q - 4N_{A1} = 1500. \qquad (2)$$

Adding equations 1 and 2,

$$2N_Q = 6500,$$

or

$$N_Q = 3250 \text{ r.p.m. clockwise.}$$

WORKED EXAMPLE (U.L.2 1950 Int. (Modified))

5.4. The compound epicyclic gear shown in Fig. 5.6, has a driving shaft *D* and a driven shaft *E* to which the arms *F* and *G* are fixed.
The arms carry planet wheels which mesh with annular wheels *A* and *B*; and the sun wheels *H* and *J*. The sun wheel *H* is part of

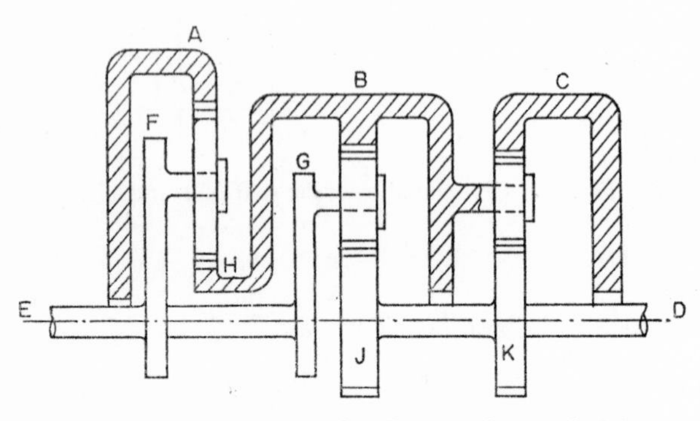

FIG. 5.6. Compound epicyclic gear of example 5.4

B. Wheels *J* and *K* are fixed to the shaft *D*. *K* engages with a planet wheel carried on *B* and this planet wheel engages the fixed annular wheel *C*. The numbers of teeth on the wheels are *A*–120, B–100, C–100, H–30, J–20 and K–25. Find the speeds and directions of rotation of the driven shaft *E* and the wheel *A* when the driving shaft *D* makes 1500 r.p.m. clockwise.

Solution

Referring to Fig. 5.6, consider epicyclic train K, C, arm B,

$$\frac{N_K - N_B}{N_C - N_B} = \frac{-100}{25} = -4,$$

and so

$$\frac{1500 - N_B}{0 - N_B} = -4$$

and

$$1500 - N_B = 4N_B \text{ and } N_B = 300 \text{ r.p.m.}$$

Consider epicyclic train B, J, arm G,

$$\frac{N_J - N_G}{N_B - N_G} = \frac{-100}{20} = -5,$$

and so

$$\frac{1500 - N_G}{300 - N_G} = -5,$$

whence

$$N_G = 500 \text{ r.p.m. clockwise} = \text{speed of } E.$$

Consider epicyclic train A, H, arm F,

$$\frac{N_H - N_F}{N_A - N_F} = \frac{-120}{30} = -4,$$

and so

$$\frac{300 - 500}{N_A - 500} = -4,$$

giving

$$N_A = 550 \text{ r.p.m. clockwise.}$$

5.3. Transmission of Power and Equilibrium or Epicyclic Gear

The transmission of power by a gear train results in torques being applied to the gears. Knowledge of these torques is required if the assembly is to be made adequately rigid and the teeth of suitable proportions. Assuming in the first instance that the gears of the train are rotating at their individually steady speeds and that power is supplied to one shaft and leaves the gear on one other shaft, then, two conditions are apparent.

(i) Since the gear box, in whole or in part, is not being accelerated the resultant torque acting must be zero.

(ii) If there is no loss of energy, in friction etc., then the rate of working on the input shaft is equal to the rate of output working on the output shaft, and since the rate of working is proportional to the product of speed and torque, then, input speed × input torque = output speed × output torque. If the gear box efficiency is $x\%$ then $x/100$ = ratio of the output and input torque–speed products.

These two simple principles may be applied to problems and no attempt is made to express them in symbols since this can lead to confusion over signs and examination candidates are advised to work from basic principles rather than apply equations blindly. To illustrate this, the following worked example is given.

WORKED EXAMPLE (U.L.1 Ext., 1947)

5.5. In the epicyclic gear shown in Fig. 5.7, the driving wheel A has 14 teeth and the fixed annular wheel C, 100 teeth; the ratio of the tooth numbers in wheels E and D is 98: 41. If $2\frac{1}{2}$ h.p. at 1200 r.p.m. is supplied to the wheel A, find the speed and direction of rotation of E, and the fixing torque required at C.

Solution

Referring to Fig. 5.7,

$$t_B = \tfrac{1}{2}t_C - \tfrac{1}{2}t_A = 50 - 7 = 43.$$

Considering epicyclic train A, B, C, arm M,

$$\frac{N_A - N_M}{N_C - N_M} = \frac{-100}{14}$$

and so

$$\frac{1200 - N_M}{0 - N_M} = \frac{-100}{14},$$

$$N_M = \frac{1200 \times 14}{114} = 147 \cdot 5 \text{ r.p.m.}$$

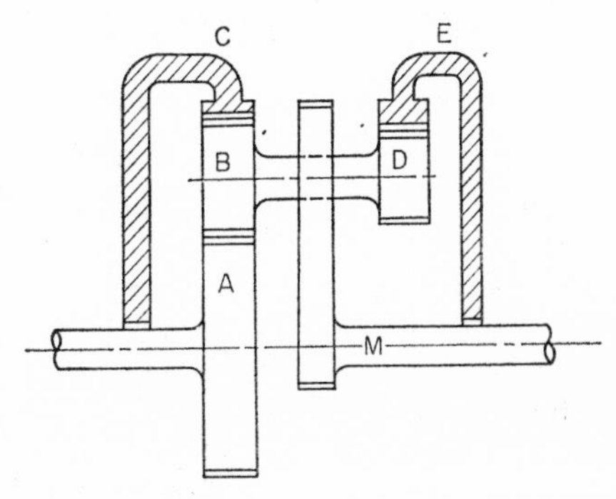

FIG. 5.7. Compound epicyclic gear of example 5.5

Considering epicyclic train A, BD, E, arm M,

$$\frac{N_A - N_M}{N_E - N_M} = \left(\frac{-43}{14}\right) \times \left(\frac{+98}{41}\right) = -7 \cdot 33,$$

giving

$$\frac{1200 - 147 \cdot 5}{N_E - 147 \cdot 5} = -7 \cdot 33,$$

and thus

$$N_E = 4 \cdot 0 \text{ r.p.m. same direction as } A.$$

The direction of speeds of rotation of A and E are shown in Fig. 5.8a.

The input torque

$$T_A = \frac{2 \cdot 5 \times 33{,}000}{2\pi \times 1200} = 10 \cdot 95 \text{ lb ft},$$

direction as shown in Fig. 5.8b.

The output torque

$$T_E = \frac{2 \cdot 5 \times 33{,}000}{2\pi \times 4} = 3285 \text{ lb ft}.$$

This torque will act on whatever the gear is driving in the direction of the output speed N_E. It is however the *reaction* of this torque that acts on the gear box as shown in Fig. 5.8b.

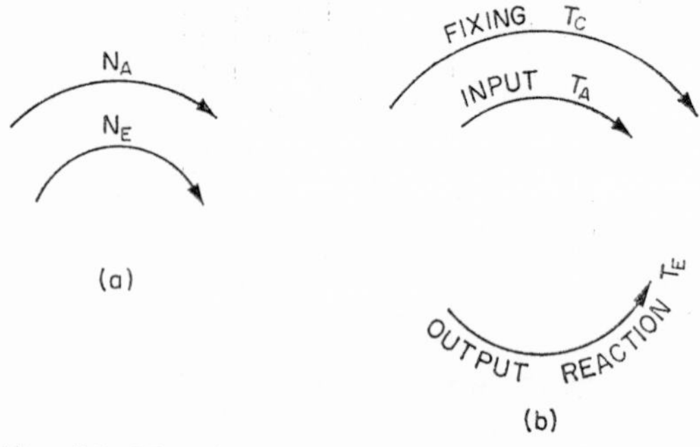

FIG. 5.8. Direction of speed and torque of the gear of example 5.5

The fixing torque has to keep the gear box in equilibrium and so fixing torque = 3285 − 10·95 = 3274 lb ft approximately in the direction shown in Fig. 5.8b.

5.4. Torque to Accelerate and Energy of an Epicyclic Gear Train

Since an automobile has to function under conditions of greatly varying speed and power, the torque required to accelerate the gear train and the energy that it has when all its parts are moving are factors that need considering. Since the gear train consists of rotating elements the torque and energy can be found by applying the well-known formulae $T = I \cdot \alpha$ and K.E. $= \frac{1}{2}I \cdot \omega^2$. It is however the inertia of the planet wheels that make the calculation a little more complex than in the case of non-epicyclic gears, as shown in the following worked examples.

WORKED EXAMPLE (U.L.2 Ext., 1951)

5.6. An epicyclic gear train has a fixed annulus, a sun wheel with 50 teeth and three planets (each 25 teeth) carried on a spider.

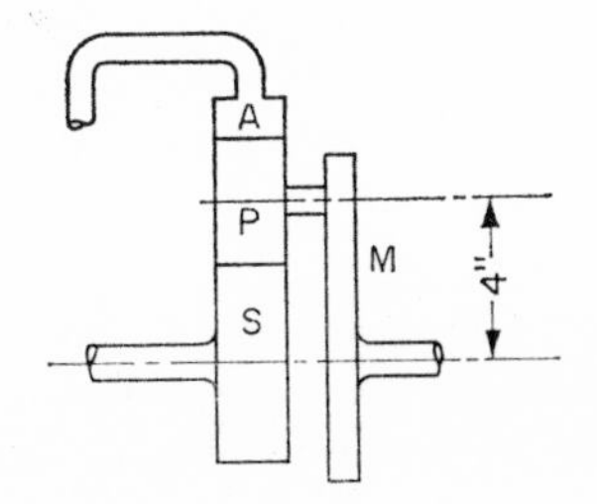

FIG. 5.9. Epicyclic gear of example 5.6

The radius of the path of the centre of each planet wheel is 4 in. The weights of the various members and their radii of gyration about their respective polar axes are:

	Weight	Radius of gyration
Sun wheel	8 lb	2 in.
Spider	20 lb	3 in.
Planet wheels (each)	$2\frac{1}{2}$ lb	1 in.

Determine the total kinetic energy of the gear train, in ft lb, if the sun wheel is driven at 600 r.p.m.

Solution

Referring to Fig. 5.9, before the kinetic energy can be calculated, the speeds of the gears are required.

$$t_A = 50 + 2 \times 25 = 100$$

and then

$$\frac{N_S - N_M}{N_A - N_M} = \frac{-100}{50},$$

hence

$$600 - N_M = 2N_M \text{ and } N_M = 200 \text{ r.p.m.} = 20{\cdot}94 \text{ rad/sec.}$$

$$\frac{N_P - N_M}{N_S - N_M} = \frac{-50}{25} = \frac{N_P - 200}{600 - 200}$$

and so

$$N_P = -600 \text{ r.p.m.} = -62{\cdot}84 \text{ rad/sec.}$$

The kinetic energy is the sum of that due to the rotation of the sun parts, the spider, and in the case of the planet due to its rotation and translation of the centre of mass. The linear velocity of the c. of g. of the planet = ang. vel × radius of spider

$$= 20{\cdot}94 \times \frac{4}{12} = 6{\cdot}98 \text{ ft/sec.}$$

Kinetic energy of sun

$$= \tfrac{1}{2} \times \frac{8}{32{\cdot}2} \times \left(\frac{2}{12}\right)^2 \times 62{\cdot}84^2 \text{ ft lb.}$$

Kinetic energy of spider

$$= \tfrac{1}{2} \times \frac{20}{32{\cdot}2} \times \left(\frac{3}{12}\right)^2 \times 20{\cdot}94^2 \text{ ft lb.}$$

Kinetic energy of three planets

$$= \tfrac{1}{2} \times \frac{7{\cdot}5}{32{\cdot}2} \times \left(\frac{1}{12}\right)^2 \times 62{\cdot}84^2 + \frac{7{\cdot}5 \times 6{\cdot}98^2}{2 \times 32{\cdot}2} \text{ ft lb.}$$

(using 3 × wt. of one planet)

Thus total K.E. = 31 ft lb.

WORKED EXAMPLE (U.L.2 Ext., 1950)

5.7. In the epicyclic train shown in Fig. 5.10, all the teeth are of $4D\,.\,P$. Wheel F (40t) mounted on shaft A, is stationary. D(50t) and E(30t) are made of one piece of metal, and can rotate freely

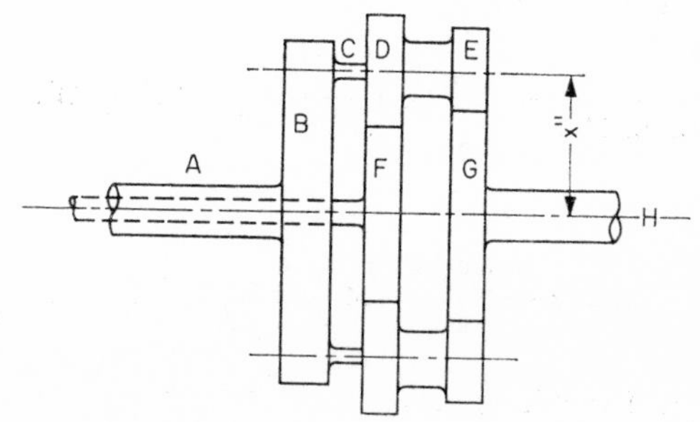

FIG. 5.10. Epicyclic gear of example 5.7

on a pin C, attached to the plate B. A similar pair of pinions D' and E' are mounted on a pin C'. B can rotate freely on a shaft A. Wheel G is mounted on the driving shaft H. The polar moment of inertia of the disc B including the two pins C and C' is 1200 lb in^2 D and E together weigh 7 lb with polar radius of gyration about their own centre line of 3 in. G has a polar moment of inertia 200 lb in^2. Find the torque required on shaft H to accelerate the system so that B has an angular acceleration of 5 rad/sec^2.

Solution

Referring to Fig. 5.10, the first part of the solution will be the calculation of the velocity ratios since the accelerations of the gears will be in the same proportion. This part is left to the reader.

$$N_G = N_H = 0{\cdot}6\, N_B \text{ and } N_{DE} = 1{\cdot}8 N_B$$

Let acceleration of B be α rad/sec^2, then acceleration of $G = 0{\cdot}6\alpha$, and acceleration of $DE = 1{\cdot}8\alpha$ rad/sec^2.

Torque on H to accelerate

$$G = I_G \times 0{\cdot}6\alpha = \frac{200}{32{\cdot}2} \times \frac{1}{144} \times 0{\cdot}6\alpha \text{ lb ft.}$$

Inertia of parts rotating with and including B is

$$\frac{1200}{32{\cdot}2 \times 144} + 2 \times \left(\frac{7}{32{\cdot}2} \times \frac{x^2}{144}\right) \text{ slugs ft}^2.$$

But x in.

$$= \frac{(50 + 40)}{2} \times \frac{1}{4} = 11{\cdot}25 \text{ in.}$$

Torque on A for these parts

$$= \left(\frac{1200}{32{\cdot}2 \times 144} + \frac{2 \times 7 \times 11{\cdot}25^2}{32{\cdot}2 \times 144}\right) \alpha \text{ lb ft.}$$

$$\text{Torque on } H \text{ for this} = \text{torque on } A \times \frac{1{\cdot}0}{0{\cdot}6}$$

$$= \left(\frac{1200}{32{\cdot}2 \times 144} + \frac{2 \times 7 \times 11{\cdot}25^2}{32{\cdot}2 \times 144}\right) \alpha \times \frac{1{\cdot}0}{0{\cdot}6} \text{ lb ft.}$$

Inertia of two sets of DE about own axis

$$= \frac{2 \times 7 \times 3^2}{32{\cdot}2 \times 144} \text{ slugs ft}^2.$$

Torque about arm axis

$$= \frac{2 \times 7 \times 9}{32{\cdot}2 \times 144} \times 1{\cdot}8\ \alpha \text{ lb ft.}$$

Torque on H for this

$$= \frac{2 \times 7 \times 9 \times 1{\cdot}8\alpha}{32{\cdot}2 \times 144} \times \frac{1{\cdot}8}{0{\cdot}6} \text{ lb ft.}$$

Hence total torque on H, when $\alpha = 5$, gives $T = 6{\cdot}2$ lb ft.

It is not proposed to deal with the composition of the various brands of automatic gear boxes since their development is rapid. The basic principles have been covered and need only be applied to whatever gear box is presented. However, the essentials of some automatic gears are given in examples at the end of the chapter.

Examples

5.8. Two parallel shafts X and Y are to be connected by tooth wheels; wheels A and B form a compound pair which can slide along but rotate with shaft X; wheels C and D are rigidly attached to shaft Y and the compound pair may be moved so that A engages with C or B with D. Shaft X rotates at 640 r.p.m. and the speeds of shaft Y are to be 340 r.p.m. exactly and 240 r.p.m. as near as possible. Using a D.P. of 2 for all wheels, find the minimum distance between the shaft axes, suitable tooth numbers for the wheels and the lower speed of Y. (Non-epicyclic box.) (U.L.1 Ext., 1949)

Answers: 12·25 in.; $t_A = 17$; $t_C = 32$; $t_B = 13$; $t_D = 36$; 231 r.p.m.

5.9. In the epicyclic gear train shown in Fig. 5.11, the shaft P rotates at 2000 r.p.m. in a clockwise direction whilst shaft Q is driven at 700 r.p.m. in an anti-clockwise direction. Determine the speed and direction of rotation of the shaft R if all the teeth are of the same D.P. and the numbers of teeth in the various gears are: $S = 15$, $T = 30$, $X = 55$, $Z = 40$ and $W = 50$.

(U.L.1 Ext., 1956)

Answer: 4340 r.p.m. anti-clockwise.

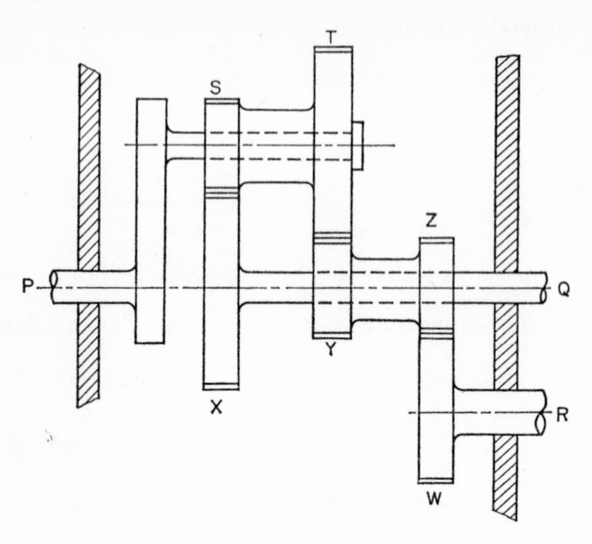

FIG. 5.11. Epicyclic gear of example 5.9

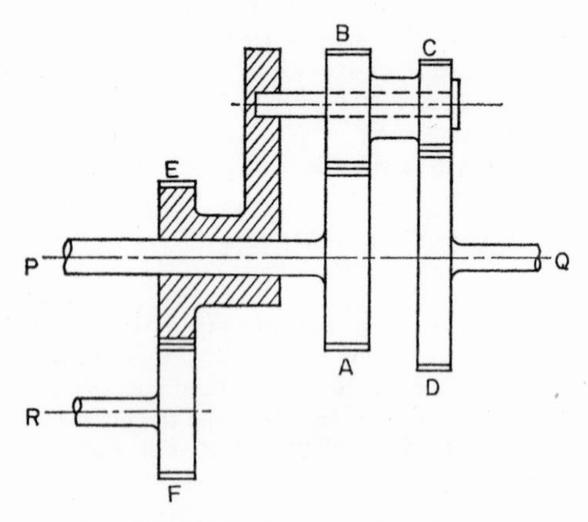

FIG. 5.12. Epicyclic gear of example 5.10

5.10. The Fig. 5.12, shows an epicyclic gear in which the shaft P is driven at 480 r.p.m. in a clockwise direction with a horsepower input at this point of 10. The shaft Q rotates at 100 r.p.m. also in a clockwise direction. Determine (*a*) the speed and direction of rotation of the shaft R, (*b*) the torque on shaft Q and on shaft R, stating whether they are inputs or outputs.

(A.M.I.Mech.E., 1959)

Answers: (*a*) 187·5 r.p.m. same direction as P, (*b*) T_Q = 196·3 lb ft output; T_R = 174·6 lb ft output.

5.11. In an epicyclic gear with a fixed outer annulus the sun wheel is to rotate at 1000 r.p.m. and the spider which carries three planet wheels is to be driven at 200 r.p.m. The teeth of all wheels are to be of 5 D.P. and the pitch

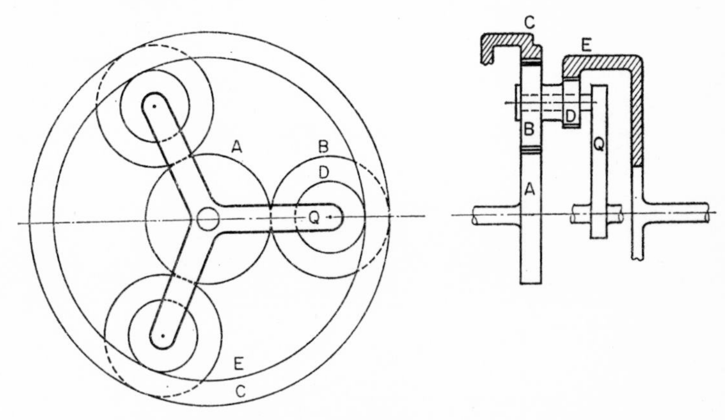

FIG. 5.13. Compound epicyclic gear of example 5.12

circle diameter of the annulus is to be as near 15 in. as possible. Determine the total kinetic energy of the gear, the following values being given:

	Weight (lb)	Radius of gyration about polar axis (in.)
Sun with shaft and coupling	9	$1\frac{1}{2}$
Spider with shaft and coupling	20	3
Planet wheel (each)	4	2

(U.L.2 Ext., 1947)

Answer: 50·2 ft lb.

5.12. In the compound epicyclic train shown in Fig. 5.13, of the three independent wheels concentric about O, wheel A is keyed to the driving shaft, E to the driven shaft and wheel C is fixed. The planet wheels B and D rotate together about the axis Q on the three-armed carrier. Wheels A, B and D have 20, 30 and 25 teeth respectively and all the wheels have a module pitch of 0·25 (i.e. 4 D.P.). The moments of inertia of the wheels A and E, the carrier and each compound planet pair are 15, 6500,250 and 125 lb in² respectively, the total weight of the three sets of planet wheels is 36 lb. Find the velocity ratio between the driving and driven shafts and the torque required to give the driven shaft an acceleration of one radian/sec². (U.L.1 Ext., 1954)

Answers: 45; 1·25 lb ft.

5.13. Figure 5.14 shows an arrangement of the Wilson epicyclic gear box giving four forward and one reverse speed of shaft E for an input speed of

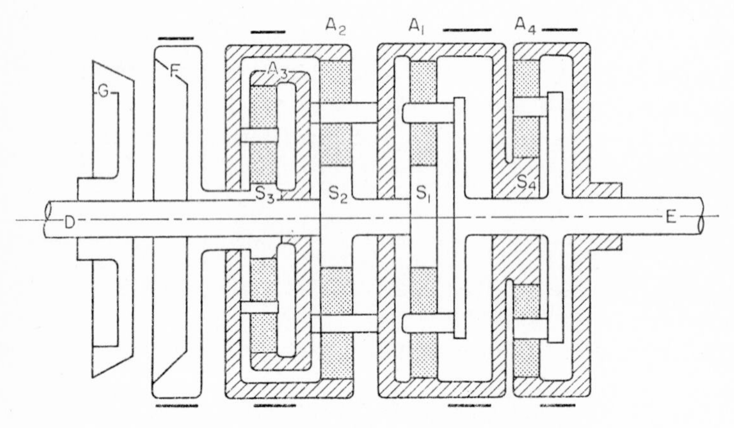

FIG. 5.14. Wilson epicyclic gear of example 5.13

shaft D. In 1st gear A_1 is fixed. In 2nd gear A_2 is fixed. In 3rd gear S_3 is fixed. Top gear F, is locked to G. Reverse gear A_1 is connected to S_4 and A_4 is fixed. The numbers of teeth on the gears are: $S_1 = 20$, $A_1 = 70$, $S_2 = 20$, $A_2 = 70$, $S_3 = 17$, $A_3 = 61$, $S_4 = 26$ and $A_4 = 70$. Calculate all the gear ratios. If 30 h.p. is transmitted in 1st gear at an engine speed of 3000 r.p.m., find the required fixing torque on the annulus A_1.

Answers: 4·5; 2·53; 1·51; 1; −8·43; 1840 lb ft.

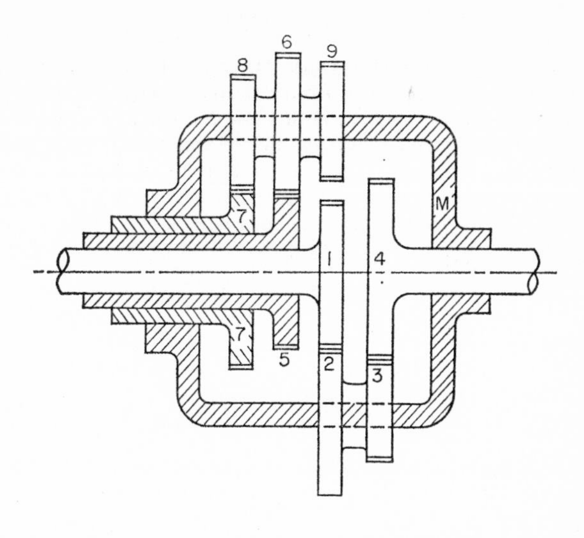

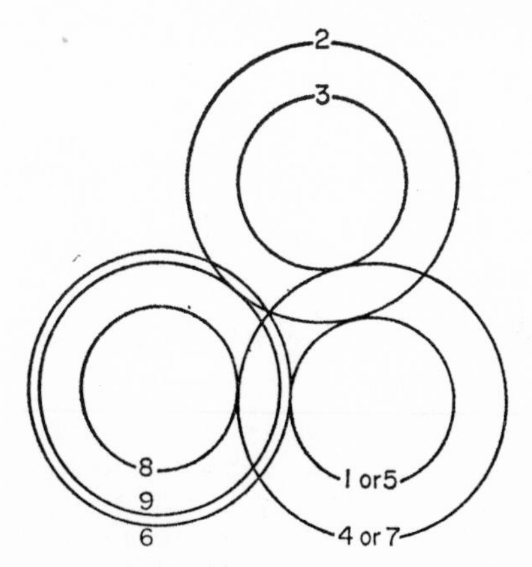

FIG. 5.15. Hobbs epicyclic gear of example 5.14

5.14. Figure 5.15 shows an arrangement of the epicyclic gearing of the Hobbs automatic transmission. Gear 5 meshes only with gear 6, and gear 1 only with 2. In 1st gear, 1 rotates at engine speed and the arm is fixed. In 2nd gear, 1 rotates at engine speed and 7 is fixed. In 3rd gear, 1 rotates at engine speed and 5 is fixed. In top gear, both 1 and 5 rotate at engine speed. In reverse, 1 is free 5 rotates at engine speed and the arm is fixed. The numbers of teeth on the various gears are: 1=3=5=8=30 teeth, 2=4=6=7=60 teeth, 9 = 40 teeth. Calculate all forward and reverse gear ratios. (Note the simplicity of this box and the absence of annular gears.)

Answers: 4, 2·2; 1·43; 1, −6.

CHAPTER SIX

COUPLINGS BETWEEN NON-AXIAL SHAFTS

6.1. Universal Joint (Hooke's) Angular Displacement and Velocity

These joints are used extensively in automobiles to connect the output shaft of the gear box to the input shaft of the differential. The connection is between shafts that are parallel but do not lie

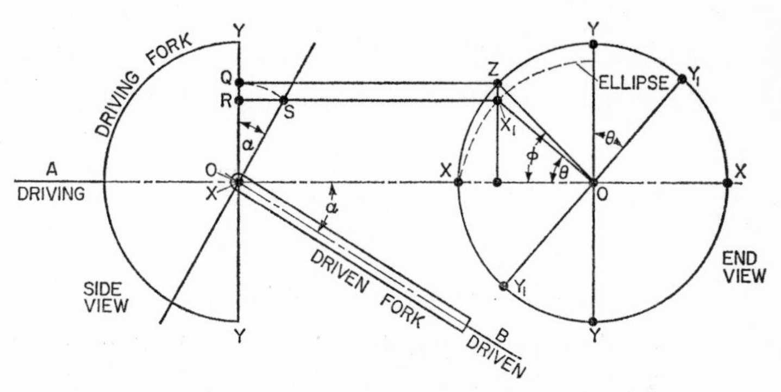

FIG. 6.1. Diagrammatic arrangement of a Hooke's joint

in the same axis and although in such a case, two universal joints are needed, the basis of the motion is that due to a single joint as shown diagrammatically in Fig. 6.1.

The driving shaft A is connected to the arm YY and the driven shaft B is connected to the arm XX. The driving fork lies in the vertical plane with its axis YY vertical, and the driven fork lies in a plane inclined at an angle α to the horizontal with its axis XX horizontal.

The driving shaft is turned an angle θ so that in the end view points Y move to Y_1. Points X which in a vertical plane move in an elliptical path, move to X_1, but the real movement, i.e., about an axis OB, is through an angle ϕ subtended by an arc XZ.

$$\tan\theta = \frac{X_1P}{PO} = \frac{RO}{PO},$$

and

$$\tan\phi = \frac{ZP}{PO} = \frac{QO}{PO}$$

thus

$$\frac{\tan\theta}{\tan\phi} = \frac{RO}{QO} = \frac{RO}{OS} = \cos\alpha,$$

giving

$$\tan\theta = \tan\phi \,.\, \cos\alpha. \tag{6.1}$$

The velocity ratio is obtained by differentiation which, if $\cos\alpha$ is constant, gives

$$\sec^2\theta \,.\, \frac{d\theta}{dt} = \cos\alpha \,.\, \sec^2\phi \,.\, \frac{d\phi}{dt},$$

or

$$\sec^2\theta \,.\, \omega_A = \cos\alpha \,.\, \sec^2\phi \,.\, \omega_B$$

where, ω_A and ω_B are the angular velocities of the driving and driven shafts respectively, therefore

$$\frac{\omega_B}{\omega_A} = \frac{\sec^2\theta}{\cos\alpha \,.\, \sec^2\phi} \tag{6.2}$$

Elimination of ϕ between equations 6.1 and 6.2 giving

$$\frac{\omega_B}{\omega_A} = \frac{\cos\alpha}{1 - \cos^2\theta \,.\, \sin^2\alpha} \tag{6.3}$$

Note that the velocity ratio is NOT constant, but is a maximum when $\theta = 0°$ or $180°$ and is a minimum when $\theta = 90°$ or $270°$. This variation of the speed of the driven shaft for various positions of the driving shaft, makes a SINGLE joint unsuitable for use in automobiles, but a constant velocity ratio can be obtained by the correct use of a double joint.

6.2. Constant Velocity Ratio Using a Double Hooke's Joint

Fig. 6.2 shows an arrangement of a double Hooke's joint coupling two shafts A and C. The forks on the driving and driven

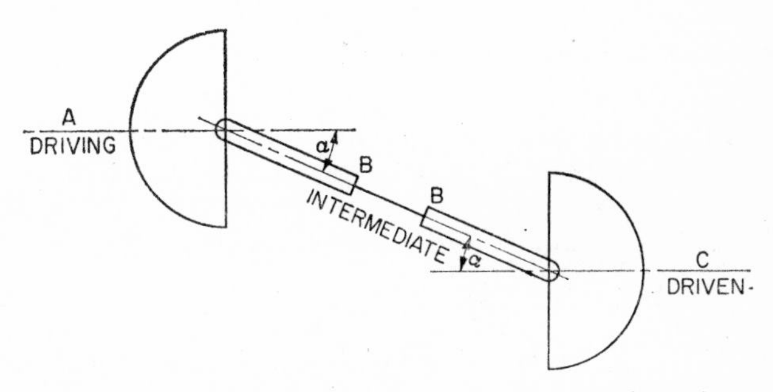

FIG. 6.2. Double Hooke's joint for constant velocity ratio

shafts A and C, lie in the same plane. Similarly the forks on the common intermediate shaft B are parallel and lie in the same plane. The driving and driven shafts are parallel. Then

$$\frac{\omega_B}{\omega_A} = \frac{\cos \alpha}{1 - \cos^2 \theta_A \, . \, \sin^2 \alpha}$$

and

$$\frac{\omega_B}{\omega_C} = \frac{\cos \alpha}{1 - \cos^2 \theta_C \, . \, \sin^2 \alpha}$$

hence

$$\frac{\omega_C}{\omega_A} = \frac{\omega_B}{\omega_A} \times \frac{\omega_C}{\omega_B} = \left[\frac{\cos\alpha}{1 - \cos^2\theta_A \sin^2\alpha}\right] \times \left[\frac{1 - \cos^2\theta_C \sin^2\alpha}{\cos\alpha}\right] \tag{6.4}$$

also

$$\tan\theta_A = \tan\phi_B \,.\, \cos\alpha$$

and

$$\tan\theta_C = \tan\phi_B \,.\, \cos\alpha,$$

and so

$$\theta_A = \theta_C \tag{6.5}$$

Equations (6.4) and (6.5) thus give

$$\frac{\omega_C}{\omega_A} = 1$$

Note that correct positioning of the forks, particularly those on the intermediate shaft, is essential for constant velocity ratio.

6.3. Angular Acceleration of a Hooke's Joint

Equation (6.3) may be differentiated to give the acceleration of the driven shaft (α_B), whence

$$\alpha_B = \frac{-\omega_A^2 \cos\alpha \,.\, \sin^2\alpha \,.\, \sin 2\theta}{(1 - \cos^2\theta \,.\, \sin^2\alpha)^2} \tag{6.6}$$

Not a great variety of problems can be set on Hooke's joint and so only two worked examples will be given. Examination candidates should note that in most examples the solution from first principles is asked.

WORKED EXAMPLE (part (a) is U.L.2 Ext., 1948)

6.1. (a) A Hooke's joint is used to couple two shafts together. The driving-shaft rotates at a uniform speed of 1000 r.p.m.

Working from first principles, determine the greatest permissible angle between the shaft axes so that the total fluctuation of speed of the driven shaft does not exceed 150 r.p.m. What will then be the maximum speed of the driven shaft?

(b) Explain the conditions necessary in a double coupling for the speed ratio to be constant. In such a double coupling, the driving pin on the intermediate shaft has been placed 90° in advance of the correct position. The driving and driven shafts are parallel and are at an angle of 22° to the intermediate shaft. Find the ratio of the maximum and minimum speeds of rotation of the driven shaft when the driving shaft rotates at 1000 r.p.m.

Solution

Refer to Fig. 6.1.

(a) Maximum value of ω_B is when $\theta = 0°$

$$= \omega_A \left[\frac{\cos\alpha}{1 - \sin^2\alpha}\right] = \frac{1}{\cos\alpha}$$

Minimum value of ω_B is when $\theta = 90° = \omega_A \,.\, \cos\alpha$, therefore, speed range

$$= \omega_A \left(\frac{1}{\cos\alpha} - \cos\alpha\right)$$

and for limiting value,

$$150 = 1000\,(1/\cos\alpha - \cos\alpha),$$

$$\cos^2\alpha + 0{\cdot}15\cos\alpha - 1 = 0,$$

$$\cos\alpha = \frac{-0{\cdot}15 \pm (0{\cdot}0225 + 4)^{\frac{1}{2}}}{2} = 0{\cdot}925,$$

giving

$$\alpha = 22°\ 18'$$

$$\omega_B\,(\text{max}) = 1000/\cos 22°\ 18' = 1080 \text{ r.p.m.}$$

(b)

$$\omega_B \max = \omega_A \,.\, 1/\cos\alpha \text{ and } \omega_B \min = \omega_A \,.\, \cos\alpha,$$

$$\omega_C \max = \omega_B \,.\, 1/\cos\alpha \text{ and } \omega_C \min = \omega_B \,.\, \cos\alpha.$$

Thus

$$\omega_C \max = \omega_A \,.\, 1/\cos^2\alpha \text{ and } \omega_C \min = \omega_A \,.\, \cos^2\alpha.$$

$$\text{Ratio} = \frac{1000}{(0{\cdot}9272)^2} \times \frac{1}{1000 \times (0{\cdot}9272)^2} = 1{\cdot}35$$

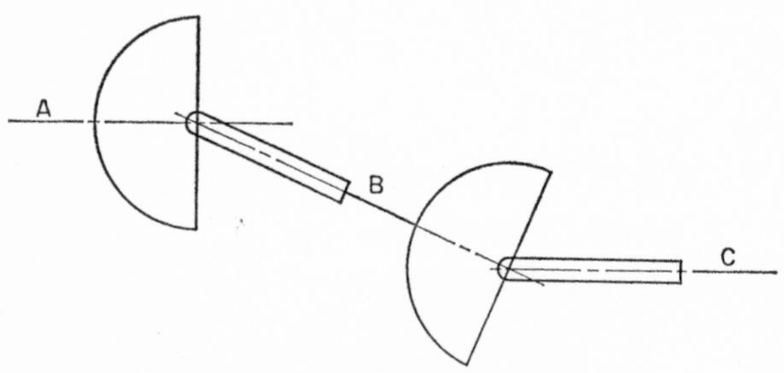

FIG. 6.3. Hooke's joint of example 6.1(b)

WORKED EXAMPLE (U.L.2 Int., 1946)

6.2. Two horizontal shafts are connected by a Hooke's joint. The angle between the shafts is 160°. The driving shaft rotates uniformly at 150 r.p.m. The driven shaft carries a flywheel weighing 20 lb having a radius of gyration 4 in. Find the torque required on the driving shaft to overcome the inertia of the flywheel when the fork end on the driving shaft has rotated 30° from the horizontal plane. Show how any formulae you use for the motion of the joint are derived.

Solution

Derivation of speed ratio is given in paragraph 6.1 and then differentiation gives for the acceleration of the driven shaft,

$$\alpha_B = \frac{-\omega_A^2 \,.\, \cos\alpha \,.\, \sin^2\alpha \,.\, \sin 2\theta}{(1 - \cos^2\theta \,.\, \sin^2\alpha)^2}$$

but $\omega_A = \dfrac{150}{60} \,.\, 2\pi = 5\pi$ rad/sec. $\theta = 30°$, $2\theta = 60°$, $\alpha = 20°$

$$\alpha_B = \frac{-25\pi^2 \times 0{\cdot}9397 \times 0{\cdot}3420^2 \times 0{\cdot}866}{(1 - (0{\cdot}3420 \times 0{\cdot}9397)^2)^2} \text{ rad/sec}^2$$

$$= 29{\cdot}3 \text{ rad/sec}^2.$$

Inertia torque on driven shaft

$$= \frac{20}{32{\cdot}2} \times \left(\frac{4}{12}\right)^2 \times 29{\cdot}3 = 2{\cdot}02 \text{ lb ft.}$$

$$\text{Velocity ratio} = \frac{\omega_B}{\omega_A} = \frac{0{\cdot}9397}{1 - (0{\cdot}866 \times 0{\cdot}342)^2} = \frac{0{\cdot}9397}{0{\cdot}913}$$

$$\text{Therefore torque on driving shaft} = 2{\cdot}02 \times \frac{0{\cdot}9397}{0{\cdot}913}$$

$$= 2{\cdot}08 \text{ lb ft.}$$

Examples

6.3. Describe, with the aid of sketches, the general arrangement and detailed construction of a universal joint for the front end of a vehicle propeller shaft, and explain why a universal coupling is fitted at each end of the shaft.

The output shaft of a gearbox runs at 3000 r.p.m. and is connected by a universal-coupling to a propeller-shaft whose axis is inclined at 12 degrees to the axis of the gearbox shaft. Calculate the maximum angular velocity of the propeller-shaft. (A.M.I.Mech.E., Auto. Eng., 1958)

Answer: 3070 r.p.m.

6.4. If a Hooke's joint connects two shafts whose axes are inclined to each other at an acute angle α, show that the instantaneous speed ratio between these shafts is given by the expression

$$\left(\frac{\sec^2\theta}{\sec^2\phi \,.\, \cos\alpha}\right)$$

where θ and ϕ are the angles through which the two halves of the joint have turned respectively from some datum. State what this datum is. Determine the maximum and minimum values of this ratio when $\alpha = 10°$.

(U.L.2 Ext., 1951)

Answer: 1·015 and 0·9848.

6.5. Two shafts are connected by a universal (Hooke's) joint, with the axis of the driven shaft inclined at an angle α to that of the driving shaft. The speed of the driven shaft must not vary more than 4 per cent above or below that of the driving shaft. Determine, from first principles, the ratio of the driven speed to driving speed, and the maximum permissible value of α.

(U.L.1 Ext., 1956)

Answer: 16° 4′.

6.6. Two shafts are to be connected by a Hooke's joint; the driving shaft rotates at a uniform speed of 500 r.p.m., and the speed of the driven shaft must lie between 475 and 525 r.p.m. determine, from first principles, the maximum permissible angle between the shafts, and prove that by a suitable arrangement of two such joints the driven and driving shafts can have the same rotational speeds.

(U.L.2 Ext., 1947)

Answer: 17° 44′.

6.7. Two shafts, the axes of which intersect but are inclined at 20° to each other, are connected by a Hooke's joint. If the driving shaft has a uniform speed of 1000 r.p.m. find, from first principles, the variation in speed of the driven shaft. The driven shaft carries a rotating mass which weighs 30 lb and has a radius of gyration of 10·4 in. Find the accelerating torque on the driven shaft for the position when the driven shaft has turned 45° from the position in which its fork end is in the plane containing the two shafts.

(U.L.2 Int., 1949)

Answers: 1064 and 939·7 r.p.m.; 957 lb ft.

6.8. A universal (Hooke's) joint connects two shafts whose axes are out of line by an angle α. The driving shaft rotates at a uniform speed ω rad/sec. Show that the speed of the driven shaft is

$$\left(\frac{\omega \cos \alpha}{1 - \cos^2 \theta \,.\, \sin^2 \alpha}\right)$$

where θ is measured from the position in which the driving fork lies in the plane of the shafts.

The driving shaft of such an arrangement runs at a uniform speed of 250 r.p.m., and the angle α between the shaft axes is 25°; the driven shaft with attached masses has a weight of 120 lb at a radius of gyration of 0·5 ft. If a steady torque of 150 lb ft resists rotation of the driven shaft find the torque required at the driving shaft when θ is 45°. (U.L.2 Ext., 1952)

Answer: 25·1 lb ft. Note. Inertia of driven shaft helps to overcome resisting torque.

CHAPTER SEVEN

BALANCE OF RECIPROCATING ENGINES

7.1. Out of Balance Forces and Couples Due to the Reciprocating Engine Parts

Figure 7.1 shows a diagram of the moving parts of a reciprocating engine cylinder. The force mainly causing rotation of the crank is that due to the intensity of gas thrust acting on the piston and can be represented by $p \, . \, A$ where, p is the pressure and A the effective piston area. This thrust will act not only on the piston face but also on the cylinder head and under these static forces, the complete engine would be in equilibrium. However, due to the motion of the piston, the gas thrust on it may be opposed, or aided, by an inertia force arising mainly from the linear acceleration of the piston parts. Thus if friction is ignored the resultant thrust of the piston on the connecting rod will be

$$p \, . \, A \pm \frac{W}{g} \, . \, f, \tag{7.1}$$

where W = weight of reciprocating parts and f their acceleration ($\pm$ sign used to show that inertia force may help or hinder the gas thrust).

If the inertia effect of the connecting rod is ignored or, in part, allowed for by a modified value of W, then the force acting on the crankshaft bearings will be that transmitted by the mechanism

$$= p \,.\, A \pm \frac{W}{g} \,.\, f.$$

The gas thrust acting on the cylinder head is transmitted to the crankshaft bearings by the engine frame and so there is a resultant, or unbalanced, force of

$$p \,.\, A \pm \frac{W}{g} \,.\, f - p \,.\, A = \frac{W}{g} \,.\, f$$

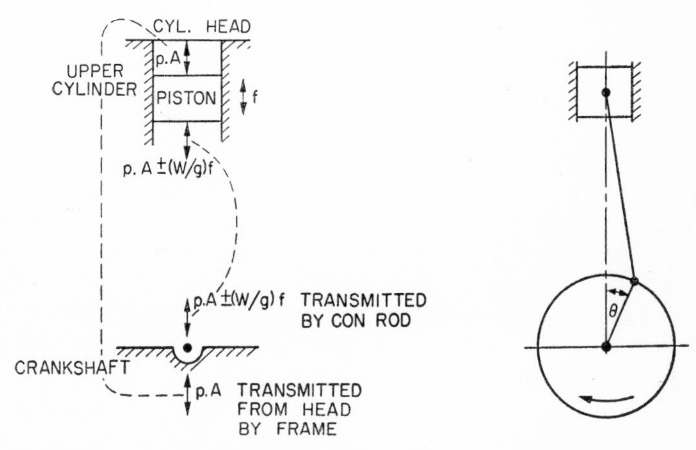

FIG. 7.1. Unbalanced force in single cylinder reciprocating engine

acting at the crankshaft in the direction of reciprocation, as shown in Fig. 7.1 ($\pm$ sign no longer shown).

The acceleration f is given approximately by

$$f = \omega^2 r \left(\cos \theta + \frac{\cos 2\theta}{n} \right), \qquad (7.2)$$

where ω is the angular velocity of the crank in rad/sec, r is the crank radius in feet, n is the ratio of the length of the connecting rods to the length of the crank, i.e., $n = l/r$, θ is the angle of the crank from the dead centre position shown in Fig. 7.1.

Thus unbalanced force in the line of reciprocation is

$$F = \frac{W \cdot f}{g} = \frac{W}{g} \cdot r \cdot \omega^2 \cos \theta + \frac{W}{g} \cdot \frac{r \cdot \omega^2}{n} \cos 2\theta \qquad (7.3)$$

i.e.,

$$F = F_1 \cos \theta + F_2 \cos 2\theta \qquad (7.4)$$

The components $F_1 \cos \theta$ and $F_2 \cos 2\theta$ are called PRIMARY and SECONDARY unbalanced forces respectively.

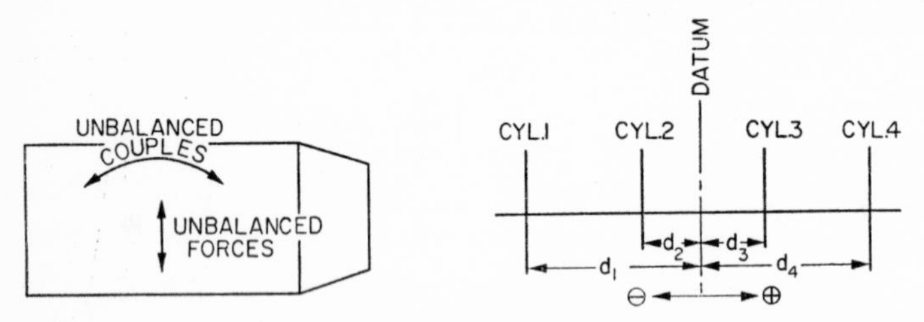

FIG. 7.2. Unbalanced forces and couples in multi-cylinder engine

In the case of a multi-cylinder in-line engine, primary and secondary forces can arise for each cylinder and so forces will be in balance when

$$\Sigma F_1 \cos \theta = 0 \quad \text{and} \quad \Sigma F_2 \cos 2\theta = 0.$$

In addition, the forces, since they do not lie in the same line of reciprocation, can give rise to couples tending to rotate the engine as shown in Fig. 7.2. The additional requirements for balance are now

$$\Sigma F_1 \cos \theta \cdot d = 0 \quad \text{and} \quad \Sigma F_2 \cos 2\theta \cdot d = 0$$

where d is the distance of the line of reciprocation of a cylinder from some datum which is usually the engine centre as shown in Fig. 7.2.

Mathematical investigation of engine balance can be made by solving the four equations given above, but this is a tedious process that can be replaced by simple accurate vectorial methods.

7.2. Vector Representation of Unbalanced Forces and Couples

(a) PRIMARY VECTORS

A vector *oa* whose length represents $\frac{W}{g} . r . \omega^2$ is drawn, as shown in Fig. 7.3, in the direction of the crank, i.e., at θ to the

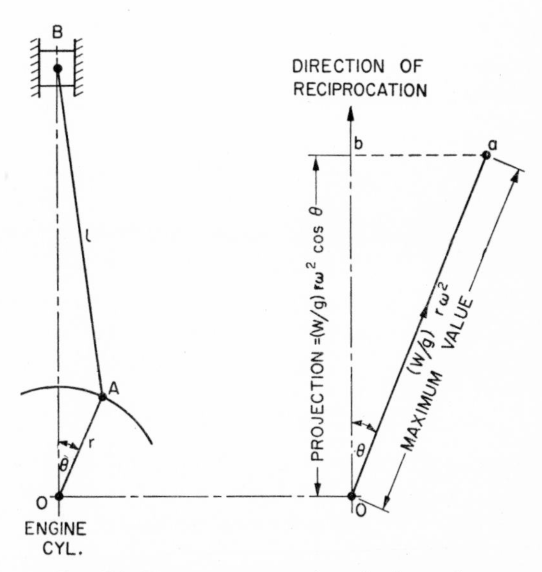

FIG. 7.3. Vector representation of primary force

direction of piston reciprocation. The primary force is then given by *ob* the projection of the vector *oa* on to the direction of reciprocation, and the maximum value of the primary force is the full length of the vector *oa*. In the case of an engine with several cylinders, a force diagram can be drawn whose sides represent, to scale if necessary, the values $\frac{W}{g} \cdot r \cdot \omega^2$ for each cylinder drawn in each case in the direction of the respective crank. The addition of the vectors gives the maximum unbalanced primary force and this value projected on to the direction of reciprocation gives the unbalance for the engine crank position considered. A closed diagram of course indicates primary force balance.

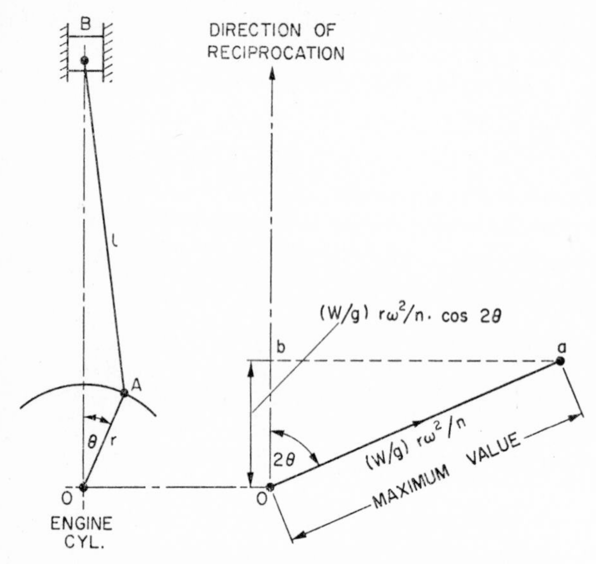

FIG. 7.4. Vector representation of secondary force

Primary couples may be similarly represented. For couples of cylinders on the "positive" side of the reference position, vectors to represent $\frac{W}{g} \cdot r \cdot \omega^2 \cdot d$ are drawn in the direction of the respective crank, whilst "negative" couples, i.e., those for cylinders on the negative side of the datum, are drawn, in directions opposite to the crank position.

(b) SECONDARY VECTORS

The procedure is similar to that for primary vectors except that since the secondary force $= \frac{W}{g} \cdot \frac{r\omega^2}{n} \cdot \cos 2\theta$, the vector is drawn, as shown in Fig. 7.4, to represent $\frac{W}{g} \cdot \frac{r\omega^2}{n}$, to scale, at an angle of 2θ to the direction of reciprocation.

Secondary couple vectors are drawn to represent, to scale, $\frac{W}{g} \cdot \frac{r\omega^2}{n} \cdot d$ either in, or opposite to, the direction of 2θ to the direction of reciprocation.

These vectorial methods are used to solve the following variety of problems and examination candidates should note that in the cases of engines whose reciprocating parts per cylinder are identical, as in most automobile engines, there is often no need to draw vector diagrams to scale.

WORKED EXAMPLE (U.L.2 Ext., 1938)

7.1. In a reciprocating engine which has four cylinders in line, the weights of the reciprocating masses are 2·25 lb per cylinder. The stroke is 5 in., the length of the connecting rod is 9 in., the cylinders are spaced 5 in. apart. If the cylinders are numbered 1 to 4 from one end, then in an end view the cranks appear at successive intervals of 90° in the order 1, 4, 2, 3. The engine speed is 2000 r.p.m. Find, with reference to the central plane of the engine, the maximum value of any primary and secondary out of balance effects.

Solution

The engine is considered in the position shown in Fig. 7.5, i.e., when the crank of cylinder 1 is at the dead centre. The positions (angularly) of the cranks are also shown for primary (at θ), and for secondary (at 2θ) in Fig. 7.5.

Primary and secondary forces. Since the cylinder parts are identical, each primary force vector representing $\frac{W}{g} \cdot r\omega^2$ has the same value and similarly each secondary force vector has the

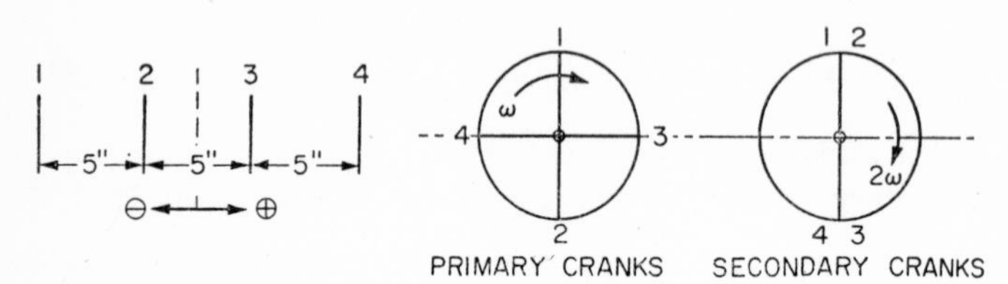

FIG. 7.5. Cylinder and crank configuration for the engine of example 7.1

same value. The primary and secondary force diagrams are drawn as shown in Fig. 7.6.

It should be noted that since each vector has the same length and the cranks are equally spaced round 360°, then these diagrams

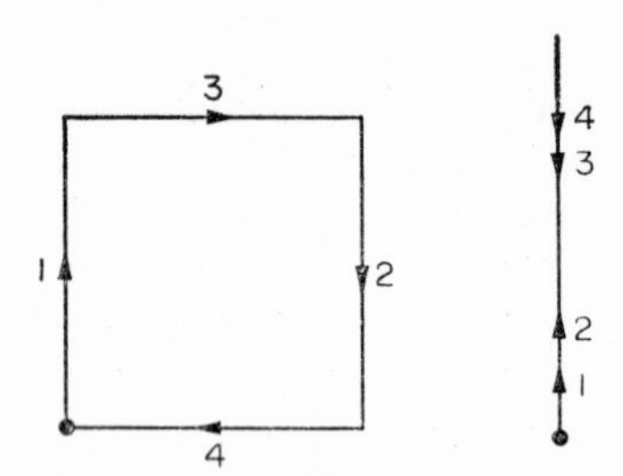

FIG. 7.6. Primary and secondary force polygons for engine of example 7.1

must be regular polygons and the engine is balanced for primary and secondary forces. There is also no need to draw diagrams at all, and in future worked examples when it can be deduced, by observation, that force diagrams are regular polygons they will not be drawn. Examination candidates are advised to do this but make certain that a statement to this effect is given.

Primary couples (datum as shown in Fig. 7·5). Values of couples are $1 = F_1 \cos \theta_1 (-7{\cdot}5)$ lb in.; $2 = F_2 \cos \theta_2(-2{\cdot}5)$; $3 = F_3 \cos \theta_3(+2{\cdot}5)$; $4 = F_4 \cos \theta_4(+7{\cdot}5)$ lb in., where $F_1 = F$ $= F_3 = F_4 = \dfrac{W}{g} . r\omega^2$ lb.

The primary couple diagram is then drawn as in Fig. 7.7 to a suitable scale, e.g., 1 in. $= \dfrac{W}{g} . r\omega^2 \times 5$ lb in.

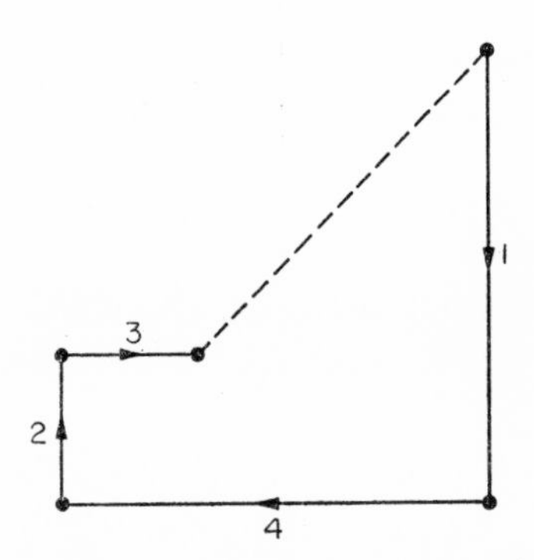

FIG. 7.7. Primary couple polygon for engine of example 7.1

The maximum unbalanced primary couple is given by vector *oa*, which by measurement gives

$$7{\cdot}07 \frac{W}{g} . r\omega^2 = 7{\cdot}07 \times \frac{2{\cdot}25}{32{\cdot}2} \times \frac{2{\cdot}5}{12} \left(\frac{2000}{60} \times 2\pi\right)^2$$

$$= 4500 \text{ lb in.}$$

Secondary couples (datum as shown in Fig. 7.5). Values are the same as primary except that $F_1 = F_2 = F_3 = F_4 = \dfrac{W}{g} \cdot \dfrac{r\omega^2}{n}$.

The couple diagram is drawn as shown in Fig. 7.8 and a suitable scale is 1 in. $= \frac{W}{g} \cdot \frac{r\omega^2}{n} . 5$ lb in.

The maximum unbalanced secondary couple is the sum of the vectors

$$= 20 \times \frac{W}{g} \cdot \frac{r\omega^2}{n} = 20 \times \frac{2{\cdot}25}{32{\cdot}2} \times \frac{2{\cdot}5}{12} \times \frac{2{\cdot}5}{9}\left(\frac{2000 \times 2\pi}{60}\right)^2 \text{ lb in.}$$

$$= 3540 \text{ lb in.}$$

FIG. 7.8. Secondary couple polygon for engine of example 7.1

WORKED EXAMPLE (A.M.I.Mech.E., 1958)

7.2. A six-cylinder, in-line engine, of the four-stroke internal combustion type, has a firing order 1, 4, 2, 6, 3, 5. The distance between successive cylinder bores is 4 in., the stroke of each piston is 3 in., the connecting rod length is 6 in., the reciprocating mass per cylinder is 12 oz and the engine speed is 2400 r.p.m.

(a) Determine, by calculation, the maximum value of the inertia force along each cylinder centre-line.

(b) Examine, graphically, the state of balance of the engine so far as primary and secondary forces and couples are concerned, taking a point midway between cylinders 3 and 4 as the reference plane.

Solution

(a) It is assumed that the approximate value of $f = \omega^2 r \left(\cos\theta + \frac{\cos 2\theta}{n}\right)$ can be used so that the inertia force in a cylinder is given by

$$F = \frac{W}{g} \cdot r\omega^2 \left(\cos\theta + \frac{\cos 2\theta}{n}\right)$$

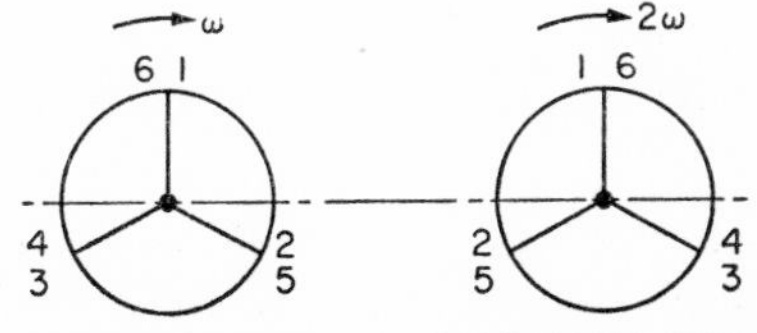

FIG. 7.9. Cylinder and crank configuration for engine of example 7.2

and the maximum value is when $\theta = 0°$

$$F_{\max} = \frac{W}{g} \cdot r\omega^2 \left(1 + \frac{1}{n}\right) = \frac{12}{16 \times 32{\cdot}2} \times \frac{1{\cdot}5}{12} \left(\frac{2400 \times 2}{60}\right)^2 \times \left(1 + \tfrac{1}{4}\right) \text{ lb} = 230 \text{ lb.}$$

(b) Since the engine is working on the four-stroke cycle, the six cylinders have to be fired (piston to come to dead centre) whilst the crank turns through two revolutions. The angle between successive cranks is therefore 120° and the primary and secondary crank positions are as shown in Fig. 7.9.

Primary and secondary forces. Since the reciprocating parts per cylinder are identical and their cranks, primary and secondary, are equispaced angularly, the primary and secondary force diagrams form regular polygons and indicate balance of both forces.

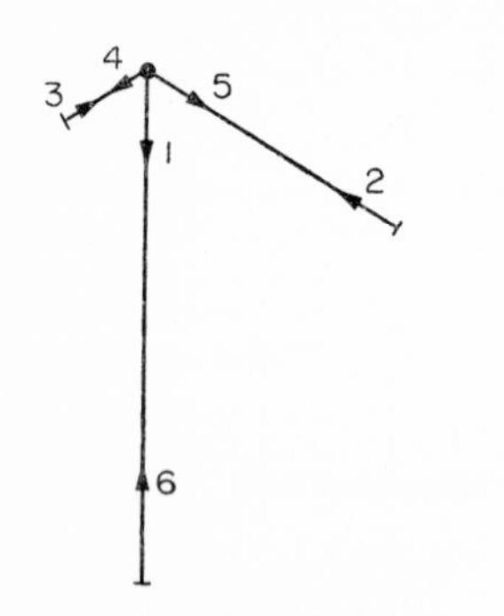

FIG. 7.10. Primary couple polygon for engine of example 7.2

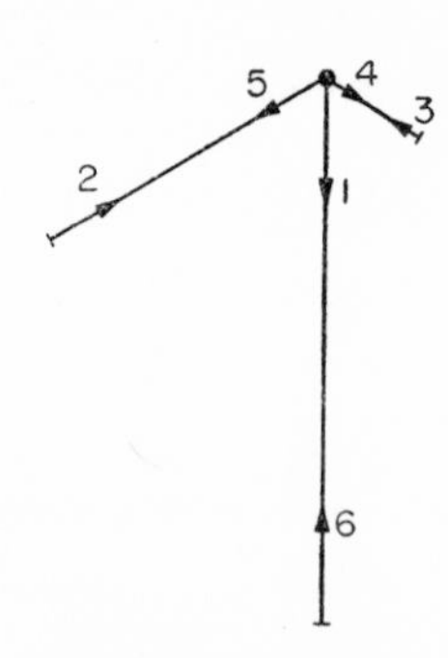

FIG. 7.11. Secondary couple polygon for engine of example 7.2

Primary couples $1 = F_1 \cos \theta_1(-10)$; $2 = F_2 \cos \theta_2(-6)$; $3 = F_3 \cos \theta_3(-2)$; $4 = F_4 \cos \theta_4(2)$; $5 = F_5 \cos \theta_5(6)$; $6 = F_6 \cos \theta_6(10)$. Couple polygon is shown in Fig. 7.10 drawn to scale.

The polygon closes and thus primary couples are balanced.

Secondary couples $1 = \frac{F_1}{n} \cos 2\theta_1(-10)$ and similarly for other cylinders.

The polygon closes and thus secondary couples are balanced. The engine is completely balanced for primary and secondary effects.

WORKED EXAMPLE (U.L.2 Ext., 1946)

7.3. An engine having five cylinders in line has successive cranks 144° apart, the distance between cylinder centre lines being 15 in. The reciprocating mass for each cylinder is 35 lb, the crank radius is 4·5 in. and the connecting rod length is 18 in. The engine runs at 600 r.p.m. Examine the engine for balance of primary and secondary forces and couples. Determine the maximum values of these and the position of the central crank at which these maximum values occur.

Solution

Since the reciprocating parts per cylinder are identical and the primary and secondary cranks, as shown in Fig. 7.12, are equi-spaced round 360°, then the primary and secondary diagrams are

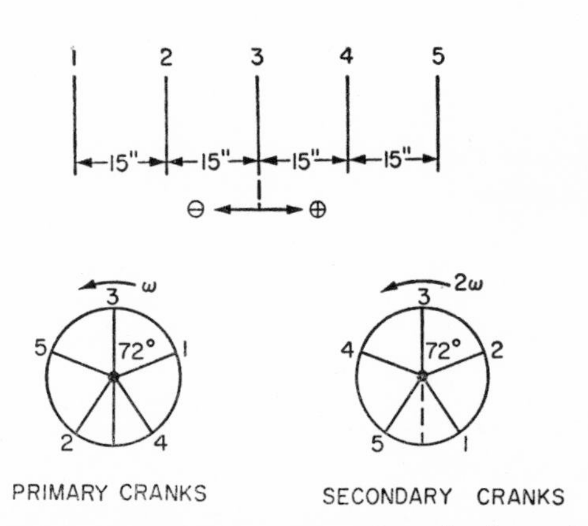

FIG. 7.12. Cylinder and crank configuration for engine of example 7.3

regular pentagons indicating that the primary and secondary forces are in balance.

Primary couples. Cylinder 3 is datum and values are, all lb in., $1 = F_1 \cos \theta_1(-30)$; $2 = F_2 \cos \theta_2(-15)$; $3 = 0$; $4 = F_4 \cos \theta_4$

(15); $5 = F_5 \cos \theta_5(30)$. The primary couple polygon is shown in Fig. 7.13 and by measurement, the maximum unbalanced couple

$$= 2{\cdot}65 \times 15 \frac{W}{g} . r\omega^2$$

$$= 2{\cdot}65 \times 15 \times \frac{35}{32{\cdot}2} \times \frac{4{\cdot}5}{12} \left(\frac{600 \times 2\pi}{60}\right)^2 \text{ lb in.}$$

$$= 63{,}800 \text{ lb in.}$$

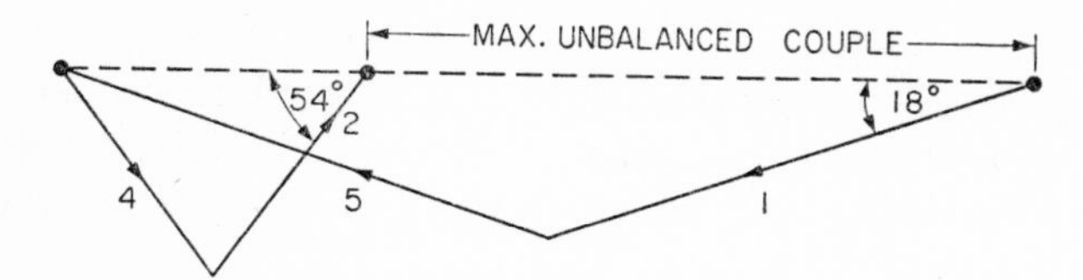

FIG. 7.13. Primary couple polygon for engine of example 7.3

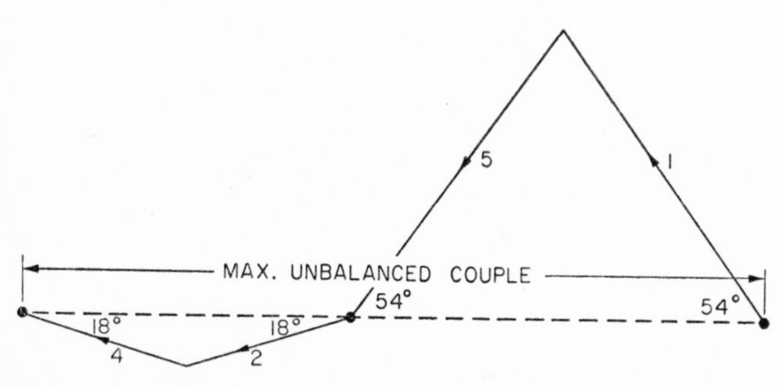

FIG. 7.14. Secondary couple polygon for engine of example 7.3

For the engine position shown, the couple is 0 since the closing vector is perpendicular to the line of reciprocation (projection is zero) and this vector will be maximum when it lies wholly in the direction of reciprocation, i.e., when the crank has turned through 90° or 270° from the dead centre position shown.

Secondary couples. Cylinder 3 is datum. The secondary couple diagram is shown in Fig. 7.14 drawn to a scale of 1 in. $= \frac{W}{g} \cdot \frac{r\omega^2}{n}$ (15) lb in.

The maximum unbalanced secondary couple is, by measurement

$$4{\cdot}25 \times 15 \times \frac{35}{32{\cdot}2} \times \frac{4{\cdot}5}{12} \times \frac{1}{4}(20\pi)^2 = 25{,}700 \text{ lb in.}$$

The maximum value is when the closing vector is vertical, but since the secondary cranks are drawn at twice crank angle, the

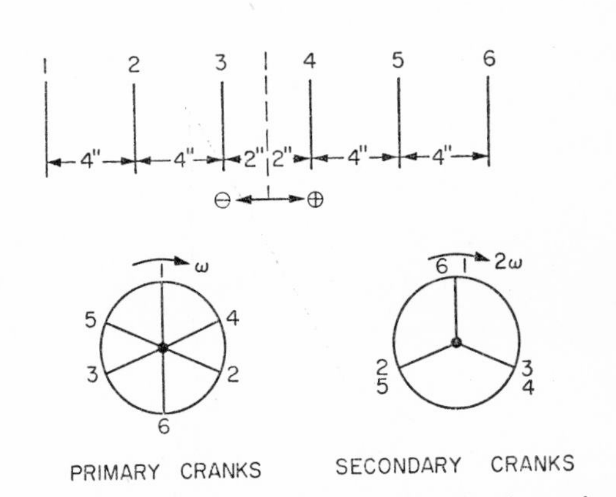

FIG. 7.15. Cylinder and crank configuration for engine of example 7.4

crank has to turn 45° from its position for the vector to turn 90° and maximum value is at 45°, 135°, 225°, 315° to dead centre.

WORKED EXAMPLE

7.4. The firing order of a six-cylinder in-line two-stroke diesel engine is 1–5–3–6–2–4. The cylinder centres are spaced at intervals of 4 in. and each piston has a stroke of 4 in. The length of each connecting rod is 8 in. and the reciprocating parts of each cylinder weigh 2 lb. The rotating masses of each cylinder, assumed to be concentrated at crank radius, weigh 1·5 lb. The The engine speed is 3000 r.p.m.

(a) Considering primary and secondary balance of reciprocating masses only, determine the magnitude of any unbalanced forces or couples.

(b) Allowing for rotating as well as for reciprocating masses, determine the maximum total unbalanced couple on the engine.

Solution

(a) Since the reciprocating parts per cylinder are identical and the primary and secondary cranks are equally spaced through 360°

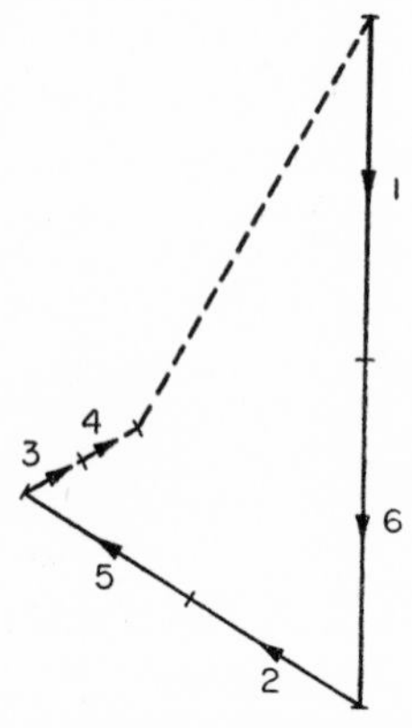

FIG. 7.16. Primary couple polygon for engine of example 7.4

(note with two-stroke, all six cylinder cranks lie in 360°), the force diagrams will be regular polygons and so engine is balanced for primary and secondary forces.

Primary couples: Engine centre is datum and couple polygon drawn to a scale of 1 in. $= \frac{W}{g} r\omega^2 \times 10$ lb in. is shown in Fig. 7.16.

Maximum unbalanced couple by measurement

$$= 13{\cdot}8 \times \frac{W}{g} r\omega^2 \text{ lb in.}$$

$$= 13{\cdot}8 \times \frac{2}{32{\cdot}2} \times \frac{2}{12} \left(\frac{3000 \times 2\pi}{60}\right)^2 = 14{,}000 \text{ lb in.}$$

Secondary couples: Engine centre is datum and the couple polygon is shown in Fig. 7.17:

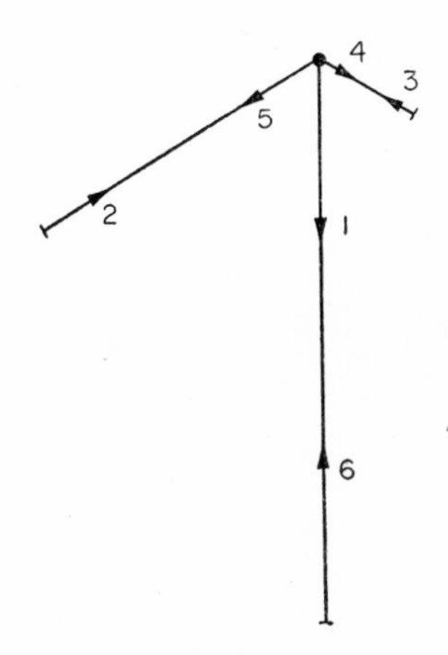

FIG. 7.17. Secondary couple polygon for engine of example 7.4

The engine is balanced for secondary couples.

(b) Centrifugal forces due to rotating masses $= C = \frac{W}{g} \,.\, r\omega^2$, where W is the rotating mass weight. These values will be similar to the quantities represented in the primary couple polygon and so the centrifugal force polygon will be similar to the primary force polygon. The closing vectors of both will be parallel and so the total effect is an addition, thus total couple on engine

$$= 13{\cdot}8(F + C) \text{ lb in.}$$

$$= 13{\cdot}8 \times \frac{(2 + 1{\cdot}5)}{32{\cdot}2} \times \frac{2}{12} (100\pi)^2$$

$$= 24{,}500 \text{ lb in.}$$

7.3. Method of Direct and Reverse Cranks

This is a simple method giving a clear picture of the unbalanced forces in a reciprocating engine and providing ready means of

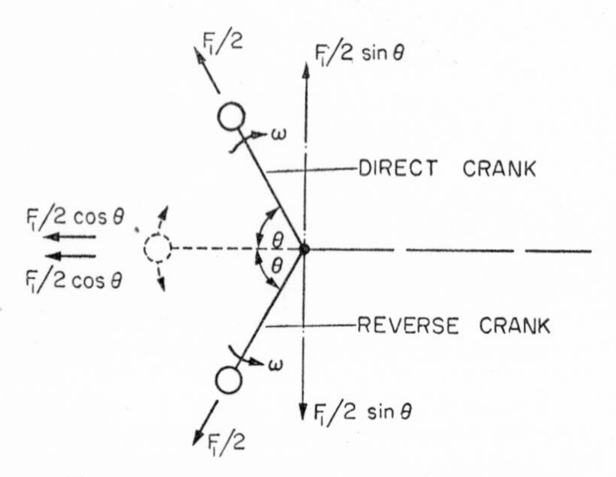

FIG. 7.18. Primary direct and reverse cranks

determining a solution to a problem. It is of particular value in dealing with radial or vee engines where mathematical solutions, whether involving complex numbers or not, become needlessly laborious. In vee engines, the problem of investigating balance is more complicated than in in-line engines because there is no common direction of reciprocation for all the cylinders. Thus for example the primary force balance is given by

$$\frac{W}{g} r \,.\, \omega^2 \cos\theta \,.\, \cos\alpha = 0 \quad \text{and} \quad \frac{W}{g} r \,.\, \omega^2 \cos\theta \,.\, \sin\alpha = 0,$$

where α = angle of a cylinder to some datum. In the method of direct and reverse cranks, the reciprocating effects are simulated by rotating effects as follows.

Considering the primary, or 1st harmonic, force $= F_1 \cos\theta$ and imagine two equal masses rotating in opposite directions and, as

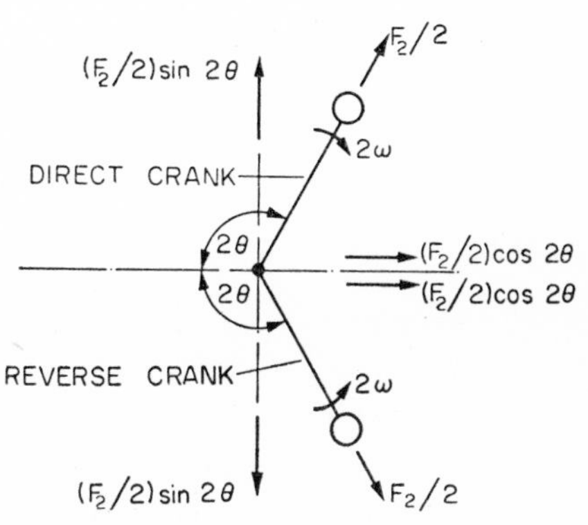

FIG. 7.19. Secondary direct and reverse cranks

shown in Fig. 7.18, coincident when the engine crank is at dead centre position. If the engine crank rotates to a position of θ to dead centre, one mass rotating at engine speed also moves to this position whilst the other moves through the same angle at engine speed but in the reverse direction. Provided the centrifugal force due to the rotation of each mass is $F_1/2$, then the components of these forces in the direction of engine reciprocation add to give $F_1 \cos\theta$, whilst the components at right angles are in equilibrium, i.e., cancel out. This will happen for any engine position. Thus the primary out of balance due to a cylinder is equivalent to, and can be replaced for analysis by, the two rotating masses. The mass rotating in the same direction as the engine crank is called the direct crank mass and the other the reverse crank mass.

Similarly the secondary (2nd harmonic) force $F_1 \cos 2\theta$ is equivalent to two rotating masses each of which gives rise to a centrifugal force of $F_2/2$. The masses must rotate at TWICE engine speed in opposite directions, as shown in Fig. 7.19.

This procedure may be carried out for any harmonic and is no more difficult for an nth order harmonic than for the 1st, the reciprocating system being replaced by a rotating system that can be readily analysed. The first of the following worked examples will be explained very comprehensively and the solution will be longer than is required in examinations.

WORKED EXAMPLE (U.L. Int., 1952)

7.5. An engine has two cylinders in the form of a V, the centre-lines of the cylinders being in one plane and inclined at 45° on either side of a central vertical line. The two connecting rods work on the same crank. The weight of the reciprocating parts for each cylinder is 1 lb, the crank radius is 1·75 in. and the connecting rod length is 6·5 in. Show that the vertical force on this engine due to secondary inertia forces is zero, and that if suitable balance weights are attached to the crankshaft the primary inertia forces can also be reduced to zero. For this value of the balance weights, find the greatest out of balance force acting on the engine in the horizontal direction when the crankshaft speed is 3000 r.p.m.

Solution

Consider the engine crank in the position shown in Fig. 7.20, and for this crank position, place the primary direct and reverse crank masses in their angular position.

For cylinder 1, the engine crank is 45° after dead centre so that the primary direct mass centrifugal force will be $F_1/2$ shown, in

Fig. 7.21, as a rotating vector by an arrow pointing in a direction 45° after dead centre, i.e., vertically.

The primary reverse mass vector will at 45° before the dead centre position of cylinder 1, i.e., pointing in a horizontal direction

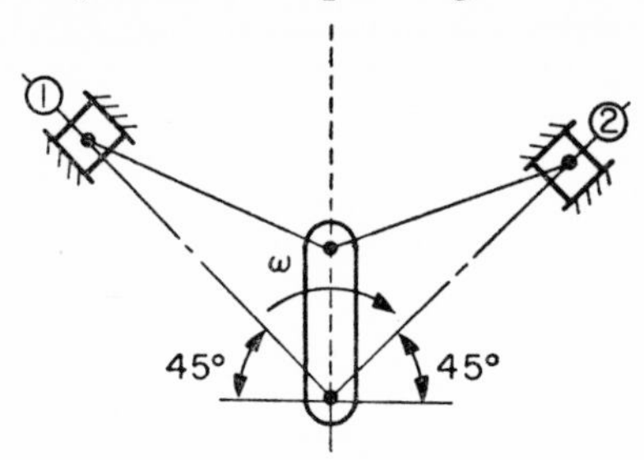

FIG. 7.20. Cylinder and crank configuration for engine of example 7.5

as shown in Fig. 7.21. Similarly for cylinder 2. The two primary reverse forces balance whilst the two primary direct rotating forces add to give a resultant force of $2F_1/2 = F_1$ pointing upwards for the engine crank position and rotating at engine speed in the same direction as the engine crank, as shown in Fig. 7.21.

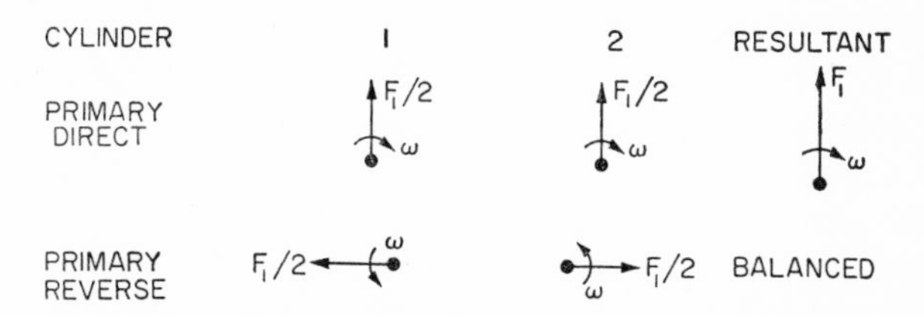

FIG. 7.21. Primary direct and reverse crank vectors of example 7.5

Balance of this force is achieved by placing a balance mass to rotate with the crank but displaced 180° to it so that the centrifugal force of the balance mass (wt., W_B at some radius r_B) equals F_1.

The engine crank is 45° after dead centre position of cylinder 1 and so the secondary direct mass is twice this angle, i.e., 90° after the dead centre position of cylinder 1. The secondary reverse mass for cylinder 1 will be 90° before the dead centre position. Similarly for cylinder 2, giving the rotating vectors shown in Fig. 7.22. The two secondary direct vectors add to give $\frac{2F_2}{2} \cdot \cos 45°$ $= 0{\cdot}707F_2$ acting vertically for the engine position and rotating in engine direction at twice engine speed. The two secondary

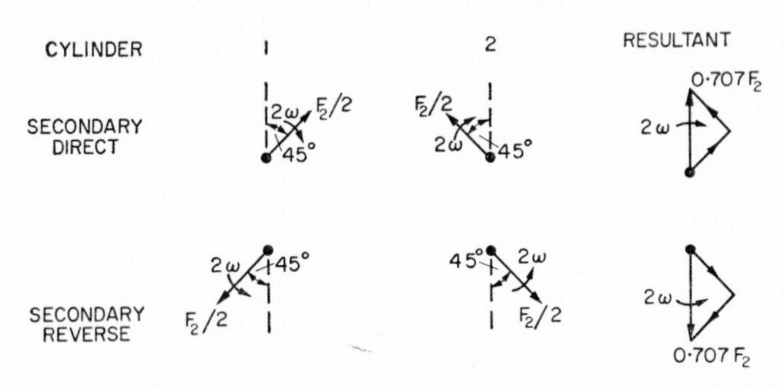

FIG. 7.22. Secondary direct and reverse crank vectors of example 7.5

reverse vectors add to give $0{\cdot}707F_2$ acting vertically downwards for the engine position and rotating at twice engine speed in opposite direction. For this position the resultant of the secondary direct mass forces balances those due to the secondary reverse masses and the resultant will be zero in a vertical direction for all positions of the engine. However when the crank has moved a further 45° the combined secondary direct forces rotate to the horizontal position and the secondary reverse forces move into the horizontal position, by reverse rotation, and then the secondary direct and reverse forces add to give a maximum horizontal force of magnitude

$$= 1{\cdot}414F_2 = 1{\cdot}414 \times \frac{1}{32{\cdot}2} \times \frac{1{\cdot}75}{12} \times \frac{1}{6{\cdot}5/1{\cdot}75}\left(\frac{3000 \times 2\pi}{60}\right)^2 \text{ lb}$$

$$= 171 \text{ lb.}$$

Note. This maximum force will occur at successive angular interval of 90° crank movement.

WORKED EXAMPLE

7.6. The pistons of a 60° V-twin engine have a stroke of 4·5 in. The two connecting rods operate on a common crankpin and each is 8 in. long. If the weight of the reciprocating parts is 2·5 lb per cylinder and the crankshaft speed 2500 r.p.m., find the maximum

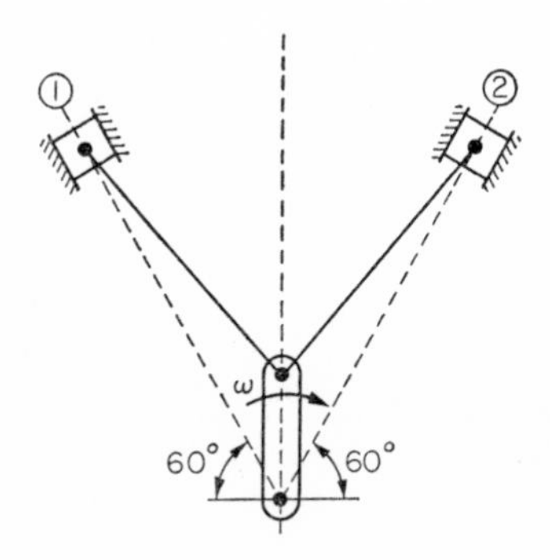

FIG. 7.23. Cylinder and crank configuration for engine of example 7.6

and minimum values of (a) primary forces; (b) secondary forces. In each case state the directions in which the forces act and the crank positions at which the maximum and minimum values occur.

Solution

Considering the engine in the position shown in Fig. 7.23, the primary direct and reverse forces are as shown in Fig. 7.24.

Maximum unbalanced primary force is when the resultant primary direct force adds to the resultant reverse force, this is when the engine crank is in the position shown and the maximum force

$$= 3F_1/2 = \frac{3}{2} \times \frac{2\cdot5}{32\cdot2} \times \frac{2\cdot25}{12}\left(\frac{2500 \times 2\pi}{60}\right)^2 = 1500 \text{ lb.}$$

The maximum force will also occur when the crank is 180° to the position shown.

The minimum primary force is when the resultant direct and reverse forces subtract, i.e., in a horizontal direction when the

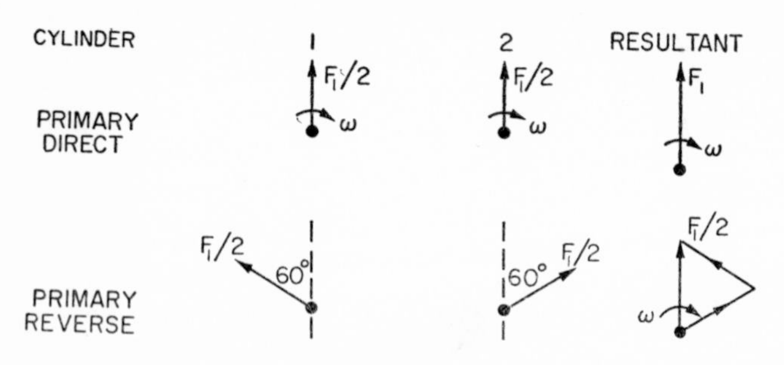

FIG. 7.24. Primary direct and reverse crank vectors of example 7.6

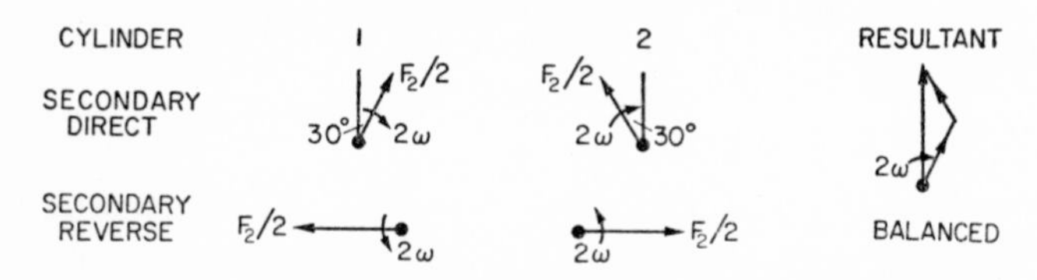

FIG. 7.25. Secondary direct and reverse crank vectors of example 7.6

engine crank is 90° before or after the position shown. The minimum primary force $= F_1/2 = 500$ lb.

The secondary direct and reverse forces are as shown in Fig. 7.25. The secondary reverse forces are balanced whilst the secondary direct forces add vectorially to give a resultant of

$F_2 \cos 30°$ rotating at twice engine speed and vertical when the crank is vertical. The maximum (which is the only) value

$$= \frac{2 \cdot 5}{32 \cdot 2} \times \frac{2 \cdot 25}{12} \times \frac{2 \cdot 25}{8} \left(\frac{2500 \times 2\pi}{60}\right)^2 \times 0 \cdot 866 = 241 \text{ lb.}$$

Worked Example

7.7. An engine has its twelve cylinders arranged in three rows each row containing four cylinders. The outer rows are at 60° to the central row. A flat, four-throw, crankshaft is used with three

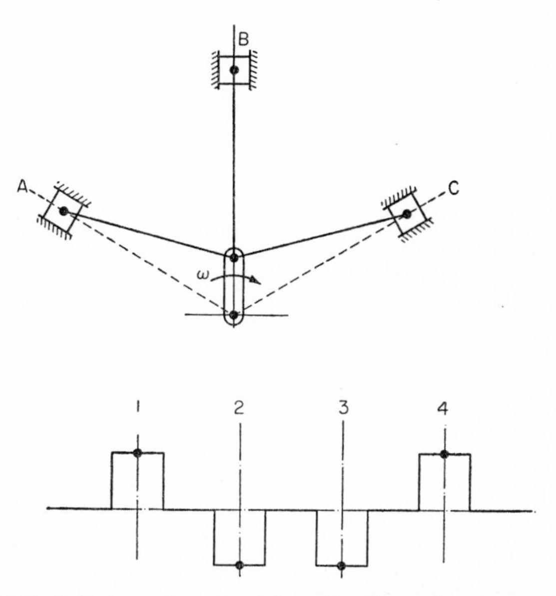

Fig. 7.26. Cylinder and crank configuration for engine of example 7.7

cylinders working off each crank. The angular positions of the cranks are 0°–180°–0°–180° with respect to the first. The reciprocating parts weigh 10 lb per cylinder, the stroke is 8 in. and the length of connecting rod 12 in. The engine speed is 1800 r.p.m.

Show that the primary forces are balanced and determine the maximum and minimum values of the secondary forces.

Solution

Consider the engine crank in the position shown in Fig. 7.26. The primary and secondary direct and reverse forces are shown as rotating force vectors in Fig. 7.27. (Vectors are either pointing up or down or are at 30° to the horizontal.)

Inspection of the forces show that the primary direct and reverse forces are balanced.

The secondary direct forces have a resultant rotating force of magnitude $8F_2/2 = 4F_2$ and the resultant secondary reverse force is $2F_2$. The maximum secondary force is therefore when these direct and reverse resultants add, $= 6F_2$

$$= 6 \times \frac{10}{32{\cdot}2} \times \frac{4}{12} \times \frac{4}{12} \times \left(\frac{60 \times 2\pi}{1800}\right)^2 = 7350 \text{ lb.}$$

The minimum secondary force is when the secondary direct resultant and secondary reverse resultant are subtracted $= 2F_2$ $= 2450$ lb.

Examples

7.8. A three-cylinder engine has the cranks spaced at equal angular intervals of 120°. Each crank is 6 in., each connecting rod is 18 in., and the speed is 500 r.p.m. If the reciprocating parts per cylinder weigh 150 lb, find the maximum unbalanced primary and secondary effects of the reciprocating parts. (A.M.I.Mech.E., 1946)

Answers: 20,100 lb in., 4310 lb in.

7.9. The four cylinders *A*, *B*, *C* and *D* of a vertical engine are spaced at 24 in., 18 in. and 24 in. centres. The reciprocating masses of cylinders *A* and *D* each weigh 160 lb and their cranks are at 90° to one another. The stroke is 12 in. and the connecting rod length is 20 in. Determine the weights of the reciprocating masses for *B* and *C* and their crank positions relative to that of *A* if all primary forces and couples balance one another.

Calculate the maximum unbalanced secondary force when the engine is running at 450 r.p.m. (U.L.1 Ext., 1948)

Answers: 430 lb, 150°, 300°; 7750 lb.

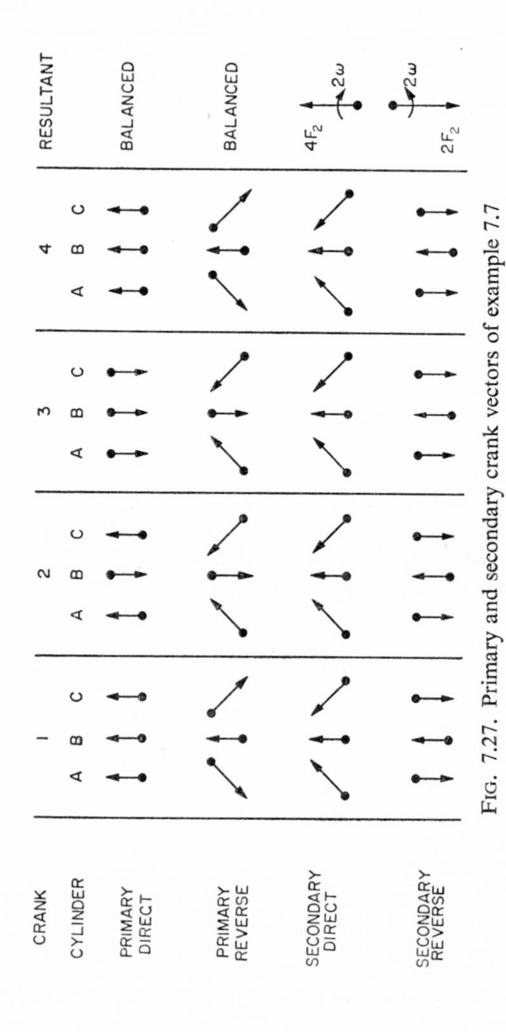

FIG. 7.27. Primary and secondary crank vectors of example 7.7

7.10. A four-cylinder in-line two-stroke oil engine has the cranks equally spaced along the shaft and so arranged as to give uniform firing intervals. If the cranks are numbered 1 to 4 from one end, show in an end view the relative positions of the four cranks which will give (*a*) the least unbalanced primary effect, and (*b*) the least unbalanced secondary effect.

(A.M.I.Mech.E., 1948)

Answers: Several firing orders will do.

7.11. A four-stroke engine has five identical cylinders in line, spaced at equal intervals of 4 in. The reciprocating parts per cylinder weigh 1·5 lb, the piston stroke is 3 in. and the connecting rods are 6 in. long between centres. The firing order is 14532 and the engine speed is 2400 r.p.m. Show that the engine is in balance for primary and secondary forces. Determine the maximum value of the primary and secondary couple acting on the engine and state the positions of no. 1 crank at which these maximum values occur. Take the plane of no. 3 cylinder as the reference plane for couple calculations.

(A.M.I.Mech.E., 1959)

Answers: 2350 lb in. 29°, 209°; 1760 lb in. 20°, 110°, 200°, 290°.

7.12. The firing order in a six-cylinder four-stroke in-line engine is 1–4–2–6–3–5. The piston stroke is 4 in. and the length of each connecting rod is 8 in. The pitch distance between cylinder centre lines are 4 in., 4 in., 6 in., 4 in., 4 in. The reciprocating mass per cylinder = 1·5 lb and the engine runs at 3000 r.p.m. Determine the out of balance primary and secondary forces and couples taking a plane midway between cylinders 3 and 4 as reference. (A graphical solution is suggested. Label all diagrams and vectors.)

(U.L.2 Ext., 1953)

Answer: Engine balanced.

7.13. Two alternate designs are contemplated for a single acting two-stroke diesel engine having six cylinders in line with centre lines spaced 36 in. apart. In the end view the cranks are to be 60° apart either in order 1–5–3–6–2–4 or in order 1–4–5–2–3–6. The stroke is to be 10 in. and each connecting rod 22 in. long. The reciprocating parts of each cylinder weigh 2100 lb and the rotating parts 1500 lb at crank radius. The engine rotates at 250 r.p.m. Show that with either arrangement the primary and secondary forces are balanced and that secondary moments are balanced in the first case and the primary moments in the second. Calculate the maximum unbalanced moment in each case.

(U.L.2 Ext., 1952)

Answers: 330,000 lb ft; 87,500 lb ft.

7.14. A vee-twin engine has the cylinder axes at right angles and the connecting rods operate a common crank. The reciprocating mass per cylinder is 25 lb, the crank is 3 in. long, and each connecting rod is 14 in. long. Show that the engine may be balanced for primary effects by means of a revolving balance weight. If the speed of the crank is 500 r.p.m., what is the maximum value of the resultant secondary force and in which direction does it act?

(A.M.I.Mech.E., 1948)

Answers: 162 lb, 90°, 180°, 270°, 0° to cylinder.

7.15. The three cylinders of an air compressor are arranged in one plane, one cylinder being vertical and the others inclined at 50° to the vertical on either side. The three connecting rods work on one crank. The stroke is 8 in., the connecting rod length is 14 in., and the reciprocating weight for each cylinder is 10 lb. In order to balance part of the inertia forces produced by the reciprocating weight, balance weights totalling 12 lb are attached to the crank webs opposite the crank at 5 in. radius. The rotating masses are separately balanced. Find the greatest amount of the vertical force acting on the machine at 500 r.p.m. (U.L.2 Int., 1946)

Answer: 156 lb.

7.16. The cylinders of a two-cylinder V engine are inclined at an angle ϕ with both pistons connected to a single crank of radius r ft. Each connecting rod is of length L ft; and the reciprocating mass for each cylinder is m lb. Using the method of direct and reverse cranks, investigate the values of ϕ which gives the least disturbing effects due to the primary and secondary inertia forces. Assume that the primary forces are half balanced.

(U.L.2 Ext., 1957)

7.17. Explain the terms "primary" and "secondary" balance as applied to reciprocating engines. A crankshaft has four throws all in one plane; a second crankshaft has four throws in two planes at right angles. The former is suitable for a four-cylinder in-line engine and the latter for a 90°-V, eight-cylinder engine, all the cylinder units being identical. Show to what extent primary and secondary balance can be obtained with each engine and suggest suitable firing orders, if the four-stroke cycle is used.

(U.L.2 Ext., 1944)

CHAPTER EIGHT

CAMS AND VALVE GEAR

MODERN automobile engines using a push rod type valve gear operate commonly at engine speeds up to 4000 r.p.m. and in some cases at speeds considerably in excess of this. The valve is thus raised and lowered several million times in a few hours of running and the time taken for one operation is a few hundredths of a second. Clearly the designer is faced with difficult problems to solve, not the least are those concerned with the selection of a suitable cam profile and the inertia and vibrational aspects. Similar problems exist in oil injection equipment.

The possible combinations of cam profile and type of follower are numerous, consisting of those that give a desired motion but are uneconomical to produce, and those that are relatively cheap to produce but do not fully satisfy the ideal motion. The preference for many years has been to use cams having profiles consisting of simple geometrical forms such as tangents and circular arcs, and in this chapter most attention will be given to these cams with roller and flat followers. In recent years, however, the production of cams to give specific follower motion has improved and now serious attention is being given to cams having a single continuous profile. These cams, known as polydyne cams, will largely supersede the present type of cam. Analysis of polydyne cam form is beyond the scope of this book, but readers interested should refer to recent articles in *Machine Design and Automobile Engineer*.

8.1. Displacement, Velocity and Acceleration of Cam Follower

In the case of cams of specified profile, the kinematics of a follower, such as a roller or flat faced tappet, can be determined by either analytical or vectorial methods. In the former case, an expression relating the displacement, or lift, of the follower in terms of the constant cam and follower dimensions and a parameter defining the cam position is obtained. The displacement equation may then be successively differentiated, graphically or mathematically, to give corresponding equations for velocity and acceleration. This often yields unwieldly expressions that are consequently unsuitable for practical design. Alternatively, it may be possible to determine the displacement, velocity and acceleration of the follower by vector diagrams. Readers not familiar with velocity and acceleration diagrams should refer to the book by the author on *Mechanics of Machines*, or, to other standard work.

To illustrate the application of the methods outlined above, the following examples are worked out.

WORKED EXAMPLE (U.L.2 Int., 1949)

8.1. A cam has straight working faces which are tangential to a base circle of diameter D. The follower is a roller of diameter d, and the centre of the roller moves along a straight line passing through the centre line of the camshaft. Show that the acceleration of the follower is given by

$$\omega^2 \left[\frac{D+d}{\cos^3\theta}\right]\left[1-\frac{\cos^2\theta}{2}\right],$$

where θ is the angle turned through by the cam, measured from the start of rise of the follower and is the angular velocity.

In such a cam the base circle diameter is 3·5 in. and the roller diameter 1·5 in. The angle between the tangent faces of the cam is 90° and the faces are joined by a nose circle of 0·4 in. radius.

The speed of rotation of the cam is 120 r.p.m. Find the acceleration of the roller centre (a) when, during lift, the roller is just about to leave the straight flank, (b) when the roller is at the outer end of its lift.

Solution

Figure 8.1, shows the cam in the given position, with the roller centre at Y. X is the position of the roller centre when in the lowest position.

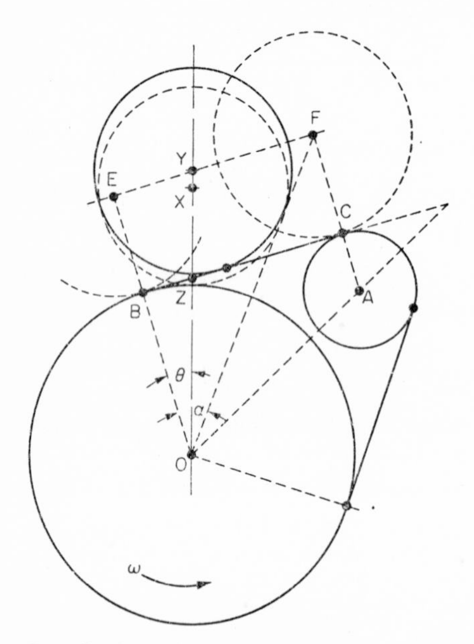

FIG. 8.1. Configuration of tangent cam of example 8.1

Lift of follower centre

$$= XY = OY - OX = OZ + ZY - OX$$

thus

$$y = \frac{D/2}{\cos\theta} + \frac{d/2}{\cos\theta} - (D/2 + d/2)$$

$$= \left[\frac{D-d}{2}\right]\left[\frac{1}{\cos\theta} - 1\right]$$

Follower velocity

$$= v = \frac{dy}{dt} = \frac{dy}{d\theta}\cdot\frac{d\theta}{dt} = \omega\,.\,\frac{dy}{d\theta}$$

if cam rotates at constant speed.

Thus

$$v = \omega\,.\left[\frac{D+d}{2}\right]\left[\frac{\sin\theta}{\cos^2\theta}\right].$$

Further differentiation gives

$$f = \frac{dv}{dt} = \omega^2\,.\left[\frac{D+d}{2}\right]\cdot\left[\frac{\cos^2\theta + 2\,.\,\sin^2\theta}{\cos^3\theta}\right]$$

$$= \omega^2\,.\left[\frac{D+d}{\cos^3\theta}\right]\cdot\left[1 - \frac{\cos^2\theta}{2}\right]$$

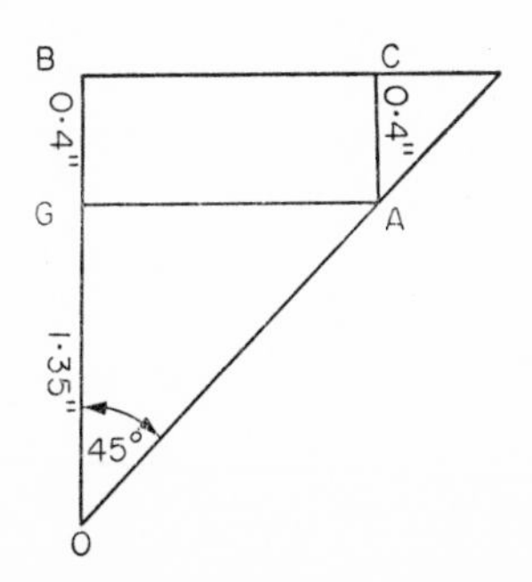

FIG. 8.2. Cam angle (of example 8.1) for contact on flank

When the follower is just about to leave contact with flank, the roller touches at C and the acceleration is given by substituting the appropriate value of θ. If the cam is assumed fixed and roller moves round it, then the angle will be α as shown in Fig. 8.1.

$$\tan \alpha = \frac{EF}{EO} = \frac{CB}{EO}.$$ Figure 8.2 shows portion $OACB$.

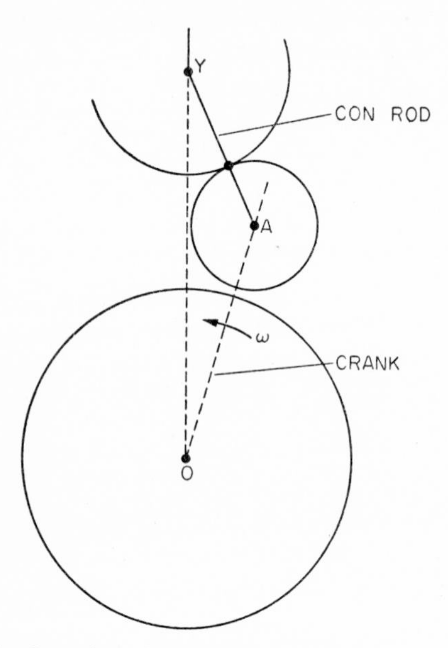

FIG. 8.3. Configuration of cam (of example 8.1) for contact on nose

Since the angle between tangent faces is 90°, then angle $BOA = 45°$

Thus,

$$CB = AG = GO = 1{\cdot}75 - 0{\cdot}4 = 1{\cdot}35 \text{ in.}$$

and

$$\tan \alpha = \frac{1{\cdot}35}{OB + BE} = \frac{1{\cdot}35}{2{\cdot}5} = 0{\cdot}54. \quad \alpha = 28^\circ\, 22',\ \cos\theta = 0{\cdot}88$$

$$f = \left(\frac{120 \times 2\pi}{60}\right)^2 \left[\frac{3{\cdot}5 + 1{\cdot}5}{0{\cdot}88^3}\right]\left[1 - \frac{0{\cdot}88^2}{2}\right] \text{ in./sec}^2$$

$$= 710 \text{ in./sec}^2.$$

The answer is a positive value and so acceleration acts upwards, i.e., same as positive value of y.

FIG. 8.4. Configuration of cam (of example 8.1) for contact on nose tip

When contact is on the nose of the cam, the cam mechanism is the same as a slider crank chain, i.e., an engine mechanism as shown in Fig. 8.3. This becomes a straight line for given cam with contact at outer end of lift as shown in Fig. 8.4. From Fig. 8.2, $OA = OG/\cos 45^\circ = 1{\cdot}35/0{\cdot}707 = 1{\cdot}9$ in. and $AY =$ sum of roller and nose radii = 1.15 in.

The velocity of A relative to

$$O = V_{AO} = \frac{120}{60} \times 2\pi \times 1{\cdot}9 = 23{\cdot}9 \text{ in./sec.}$$

and the velocity diagram is shown in Fig. 8.5.

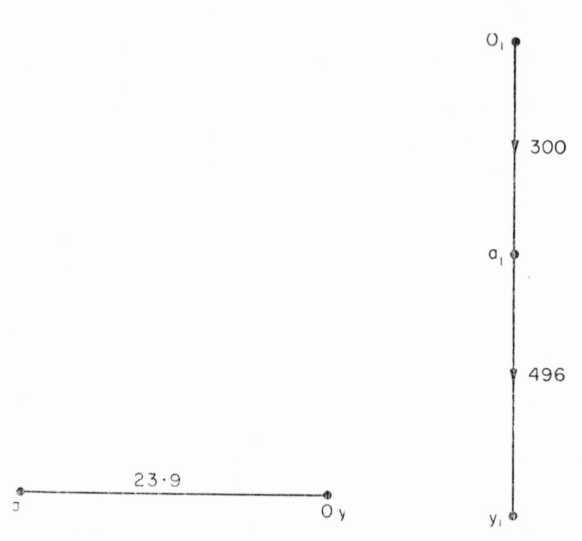

FIG. 8.5. Velocity diagram for cam follower of example 8.1

FIG. 8.6. Acceleration diagram for cam follower of example 8.1

The centripetal acceleration of A relative to

$$O = f^C_{AO} = \frac{23{\cdot}9^2}{1{\cdot}9} = 300 \text{ in./sec}^2,$$

The centripetal acceleration of A relative to

$$Y = \frac{23{\cdot}9^2}{1{\cdot}15} = 496 \text{ in./sec}^2.$$

The acceleration diagram is shown in Fig. 8.6.

The acceleration of the roller centre is given by vector o_1y_1 = 796 in./sec^2 in a downwards (negative) direction.

Note that whilst contact is on flank, acceleration is upwards, and is downwards whilst contact is on the nose, as shown in Fig. 8.7.

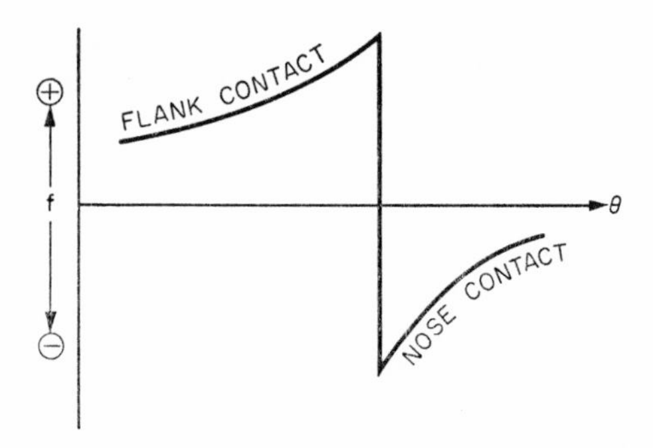

FIG. 8.7. Acceleration of roller follower and tangent cam

WORKED EXAMPLE (U.L.2 Ext., 1942)

8.2. A convex cam operating a flat-ended follower whose lift is 0·75 in., has a base circle radius of 1·5 in. and a nose radius of 0·4 in. The cam is symmetrical about a line drawn through the centre of curvature of the nose and the centre of the camshaft. If the total angle of cam action is 120°, find the radius of the convex flanks; determine the maximum acceleration and retardation when the camshaft speed is 500 r.p.m.

Solution

Figure 8.8 shows the convex flank BC touching the nose, centre A, and the base circle, centre O. Radii CA and BO produced, will intersect at the flank centre of curvature D. The total angle of action is angle BOE and thus angle $BOA = 60°$. R_f is flank radius.

$$AD = R_f - 0{\cdot}4 \text{ in.}, \quad OD = R_f - 1{\cdot}5 \text{ in.}$$

AO = base circle radius + lift − nose circle radius = 1·85 in.
Thus for triangle AOD,

$$AD^2 = AO^2 + OD^2 - 2 \, . \, AO \, . \, OD \, . \cos 120°$$

and

$$(R_f - 0{\cdot}4)^2 = 1{\cdot}85^2 + (R_f - 1{\cdot}5)^2 + 2(1{\cdot}85)(R_f - 1{\cdot}5) \times 0{\cdot}5$$

whence

$$R_f = 7{\cdot}8 \text{ in.}$$

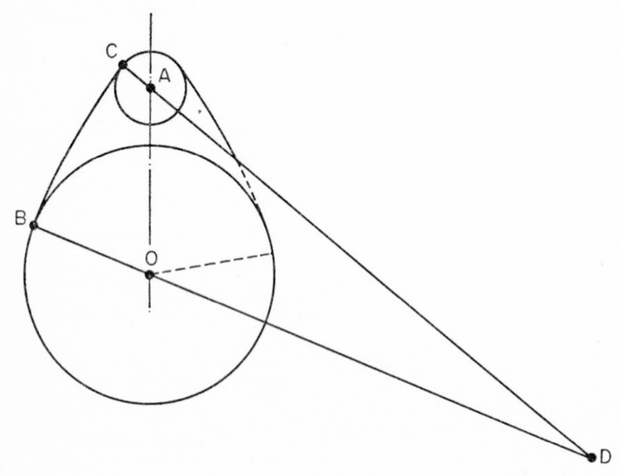

FIG. 8.8. Curvature of convex flank of cam of example 8.2

Alternatively, Fig. 8.8 could be drawn to scale and AD measured. Figure 8.9 shows contact with cam flank. θ is angle cam has turned from position when follower is at bottom of lift.

Lift = $y = QP = SQ - SP$ and if R_b is base circle radius, then

$$y = R_f - (R_b + (R_f - R_b) \cos \theta) = (R_f - R_b)(1 - \cos \theta)$$

and acceleration $f = \omega^2(R_f - R_b) \cos \theta$ and maximum value is when $\theta = 0°$.

Maximum acceleration

$$= \left(\frac{500}{60} \times 2\pi\right)^2 (7{\cdot}8 - 1{\cdot}5) = 17{,}300 \text{ in./sec}^2 \text{ upwards}$$

since value is positive.

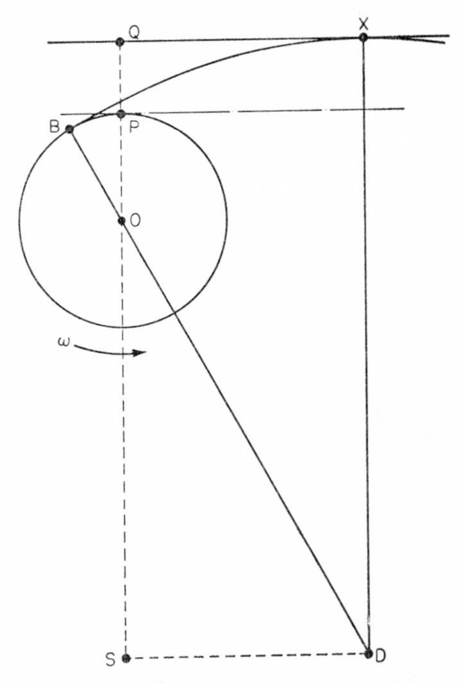

FIG. 8.9. Flank contact of cam of example 8.2

Figure 8.10 shows contact on the nose. An expression for the acceleration may be obtained in simple form provided the cam angle is expressed *from* the position of contact on the nose top and the lift is expressed from the lowest position. Thus,

$$\text{lift} = OA \cos\theta - R_b + R_n$$

where R_n is radius of nose. The acceleration is therefore equal to $-\omega^2 . OA . \cos\theta$ and the maximum value is when $\theta = 0°$, i.e., at nose top.

Maximum acceleration

$$= -\left(\frac{500}{60} \times 2\pi\right)^2 \times 1{\cdot}85 = -5070 \text{ in./sec}^2$$

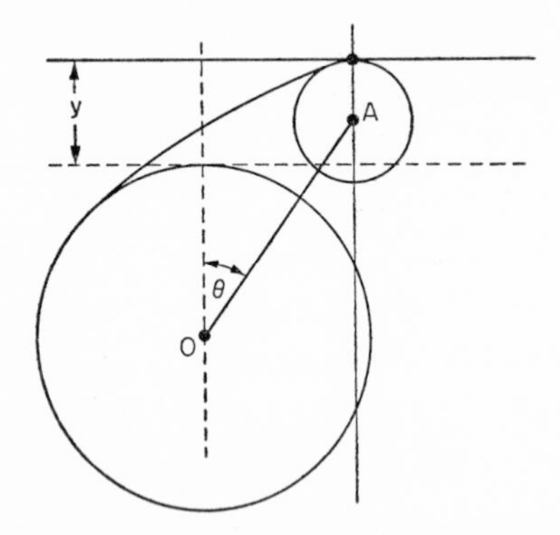

FIG. 8.10. Nose contact of cam of example 8.2

Note that a negative value indicates that acceleration is downwards, or is a retardation.

8.2. Inertia Effects

Consideration of the tangent cam with roller follower shows that whilst contact is between roller and straight flank, the acceleration of the roller is positive, i.e., upwards. When contact is between the roller and cam nose, the acceleration is negative, i.e., downwards, and at the change over points there will be sudden changes of acceleration. When the acceleration is positive, the inertia of the tappet and other moving parts of the valve gear will produce an inertia force acting in a direction opposite to the acceleration, i.e., downwards. The inertia force will then tend to keep the tappet in contact with the cam profile. When there is contact with the nose, the inertia force acts upwards and the tappet would tend to leave contact with the cam. A spring force is therefore necessary to give force closure. Similarly, with a convex cam and

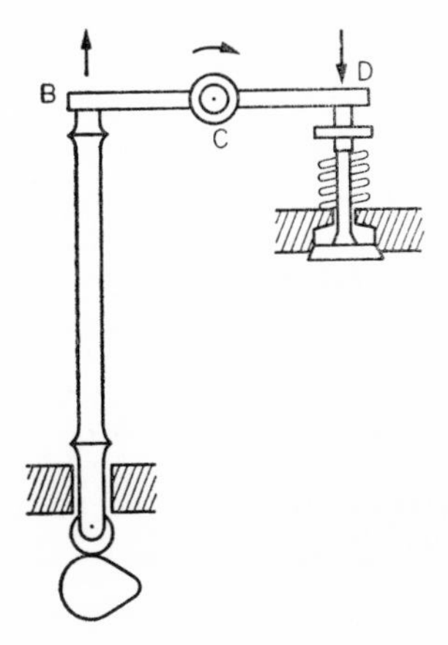

FIG. 8.11. Cam and valve gear of example 8.3

flat follower spring closure is required whilst contact is on the nose of the cam.

WORKED EXAMPLE (U.L.2 Int., 1950)

8.3. The camshaft of a petrol engine operates an overhead valve through a vertical tappet and push rod, and a horizontal rocker as shown in Fig. 8.11. A spring acting against a collar on the valve stem maintains contact between the tappet and cam. The line of action of the tappet passes through the cam axis. The weight of the moving parts are: tappet and push-rod, 0·35 lb; rocker, 0·4 lb; valve, 0·15 lb. The arm length of the rocker on the push-rod side is 1·0 in. and on the valve side 1·25 in. The radius of gyration of the rocker about its axis of rotation is 0·75 in. The cam has a base circle of 1·0 in. diameter, straight sides, a nose radius of 0·25 in. and lift of 0·25 in. The roller on the tappet is 0·5 in. diameter.

Find the spring force necessary to keep the tappet in contact with the cam when the valve has its maximum opening and the camshaft is rotating at 2000 r.p.m.

Solution

When contact is on the nose top, the valve is similar to an engine mechanism of Fig. 8.12 in the top dead centre position.

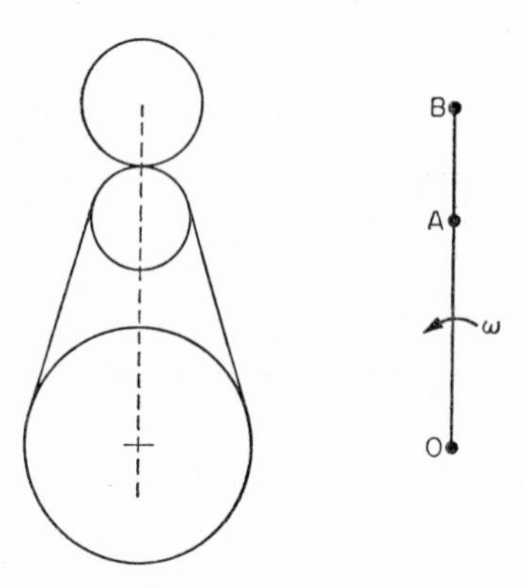

FIG. 8.12. Nose tip contact of cam of example 8.3

$$\text{Crank } OA = \text{lift} + R_b - R_n$$
$$= 0{\cdot}25 + 0{\cdot}5 - 0{\cdot}25 = 0{\cdot}5 \text{ in.}$$
$$\text{Con-rod } AB = R_n + R_r = 0{\cdot}25 + 0{\cdot}25 = 0{\cdot}5 \text{ in.}$$

(approximate formulae for acceleration cannot be used).

For velocity diagram

$$V_{AO} = \frac{2000}{60} \times 2\pi \times 0{\cdot}5 = 104{\cdot}5 \text{ in./sec.}$$

Centripetal acceleration

$$f^C_{AO} = \frac{104{\cdot}5^2}{0{\cdot}5} = 21{,}800 \text{ in./sec}^2$$

Centripetal acceleration

$$f^C_{BA} = \frac{104{\cdot}5^2}{0{\cdot}5} = 21{,}800 \text{ in./sec}^2.$$

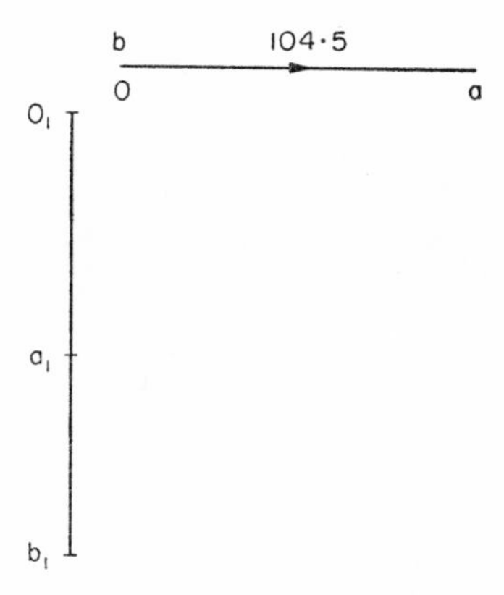

FIG. 8.13. Velocity and acceleration diagrams of example 8.3

From acceleration diagram, acceleration of $B = 45{,}600$ in./sec^2 acting downwards, or $= 3625$ ft/sec^2.

Hence acceleration of

$$D = 3625 \times \frac{1{\cdot}25}{1{\cdot}0} = 4560 \text{ ft/sec}^2 \text{ upwards.}$$

Inertia force due to valve

$$= \frac{0{\cdot}15 \times 4560}{32{\cdot}2} = 21{\cdot}3 \text{ lb downwards at } D.$$

Inertia force due to tappet, etc.

$$= \frac{0{\cdot}35 \times 3625}{32{\cdot}2} = 39{\cdot}4 \text{ lb upwards at } B.$$

Angular acceleration of rocker

$$= \frac{3625}{1/12} = 43{,}600 \text{ rad/sec}^2 \text{ anticlockwise.}$$

Inertia torque of rocker = inertia × ang. accel.

$$= \frac{0{\cdot}4}{32{\cdot}2} \times \frac{0{\cdot}75^2}{144} \times 43600 = 2{\cdot}12 \text{ lb ft clockwise, or}$$

$$= 25{\cdot}44 \text{ lb in.}$$

If spring force is S lb, then moments about C give

$$(S \times 1{\cdot}25) = (39{\cdot}4 \times 1) + 25{\cdot}44 + (21{\cdot}3 \times 1{\cdot}25) + (0{\cdot}15 \times 1{\cdot}25) - (0{\cdot}35 \times 1),$$

$$S = 73 \text{ lb.}$$

WORKED EXAMPLE (U.L.2 Ext., 1948)

8.4. A flat-ended valve tappet is operated by a symmetrical cam having circular arcs for flank and nose profiles; the base circle diameter is 1·5 in., the nose radius is 0·2 in. and the lift is 0·5 in., the total angle of action is 180°. The mass effect of valve, spring and tappet is equivalent to a mass of weight 1·7 lb concentrated at the tappet. Calculate the flank radius of the cam and the maximum reaction torque, due to the accelerated masses, acting on the camshaft when the cam rotates at 1200 r.p.m.

Solution

In Fig. 8.14, angle $AOD = 90°$, $AD = R_f - 0{\cdot}2$ in., $OD = R_f - 0{\cdot}75$ in., $AO = 0{\cdot}75 + 0{\cdot}5 - 0{\cdot}20 = 1{\cdot}05$ in., and thus

$$(R_f - 0{\cdot}2)^2 = 1{\cdot}05^2 + (R_f - 0{\cdot}75)^2,$$

giving

$$R_f = 1{\cdot}48 \text{ in.}$$

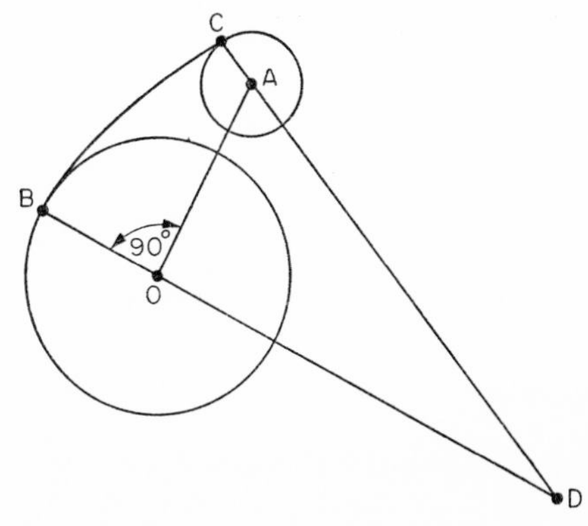

FIG. 8.14. Curvature of convex flank of cam of example 8.4

Reaction torque will occur whilst contact, as shown in Fig. 8.15, is on the flank.

Acceleration of follower $= f = \omega^2(R_f - R_b)\cos\theta$ and so inertia force

$$= \frac{1{\cdot}7}{32{\cdot}2} \times \frac{0{\cdot}73}{12}\left(\frac{1200}{60} \times 2\pi\right)^2 \cos\theta = 50{\cdot}8 \cos\theta \text{ lb.}$$

Torque on camshaft for this

$$= 50{\cdot}8 \cos\theta \times SD$$

$$= 50{\cdot}8 \cos\theta \times OD \,.\, \sin\theta \text{ lb in.}$$

$$= 37 \sin\theta \,.\, \cos\theta \text{ lb in.} = 18{\cdot}5 \sin 2\theta \text{ lb in.}$$

Maximum value of torque will be if θ is 45° provided there is 45° of cam movement whilst contact is on flank. Angle ADO is given by, $\sin\theta = AO/AD = 1{\cdot}05/1{\cdot}46 = 0{\cdot}72$ and $\theta = 46°$. Thus maximum torque is at $\theta = 45°$ and $= 18{\cdot}5$ lb in.

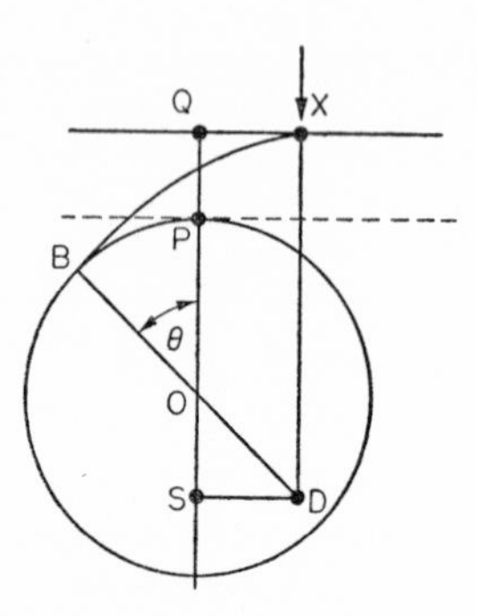

FIG. 8.15. Inertia force on cam of example 8.4

Examples

8.5. A valve is operated by a cam which has a base circle diameter of 1·75 in. and a lift of 0·625 in., the cam has tangent flanks and a circular nose and a total angle of action is 120°. The follower which has a roller of 0·75 in. diameter moves along a straight line passing through the cam axis. Find the maximum load to be exerted by the spring to maintain contact between cam and roller at all times while rotating at 1000 r.p.m. The effective weight of valve tappet and spring is 1·25 lb. (U.L.2 Ext., 1949)

Answer: $R_n = 0{\cdot}25$ in.; 212 lb.

8.6. A flat ended valve tappet is operated by a symmetrical cam having circular arcs for flank and nose profiles. The base circle diameter is 1·4 in., the nose radius is 0·15 in. and the lift is 0·45 in., the total angle of action is 180°. The inertia effect of valve, spring and tappet is equivalent to a mass of 1·75 lb at the tappet.

(*a*) Calculate the flank radius of the cam.

(*b*) Find the maximum reaction torque on the camshaft due to the accelerated mass when it rotates at 1500 r.p.m. (U.L.2 Ext., 1953)

Answer: (*a*) 1·334 in., (*b*) 22·4 lb in.

8.7. A flat ended valve tappet is operated by a symmetrical cam with circular arcs for flank and nose profiles; the straight line path of the tappet passes through the cam axis. The total angle of action is 150°, the lift is 0·25 in., the base circle of diameter is 1·25 in. and the period of acceleration is half of the deceleration during lift; the cam rotates at 1250 r.p.m. Determine (i) the nose and flank radii, (ii) the maximum acceleration and deceleration while lifting.
(U.L.2 Ext., 1946)

Answers: (i) 0·40 in., 1·484 in.; (ii) 1225 ft/sec^2, -677 ft/sec^2.

CHAPTER NINE

SUSPENSION, STEERING AND TYRES

ALL three units, suspension, steering and tyres, play important parts in the behaviour of an automobile and whilst they are separate units, having their own main functions, they are interrelated in their action on the vehicle. The suspension has considerable influence on the vehicle ride and the tyres having some elasticity also affect the ride. In performance, the tyres play the largest part in determining the vehicle motion but movements of the sprung parts give load changes which can affect tyre forces. It is however when considering vehicle stability that the influence of the three units is involved and, for example, the roll steer effect is well known.

A full consideration of the problems is clearly complex and involving many degrees of freedom and, as such, is beyond the scope of this book. Emphasis will therefore be placed on the basic geometry of suspensions and steering, the influence of this on tyre forces and, on tyre–road forces and couples that are of consequence in stability considerations. The particular aspects of vibration, gyroscopic effects, etc., are dealt with in later chapters.

9.1. Types of Suspension

Most car suspensions are nowadays fully or partially of the independent type, and the beam axle type is confined mainly to to lorries and heavier vehicles. Independent suspensions are often the four-bar link type, the sliding rod–crank type or, the trailing torque link as shown in Fig. 9.1.

In conjunction with each of these types of suspension, are the spring elements consisting of either a coil, torsion bar or leaf spring, as shown in Fig. 9.2 for a four bar linkage.

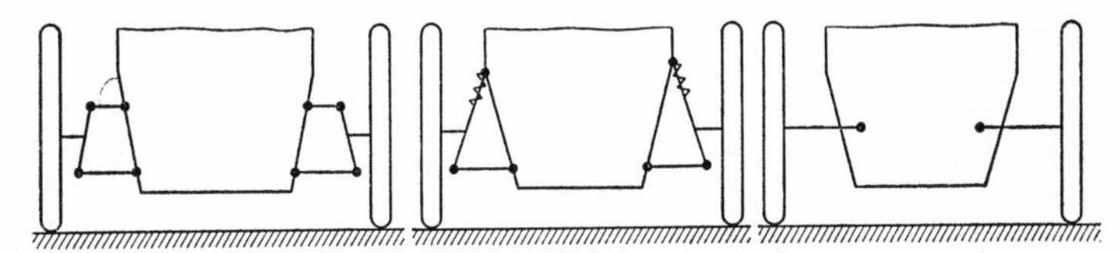

FIG. 9.1. Independent suspension linkages

A study of these suspensions to determine wheel scrub, roll axis, body side and upwards movement can be carried out most easily by means of instantaneous centres, although the general case for the four-bar linkage is complex and does not offer immediate

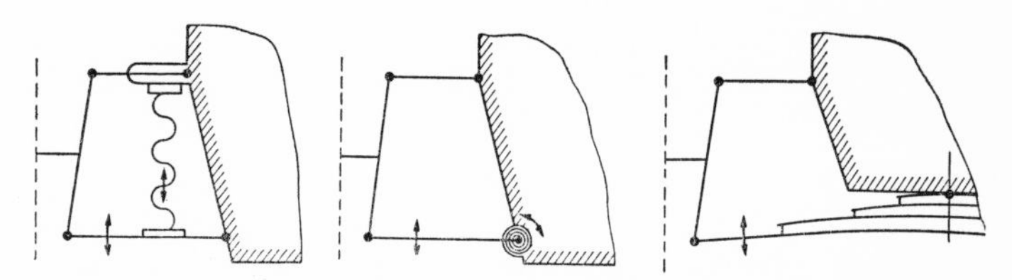

FIG. 9.2. Spring elements used with independent suspension linkages

practical advantages. It will be found that some simplifications such as considering roll only, give simple useful diagrams.

9.2. Roll Centres for Four Bar Suspension

The assumptions here are that the tyre deflections remain constant and that the wheels only rock about the point of contact with the ground. Considering the motion of the link W, as shown in Fig. 9.3, carrying the wheel, with respect to the body *B* of the car. The motion of point *b* relative to the body is a rotation about some point on the line *bc* produced. The motion of point *a* relative to the body is a rotation about some point on the line *ad* produced. Thus the motion of link *ab*, i.e., wheel *W*, relative to the body *B* is a rotation about the instantaneous centre *WB*. The motion of the wheel *W* relative to the road *R* is a rotation about

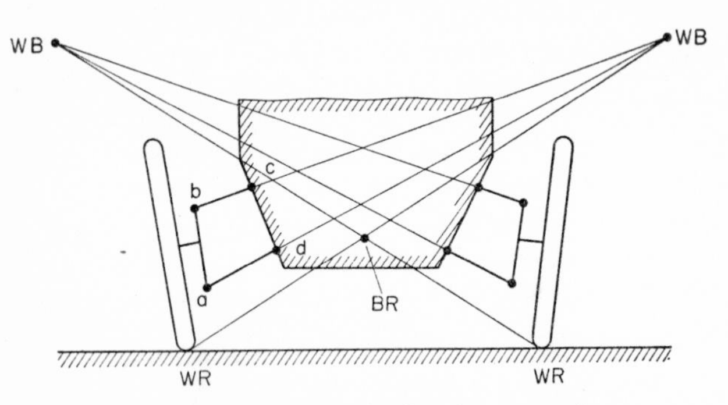

FIG. 9.3. Roll centres for four-bar suspension

the instantaneous centre *WR*. Since the three instantaneous centres for motion involving wheel *W*, road *R* and body *B* lie on a straight line, so the centre for the motion of the body relative to the road *BR* is on the line joining points *WR* and *WB*; similarly for the other wheel, giving centre *BR*. Note that when links *ab* and *cd* are nearly parallel, then some difficulty arises in confining a diagram to the drawing paper. Considerable changes of position for a roll centre can be made by modifications to the dimensions of a linkage.

9.3. Roll Centres for the Sliding Rod Suspension

With the same assumptions as in the previous case, the instantaneous centres for the link *bc* is as shown in Fig. 9.4. The link *bc* is dynamically the same as a link sliding through a pivoted block. The instantaneous centre for this motion is on a line perpendicular to the direction of sliding.

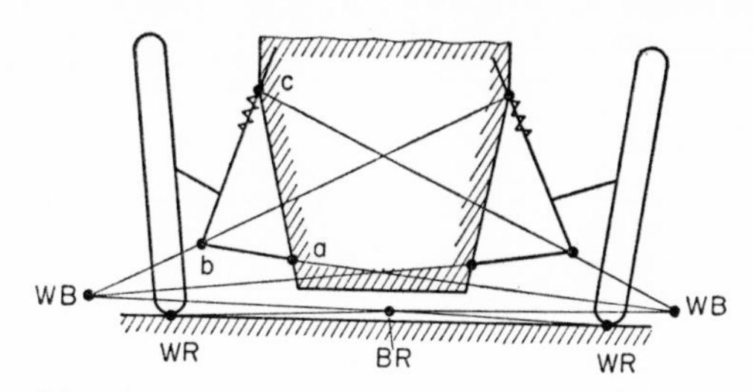

FIG. 9.4. Roll centres for sliding rod suspension

9.4. Change of Track

If the track changes then the assumption of the tyre rocking about a fixed point of contact with the road is no longer valid. The instantaneous centre *WR* is therefore no longer at the road,

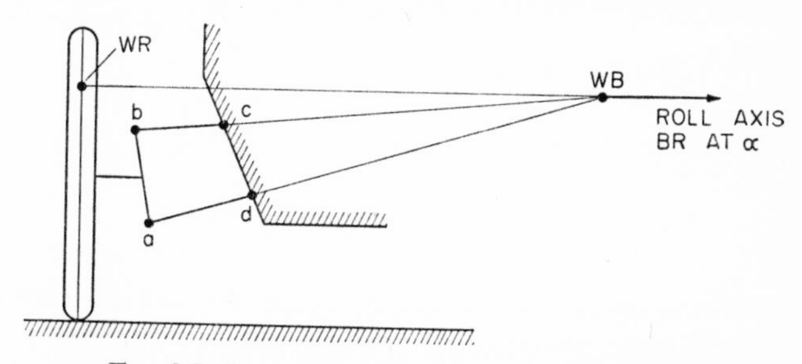

FIG. 9.5. Instantaneous centres for change of track

but at some point along a line perpendicular to the road, as shown in Fig. 9.5. Provided also the body is not considered to roll, but to move solely up or down, its instantaneous centre is at an infinite radius, i.e., along a line through *WB* parallel to the road. The wheel–road centre *WR* is at the intersection of a line through *WB* parallel to the road and, the line perpendicular to the road at point of contact of tyre with road. Note that the condition for zero track change is that centre *WR* is at the road.

9.5. Steering Interference

Movement of the stub axle up and down relative to the chassis, or roll of the chassis, can lead to interference with the steering position taken by the wheels.

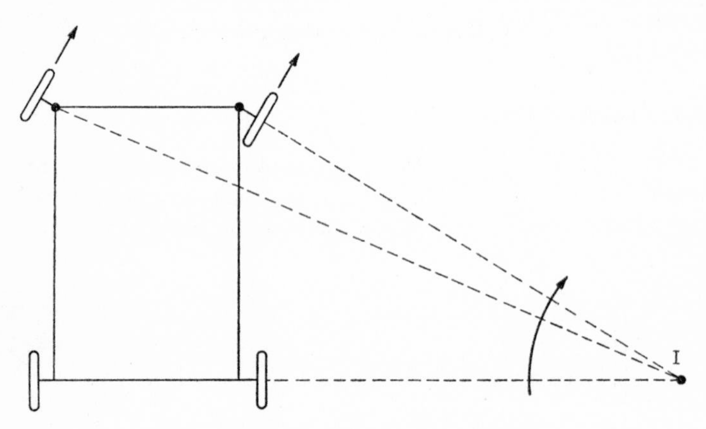

FIG. 9.6. Wheel angles for simple steering

Considerations of these effects are generally needed if undue tyre wear is to be avoided and if vehicle stability is to be investigated. No additional basic knowledge of mechanics is required for this problem which is of a three dimensional geometrical nature involving instantaneous centres. Assumptions have generally to be made to facilitate the evaluation of the problem, but these are particular to a given suspension and steering linkage and few general conclusions can be drawn.

9.6. Simple Wheel Steering Angles

For an initial simple consideration of steering, the automobile is assumed to be a box having rear wheels fixed in direction and front wheels that can be turned independently to required steering angles. This is shown in Fig. 9.6. Assuming the vehicle to turn in the circular path shown, and the wheels (assumed solid) to roll without side slip, then the steering angles for the front wheels are

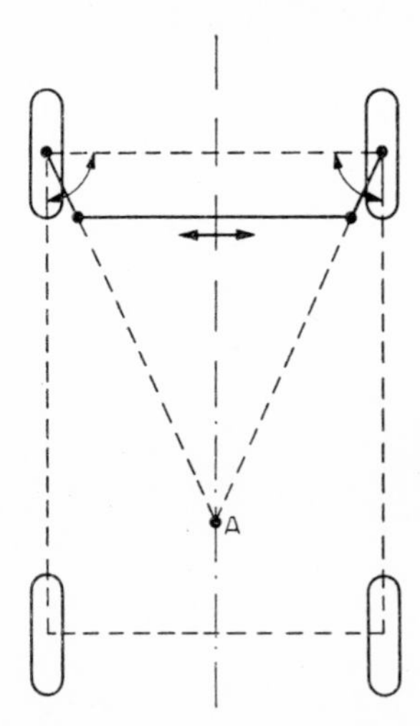

FIG. 9.7. Ackerman type steering linkage

not the same as each other. The instantaneous centre, *I*, for the wheels will lie on lines drawn perpendicular to the direction of motion of the wheels and the virtual radii of the front inner and outer wheels are different, with the inner wheel having to be turned more than the outer. The difference in steering angles of the front wheels for a vehicle of 10 ft wheelbase and 4 ft 8 in. track, can vary from 0° at zero steer angle to 11° 20′ at approximately 47° steer angle on the inner wheel. These requirements may be partially met by using a four-bar or Ackerman type of steering linkage shown in Fig. 9.7. The point of intersection, *A*, of the stub axle pivoting arms can be varied so that steering over some chosen range is nearly "exact," but over the remaining steering angle is only approximate.

It will be seen later that considerations of tyre slip angles show further limitations to the Ackerman steering.

9.7. Castor, Camber and Alignment

Castor, camber and alignment of the wheels, are all factors that have an influence on the ease and controllability of the steering.

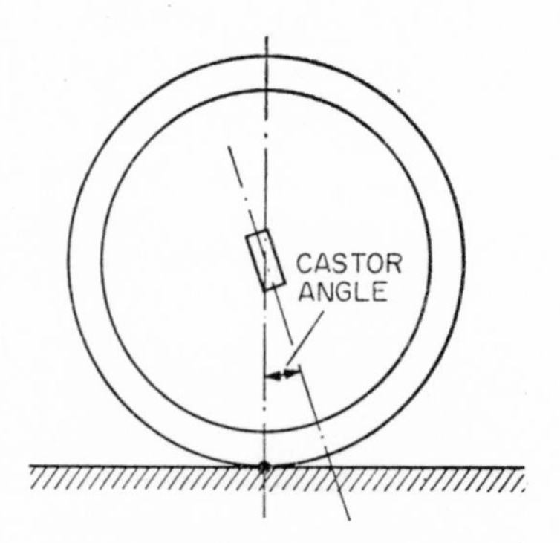

FIG. 9.8. Castor angle of wheel

Castor angle is the backward rake the swivel pin has so that the point of contact of the tyre with the road is behind the point the axis of the swivel pin makes with the road. This is shown in Fig. 9.8 with the effect exaggerated. The purpose of this castor angle (approximately 5°), is to give inherent stability to the wheels so that they tend to return to the neutral position after a turn, i.e., similar to the castors on a trolley.

In addition to castoring, the wheels are given a camber, i.e., they are not mounted vertically with the swivel pin vertical, but have the swivel pin and wheel with inward and outward camber as shown in Fig. 9.9. Note that the intersection of the wheel and swivel pin centre lines is below road level. Intersection at road level, as shown, is called centre point steering.

The amount of divergence, *d*, from centre point steering is a matter for compromise. With exact centre point conditions, there

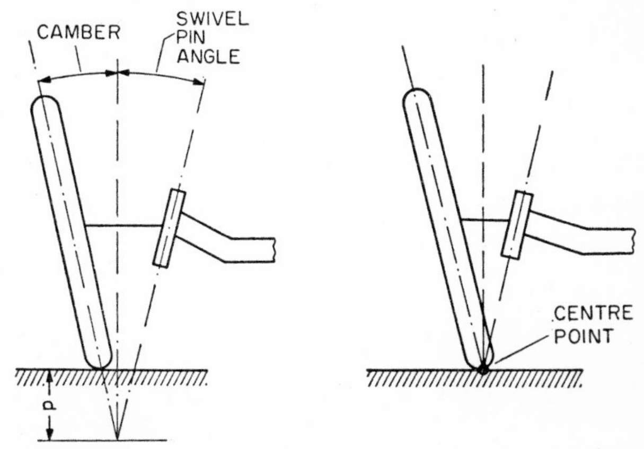

FIG. 9.9. Camber angle for divergent and centre point steering

is no tendency for forces at the tyres, due to rolling resistance, etc., to give rise to a moment about the swivel pin axis. Whilst this gives a desirable theoretical neutral condition, with light steering, it is doubtful whether it can be realized in practice and small variations on either side of the neutral, would give rise to wheel wobble. Some divergence is therefore usually given and this tends to toe-out the wheels. With divergence, there is not likely to be much tyre scrub when the wheels are turned with the vehicle at rest.

Wheel camber gives rise to road–tyre forces that tend to "stretch the axle" and if some of this load is taken along the pin axis, the frictional torque about the axis is reduced.

The wheels are generally set with a small toe-in to counteract the toe-out effect of non-centre point steering and camber torque, but the effect on tyre wear of alignment settings is of more consequence and more will be said about this later in this chapter.

9.8. Tyre–Road Forces and Couples

Apart from the forces at the tyres due to supporting the dead weight of the automobile, the main forces and couples are those arising from the performance, i.e., motion in forwards or backwards direction, or those concerned with stability. The former arise chiefly when a vehicle is accelerated, or braked, and the latter when the vehicle is steered in a circular path. Most of the tyre wear is due to these forces and couples. It is of interest to note that the braking and sideways forces are of comparable magnitude and thus tyre wear is predominantly due to cornering. The tyre forces are now considered in more detail.

9.9. Rolling Resistance

Considering the case of a wheel mounted vertically (camber ignored), and rolling in a straight path. This is often referred to as "pure rolling," but the tyre is, of course, not rigid and deformation occurs in contact with the road. The tyre therefore is stretched as it first contacts the road and then released as it leaves the road. Since the tyre is inelastic, the alternate stretching and recovery is accompanied by a hysteresis loss of energy which can be imagined equivalent to that due to overcoming a resistance to motion and called a rolling resistance. The area of contact of the tyre with the road would, if the wheels did not rotate, be of regular form symmetrical about a centre line. Owing to the creep between the tyres and the road the contact area is distorted and no longer symmetrical but with a larger area of contact to the rear or front of the original centre line.

Rolling resistance can be reduced by changes of tyre construction which by a modified arrangement of the cords, reduces the amount of deformation in the radial direction. There is also some difference in rolling resistance between tyres of natural and butyl rubber, but the effect on the reduction of fuel consumption is very small being about one-tenth of the percentage reduction of rolling

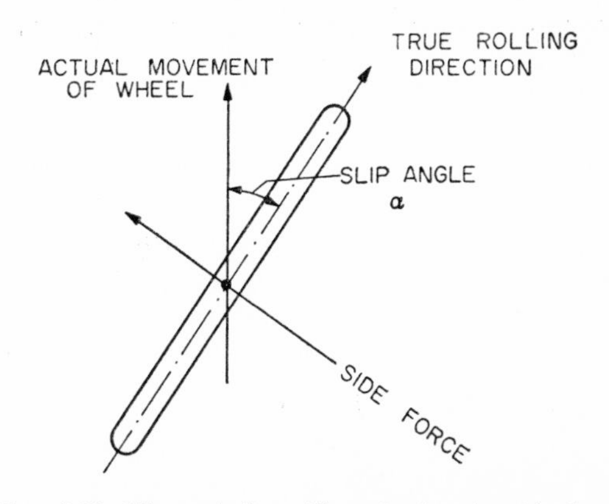

FIG. 9.10. Slip angle for rolling wheel under side thrust

resistance. However, many other factors such as speed, tyre temperature and all the various combinations of road surface, influence the value of the rolling resistance. Many of these also affect the comfort of the ride and clearly the design of tyres, which is beyond the scope of this book, is a problem of compromise between conflicting interests.

9.10. Slip Angle, Cornering Force and Self-aligning Torque

These effects arise when a wheel, whilst rolling, is acted on by a side force. The full deformation of the tyre is such that the part previously described due to performance is now accompanied by a similar type of deformation in a sideways direction, but the tyre does not however skid, or slip, in the usual meaning of these terms. The wheel centre, or axle, will move in a direction inclined to that in which the wheel points, as shown in the plan view of Fig. 9.10, the angle between these two directions being called the slip angle, α.

The side force shown in Fig. 9.10 due to centrifugal action when cornering could arise from other sources, but whatever the source, the road will react on the tyre in a direction opposing the side

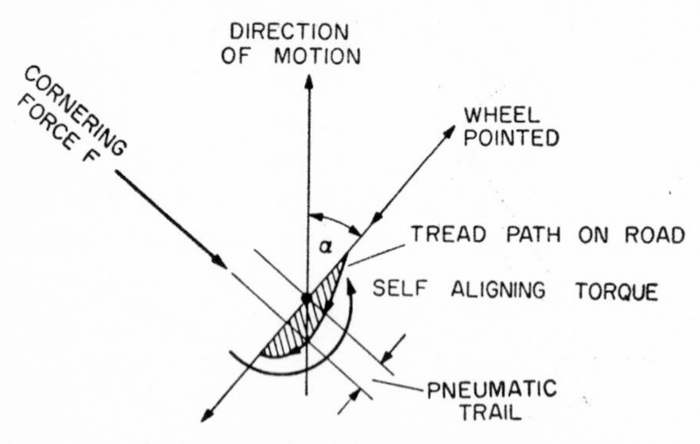

FIG. 9.11. Cornering force and torque on wheel

force. This road reaction is called the cornering force, F, and acts as shown in the plan view of Fig. 9.11.

It will be seen that the cornering force, F, is shown acting eccentrically to the point on the road directly below the wheel centre. This is due to the deformation of the tyre tread path contact area previously described. The amount of eccentricity is called the pneumatic trail and is quite distinct from castor effect. However, since the cornering force, F, is eccentric, it will produce a torque about the vertical axis of the wheel. This torque, shown in Fig. 9.11, is called a self-aligning torque, opposes the steering,

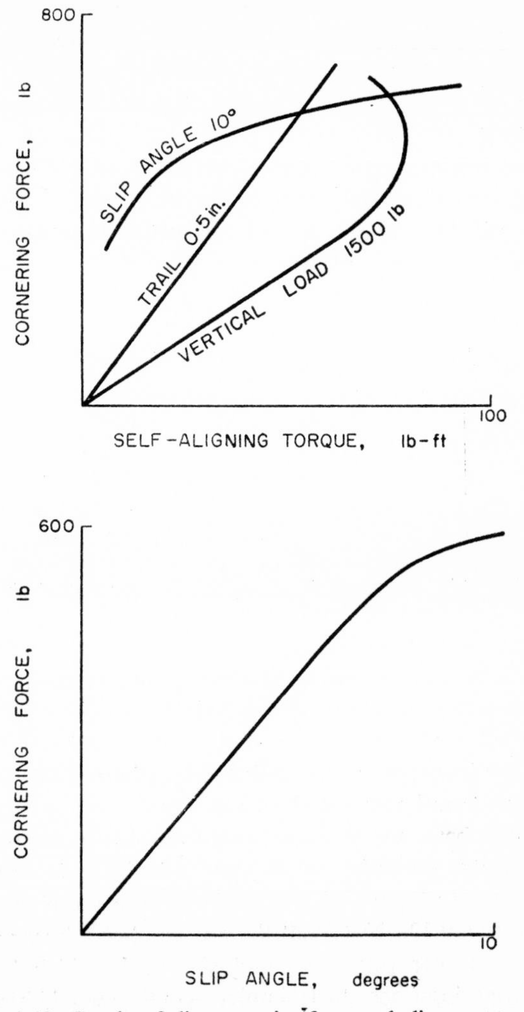

FIG. 9.12. Graphs of slip, cornering force and alignment torque

and gives feel to the steering. It will be noted that there is strictly no need, in these circumstances, for castoring, and the quantities mentioned are related by:

$$\text{Aligning torque} = \text{cornering force} \times \text{pneumatic trail.} \quad (9.1)$$

It can also be seen that side thrust due to camber is similar to cornering force in its action on a wheel and gives rise to a camber torque.

No simple relationships seem to exist between the quantities mentioned and for example, the cornering force may depend upon

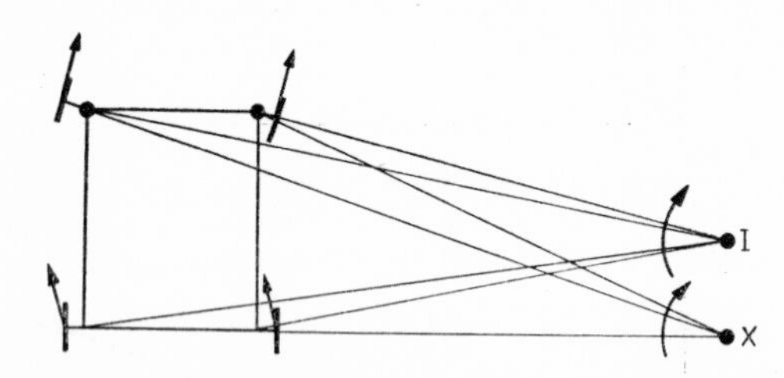

FIG. 9.13. Change of Ackerman centre due to wheel slip

tyre diameter and width, inflation pressure, vertical stiffness, coefficient of friction, nature of road and its surface, etc. Information available is too numerous and of such a varied nature that no attempt can be made in this book to reproduce graphs of actual measurements, all that will be done is to show a few general relationships between cornering force and self-aligning torque for constant values of trail, vertical load and slip angle and the between cornering force and slip angle. These are shown in the graphs of Fig. 9.12. Note that there is an almost linear relationship between cornering force and slip angle which has made stability considerations much simpler than they would have otherwise been. The ratio of cornering force to slip angle is called the cornering power.

9.11. Steering and Slip Angles

When an automobile moves round a curve with the front wheels turned to the Ackerman angles, the instantaneous centre would, in the absence of slip, be at point X as shown in Fig. 9.13. However, the centrifugal force has to be resisted by the combined cornering forces at the wheels, and each wheel must develop its

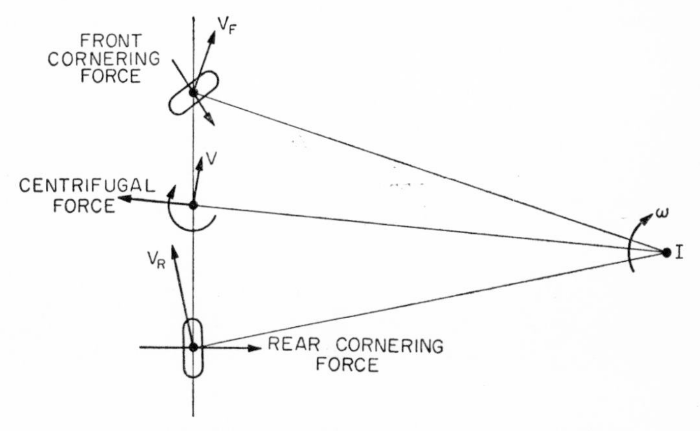

FIG. 9.14. Simplified vehicle configuration for tyre slip

appropriate slip angle. The directions of motion of the wheels is such that the slip angles adjust to give rotation about point, I, the actual instantaneous centre. It will be seen that for a slip angle to be developed at the rear wheels the centre I must be displaced from the Ackerman centre position, and the slip angles for the front wheels will not be equal. Conversely, if the front and rear wheel slip angles are to be approximately the same, then the wheels have to be steered to positions where they are more parallel than in the Ackerman position.

It is convenient when considering stability in the initial stages to assume that the two front wheels have equal slip angles which will be the same as the "front axle" slip angle and similarly for the rear wheels. The wheels can then be imagined to be compressed together at the axle centres and the vehicle behaves as though it were two wheeled as shown in Fig. 9.14.

It can be seen that the vehicle may yaw about its centroid as well as moving forwards, and considerations of dynamic stability

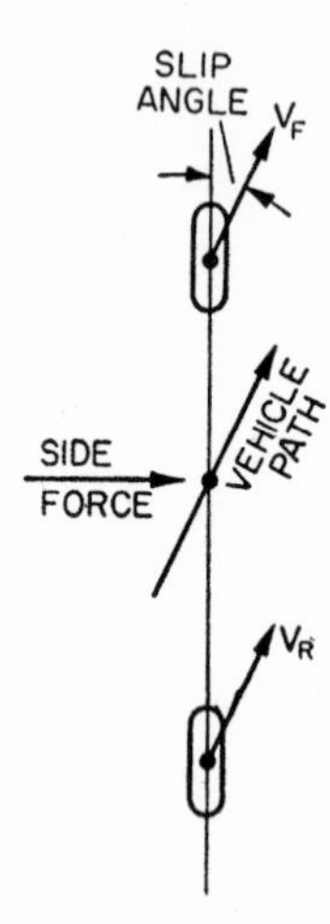

FIG. 9.15. Vehicle motion in "neutral" steer

are concerned with the behaviour subsequent to a disturbance from this position. Whilst such a consideration is beyond the scope of this book, some attention may be paid to the "static stability" or equilibrium.

Consider the vehicle moving forward in a straight path and a side force applied at the centre of gravity. If, as shown in Fig. 9.15, the applied side force produces equal steady state slip angles at the front and rear wheels, the vehicle moves off on a new straight line path. This motion will be without any yaw velocity and is called neutral steer. If the side force causes the front wheels to

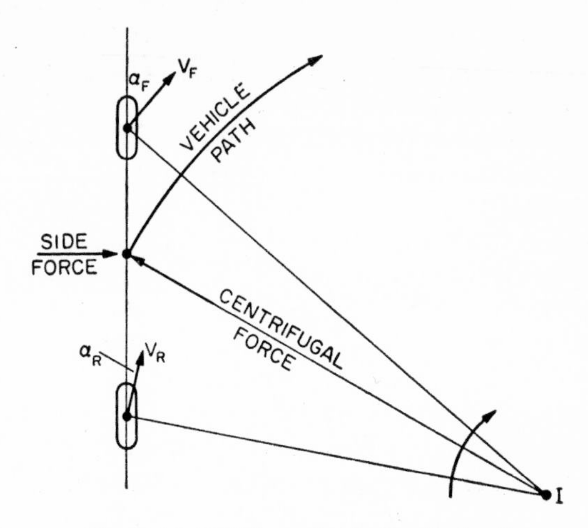

FIG. 9.16. Vehicle motion in "understeer"

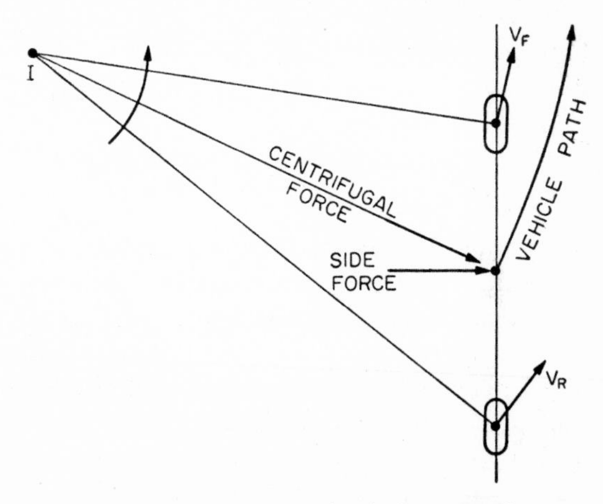

FIG. 9.17. Vehicle motion in "oversteer"

have a larger mean steady state slip angle than the rear wheels, as shown in Fig. 9.16, then the path of the vehicle is in a curve away from the applied force. The vehicle now has a yaw velocity about the centre of gravity as well as a linear velocity, with the vehicle as a whole rotating about the instantaneous centre, *I*. The rotation about *I* gives rise to a centrifugal force which resists the applied disturbing force. This condition is known as understeer. If the applied side force produces a steady state mean slip angle at the front wheels which is less than that at the rear wheels, as shown in Fig. 9.17, then the path of the vehicle is in a curve towards the direction of the applied force. The vehicle yaw is now opposite to the understeer condition and such that the centrifugal force produced acts to help the disturbing force. This condition is called oversteer and is generallly to be avoided, although it is difficult sometimes especially when the rear wheels are too heavily laden.

CHAPTER TEN

GYROSCOPIC EFFECTS

GYROSCOPIC action takes place when the axis about which a body is spinning, is moved in a particular angular way, such angular motion of the axis being called precession. Thus gyroscopic action can occur in an automobile when the axes about which the engine and transmission rotate are precessed by the automobile moving round a curve or by pitching. The wheels are precessed when the automobile moves round a curve or one wheel is lifted, or lowered, due to passage over a bump, or hollow, at the road surface. The latter effect is well known for the induction of gyroscopic wheel wobble.

However, before an analysis of the gyroscopic effects can be made for simple cases, some consideration of angular momentum is necessary as follows.

10.1. Angular Momentum and Velocity Vectors

The vector representation of linear quantities such as velocity is simple since a straight line drawn in a particular direction and of definite length is all that is needed. With angular quantities, however, representation is a little more involved owing to the necessity of drawing, on a plane sheet of paper, something that has motion about, as opposed to along, an axis or direction. Vector representation is made by using the analogy with the motion of a right-handed screw. If such a screw is rotated, its motion along the axis of rotation will be proportional to its angular motion about the axis. Thus a vector drawn to represent the axial velocity will also represent, as shown in Fig. 10.1, the angular velocity.

Since angular momentum, h, is given by the product of moment of inertia, I, and angular velocity, ω, then $h = I \,.\, \omega$ and the

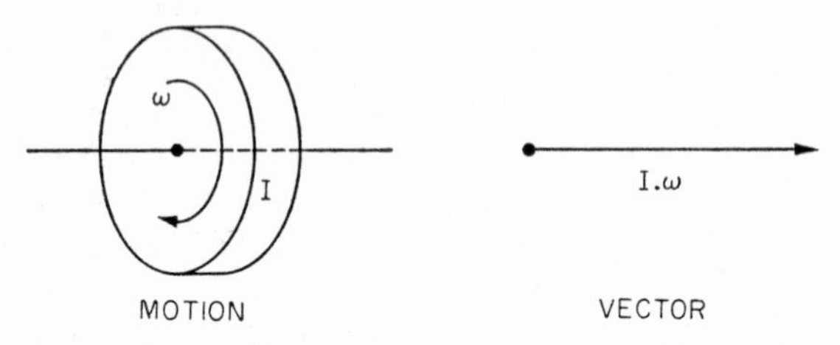

FIG. 10.1. Momentum vector for simple spinning disc

vector representing ω, will to a different scale, also represent the angular momentum of the body about the axis of spin.

10.2. Gyroscopic Action of a Rotating Disc Using Momentum Vectors

A disc is shown in Fig. 10.2, spinning about an axis OO. If a torque is applied as shown to act about an axis perpendicular to the axis of spin, then the disc does turn about this axis, but does so about a third axis perpendicular to the other two. This effect is known as the gyroscopic action and the velocity about the third axis is called the velocity of precession, ω_p. The explanation of the gyroscopic action is as follows: A disc of polar moment of inertia, I, about its horizontal axis of spin, is rotating as shown in the views of Fig. 10.3, at ω rad/sec. It is made to precess in the horizontal plane (plan view), so that in a small period of time δt sec the angle of precession is $\delta\theta$ rad. For simplicity it is assumed that whilst precessing the spin velocity remains constant. The

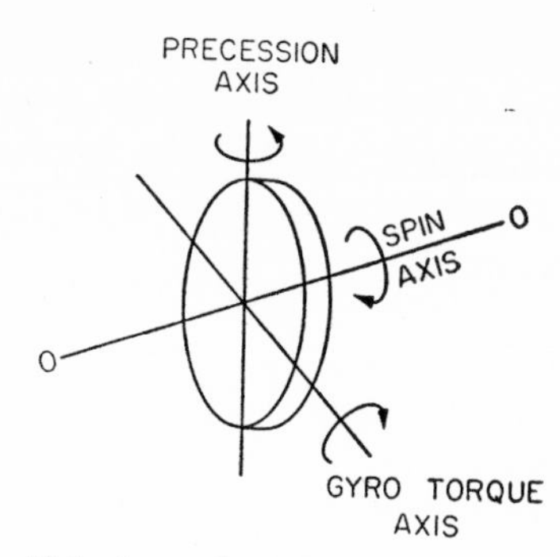

FIG. 10.2. Axes of spin, precession and torque

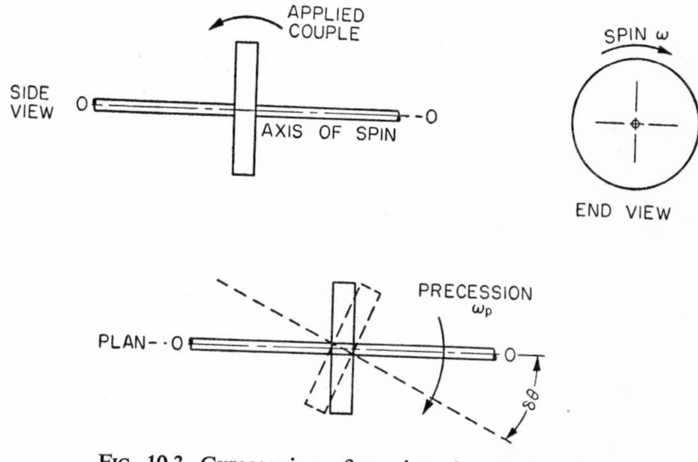

FIG. 10.3. Gyroscopic configuration of a spinning disc

vector representing the initial angular momentum $I \,.\, \omega$ is vector *oa* shown in Fig. 10.4, which has been drawn in the horizontal plane of precession. Precession causes the axis of spin to swing through $\delta\theta$ and the vector for the position after δt sec is vector *ob*. Whilst the magnitude of momentum, $I\omega$, has not changed, there is, due to change of position, a change of momentum as represented by vector *ab*. This vector is resolved into vector *ac* in a direction *ao*, and vector *cb* in a direction which is perpendicular to *ao*. From the trigonometry of Fig. 10.4, the change in angular momentum along $ao = I \cdot \omega - I \cdot \omega \cdot \cos \delta\theta$, which if $\delta\theta$ is small reduces to zero.

The change in angular momentum perpendicular to $ao = I \cdot \omega \cdot \sin \delta\theta$ which if $\delta\theta$ is small reduces to $I \cdot \omega \cdot \delta\theta$.

This change occurs in time δt and so the rate of change of angular momentum

$$= I \cdot \frac{\omega \cdot \delta\theta}{\delta t}, \quad \text{but} \frac{\delta\theta}{\delta t}$$

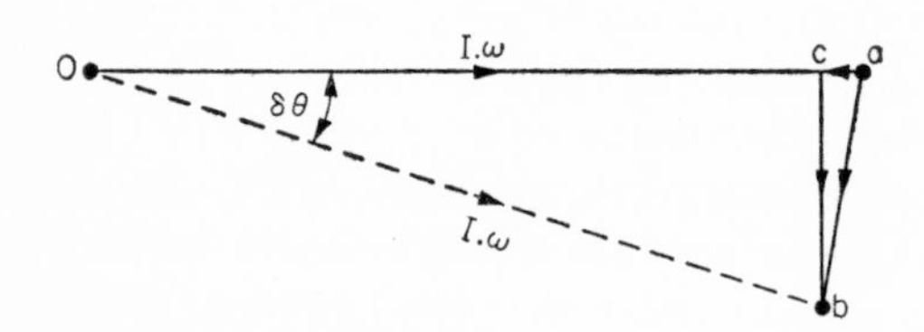

FIG. 10.4. Angular momentum vectors for system of Fig. 10.3

is the rate of precession, ω_p, thus rate of change of angular momentum $= I \cdot \omega \cdot \omega_p$ and hence,

Applied torque (gyroscopic torque)

$$= I \cdot \omega \cdot \omega_p \tag{10.1}$$

The sense and plane of action of the gyroscopic torque must be such as to give vector *cb* drawn in plan view. This vector shows a torque to act as shown in Fig. 10.3. This will be the torque on the gyroscope to make it precess, the effect of the gyroscope on the shaft holding it will be equal in magnitude but opposite in sense to the gyroscopic torque.

Students are advised when answering problems to always sketch the appropriate vectors to predict the direction of precession or gyroscopic torque. However, it should be noted that the direction of precession is such that the axis of spin tends to place itself in line with the axis of the applied torque and in the same sense.

It should also be noted that the result obtained is only applicable to simple gyroscopes which implies thin solids and of certain shapes. It is beyond the scope of the book to deal with shapes, such as two bladed fans, that give a fluctuating torque due to gyroscopic effects, and care is, therefore, necessary when applying equation (10.1).

WORKED EXAMPLE (A.M.I.Mech.E., 1959)

10.1. The crankshaft of a motor car engine is parallel to the longitudinal axis of the car and rotates in a clockwise direction when viewed from the front. The rotating parts of the engine weigh 400 lb with a mean radius of gyration of 4 in.

Calculate the magnitude of the gyroscopic couple and its effect on the loading of the four wheels when the engine is running at 3000 r.p.m. and the car turns to the right on a radius of 150 ft at a speed of 45 m.p.h.

Show clearly the gyroscopic effects of the engine, when an irregularity of the road surface causes the nose of the car to rise suddenly.

Solution

When the car turns to the right as shown in the plan view of Fig. 10.5, all parts of it rotate in a clockwise direction and the engine is precessed. The angular velocity of precession

$$= \frac{\text{linear velocity}}{\text{radius of curve}} = \frac{66}{150} \text{ rad/sec.}$$

The angular velocity of spin of the engine

$$= \frac{3000 \times 2\pi}{60} \text{ rad/sec.}$$

The moment of inertia of the engine about its axis of spin

$$= \frac{400}{32 \cdot 2} \times \left(\frac{4}{12}\right)^2 \text{ slugs ft}^2$$

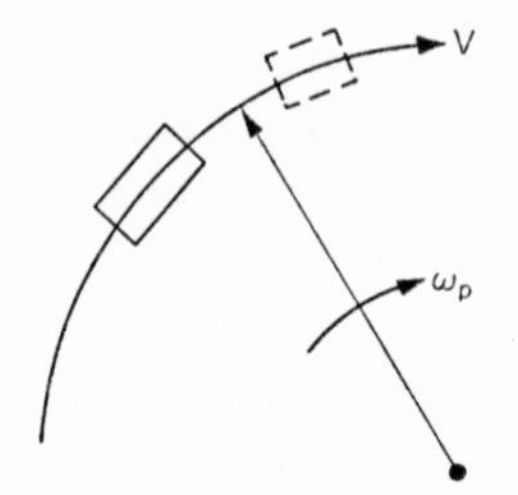

FIG. 10.5. Motion of car of example 10.1

Thus gyroscopic torque due to precession of the engine

$$= I \, . \, \omega \, . \, \omega_p = \frac{400}{32 \cdot 2} \times \left(\frac{4}{12}\right)^2 \times \frac{3000 \times 2\pi}{60} \times \frac{66}{150} = 191 \text{ lb ft.}$$

The momentum vectors for the original and new position are shown in Fig. 10.6. The torque which produces the change vector

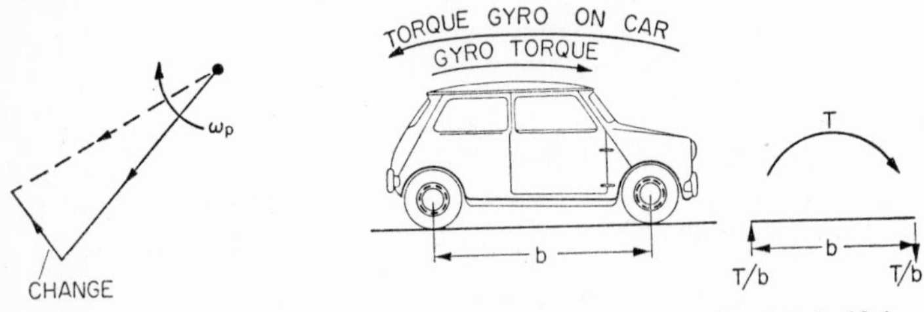

FIG. 10.6. Momentum vectors and gyroscopic torque of example 10.1

is in a clockwise direction when looking, as shown in Fig. 10.6, in the sideways view. This torque is the one applied to the gyro and is due to the road reacting on the wheels. The effect of the gyroscope on the car and road is opposite to this. Either way, the effect is to increase the road reactions on the rear wheels by an amount $T/2b$ each and to decrease those on the front wheels by an amount $T/2b$ each. T is the gyro torque and b is the wheel base. Note that no dimension for b is given in this problem and so the values of road reaction changes cannot be numerically evaluated.

When the nose of the car is raised, the effect is to cause a precession in a vertical plane, and the engine spin vectors are shown in Fig. 10.7 drawn in the side view. The change of angular

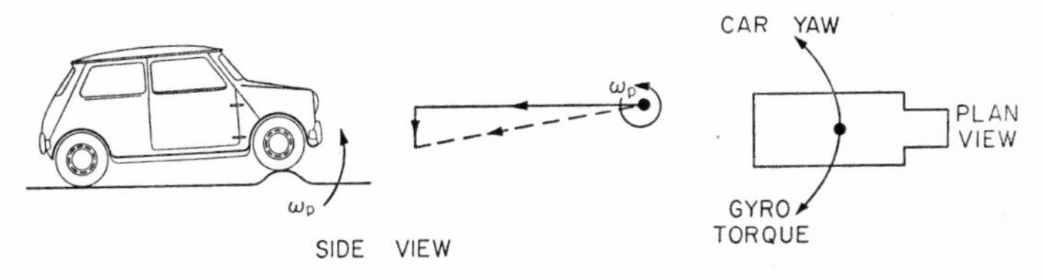

FIG. 10.7. Configuration, momentum vectors and gyroscopic torque of example 10.2

momentum is brought about by a torque (gyro torque) in a clockwise sense in plan view. The reaction to the gyroscopic torque is in an anticlockwise direction thus causing the car to yaw to left.

WORKED EXAMPLE (U.L. Ext., 1954)

10.2. The following particulars are given for a motor vehicle: total weight 3300 lb; wheel base 10·5 ft; centre of gravity 6 ft behind the front axle and 3 ft 2 in. above road level; track width 5 ft; moment of inertia of two front wheels 250 lb ft^2; moment of inertia of two rear wheels 350 lb ft^2; moment of inertia of parts turning at engine speed 50 lb ft^2; wheel diameter 2·5 ft; gear ratio engine to wheels 10 to 1. The engine turns in a clockwise direction when viewed from the front of the vehicle. The vehicle travels at a constant speed of 50 m.p.h. and enters a right-hand curve of 500 ft radius. Determine:

(a) The vertical load on each wheel taking into account (i)

the gravitational effects (ii) centrifugal effects, (iii) gyroscopic effect due to engine rotation.

(b) The rolling couple acting on the vehicle due to the gyroscopic effect of the road wheels.

Solution

(a) (i) Moments about the rear wheels give a total front wheel reaction

$$= \frac{3300 \times 4{\cdot}5}{10{\cdot}5} = 1415 \text{ lb.}$$

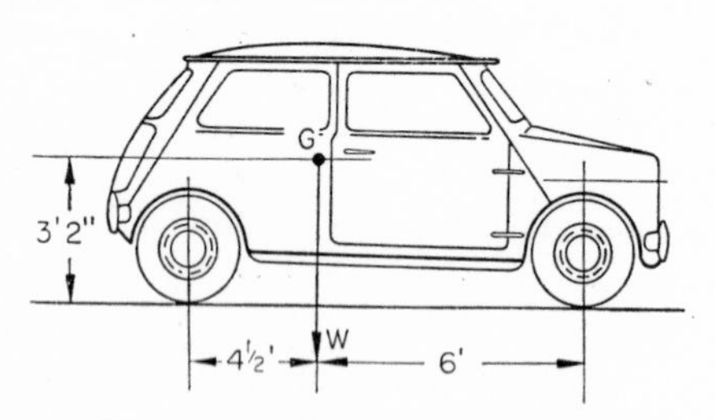

FIG. 10.8. Vehicle of example 10.2

Each front wheel vertical load = 707·5 lb and thus each rear wheel vertical load = 942·5 lb.

(a) (ii) Centrifugal force acting outwards through G is as shown in Fig. 10.9

$$= \frac{3300}{32{\cdot}2} \times 500 \times \left(\frac{50 \times 44}{30 \times 500}\right)^2 = 1100 \text{ lb.}$$

A proportion of this load will be taken by the front wheels and the rest by the back wheels and so the proportion of overturning couple at the front wheels is $\frac{4{\cdot}5}{10{\cdot}5} \times 1100 \times 38$ in. lb and this is balanced by the moment of the wheel loads = $P \times 60$ lb in.

Hence change of wheel loads due to centrifugal effects is a decrease on front inner

$$= \frac{4{\cdot}5 \times 1100 \times 38}{10{\cdot}5 \times 60} \times \frac{1}{2} = 298 \text{ lb};$$

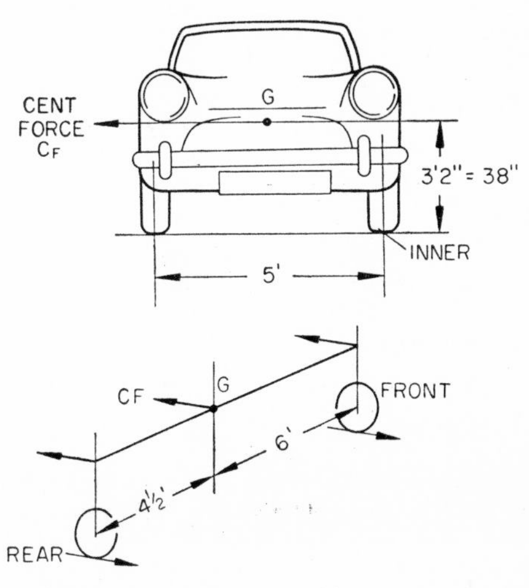

FIG. 10.9. Effect of centrifugal force on vehicle of example 10.2

an increase on a front outer of 298 lb; a decrease on the rear inner of 398 lb and an increase on the rear outer of 398 lb.

(a) (iii) Angular velocity of spin of engine = 10 × velocity of wheels

$$= 10 \times \frac{50 \times 44}{30} \times \frac{1}{1{\cdot}25} = 587 \text{ rad/sec.}$$

Angular velocity of precession

$$= \frac{50 \times 44}{30} \times \frac{1}{500} = 0{\cdot}1467 \text{ rad/sec.}$$

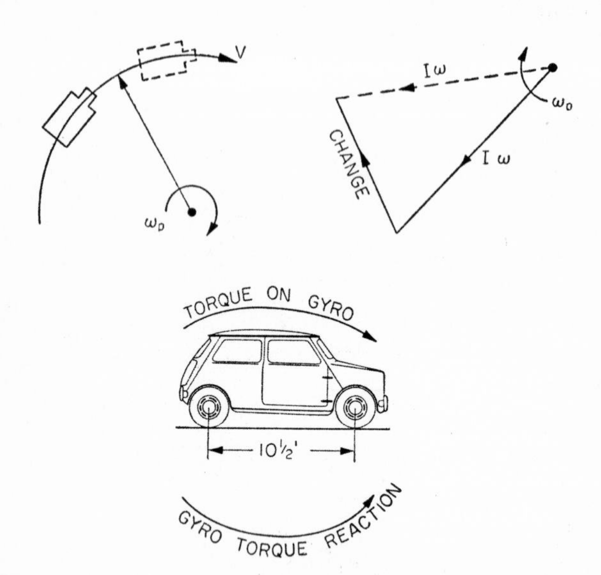

FIG. 10.10. Vehicle, momentum vectors, and gyroscopic torque of example 10.2

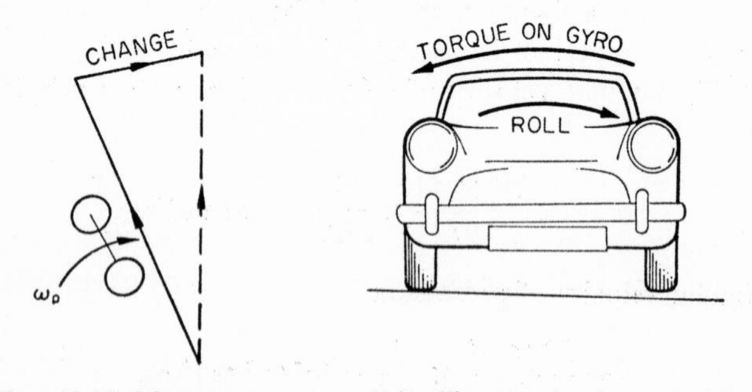

FIG. 10.11. Momentum vectors and rolling couple of example 10.2

Thus gyroscopic torque due to engine

$$= \frac{50}{32 \cdot 2} \times 587 \times 0 \cdot 1467 = 133 \cdot 5 \text{ lb ft.}$$

The effect is, as shown in Fig. 10.10, to decrease the front wheel loads by an amount $= \frac{133 \cdot 5}{10 \cdot 5} \times \frac{1}{2} = 6 \cdot 35$ lb on each.

Each rear wheel load will be increased by 6·35 lb.

(b) Since the velocity of spin and the velocity of precession is the same for the front and rear wheels, the moments of inertia may be added for the gyroscopic effects. Thus gyroscopic torque for wheels $= \frac{(250 + 350)}{32 \cdot 2} \times 58 \cdot 7 \times 0 \cdot 1467 = 160$ lb ft. The effect is as shown in Fig. 10.11 to cause the car to roll in an outwards manner similar to that caused by the centrifugal effect.

WORKED EXAMPLE (U.L.3 Ext., 1957)

10.3. A motor scooter and rider have a total weight of 300 lb and a combined centre of gravity that is 21 in. above ground level under normal straight running conditions. The two wheels of the scooter weigh 8 lb each, have a radius of gyration of 3 in. and a rolling radius of 5 in. The rotating parts of the engine weigh 10 lb, have a radius of gyration of 1·5 in. and rotate at five times the speed of the road wheels but in the opposite direction. Taking account of all forces and couples acting, determine the necessary angle of inclination to the vertical when rounding a bend of 100 ft radius at 30 m.p.h.

Solution

To counteract the overturning effect of the centrifugal force when rounding the bend, the cycle has to heel over towards the centre of turn as shown in Fig. 10.12.

Owing to the precession of the wheels and engine their gyroscopic torques will also require some heel over. Note here that the engine rotates about a transverse axis similar to the wheels, and similarly to a transversely mounted engine in a car. Let the heel over angle be θ.

Moment of the weight about the point of tyre–road contact

$$= 300 \times \frac{21}{12} \times \sin\theta \text{ lb ft.}$$

Moment of centrifugal force

$$= \frac{300}{32{\cdot}2} \times 100 \times \left(\frac{44}{100}\right)^2 \times \frac{21}{12} \times \cos\theta \text{ lb ft.}$$

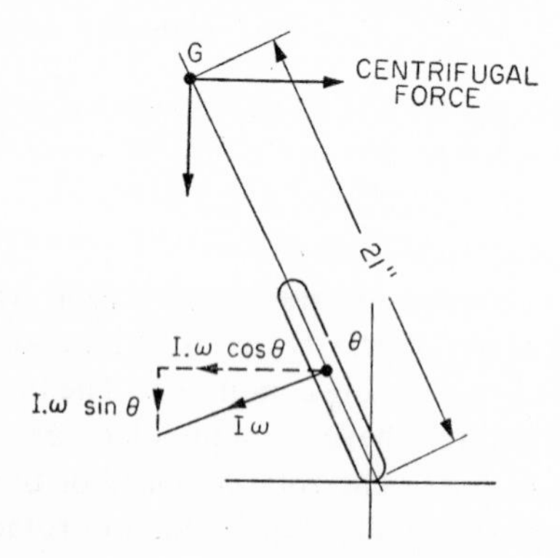

FIG. 10.12. Scooter of example 10.3

Considering the gyroscopic effects:

It will be seen that the spin vector for the wheels is, owing to the heel over, no longer at right angles to the axis about which the cycle precesses. (In the earlier worked examples this complication has been absent.) A simple method of dealing with this complication is to resolve the spin vector into two components as shown in Fig. 10.12, one vector $I_w\,\omega_w \cos\theta$ parallel to the road and the other $I_w\,\omega_w \sin\theta$ perpendicular to the road. This can also be done for the spin vector for the engine. Dealing with the wheels first. It should be noted that when the scooter rotates round the bend, motion is round an axis which is parallel to the spin momentum component $I_w\ \omega_w \sin\theta$ and so this vector is NOT PRECESSED. Gyroscopic torque is due only, therefore, to the precession of the $I_w\ \omega_w \cos\theta$ vector. This is shown together with the engine vectors in Fig. 10.13.

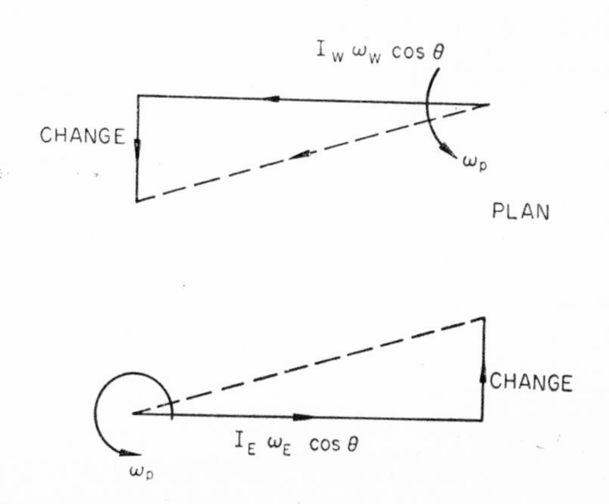

FIG. 10.13. Momentum vectors for scooter of example 10.3

The total gyroscopic torque (wheels and engine)

$$= \omega_p \cos\theta\ (I_w\omega_w - I_e\omega_e)$$

and the effect is to aid the overturning effect of the centrifugal force if the wheel effect is greater than the engine effect as in this case.

Angular velocity of wheels

$$= \frac{44}{5/12} = 105{\cdot}6 \text{ rad/sec.}$$

Angular velocity of engine $= 528$ rad/sec. Angular velocity round bend = 44/100 = 0·44 rad/sec. Hence effective gyroscopic torque

$$= 0{\cdot}44 \times \cos\theta \left[105{\cdot}6 \times \frac{16}{32{\cdot}2} \times \left(\frac{3}{12}\right)^2 - \frac{10}{32{\cdot}2} \times \left(\frac{1{\cdot}5}{12}\right)^2 \times 528\right] \text{lb ft}$$

$$= 0{\cdot}314 \cos\theta \text{ lb ft.}$$

Thus, for equilibrium,

$$\frac{300}{32{\cdot}2} \times 100 \times \left(\frac{44}{100}\right)^2 \times \frac{21}{12} \times \cos\theta + 0{\cdot}314 \cos\theta = 300 \times \frac{21}{12} \times \sin\theta$$

$$317{\cdot}3 \cos\theta = 525 \sin\theta$$

$$\tan\theta = 0{\cdot}598,$$

$$\theta = 30^\circ\ 53'.$$

WORKED EXAMPLE (U.L.3 Ext., 1958)

10.4. A motor vehicle having a rigid rear axle is travelling along a straight level road at 100 m.p.h. The rear wheel on the left-hand side of the vehicle drops into a pot-hole which lowers the end of the axle by 3 in. The track of the vehicle is 5 ft, the rolling radius of the wheels is 1 ft and the movement in and out of the pot-hole may be regarded as approximating in form to a complete

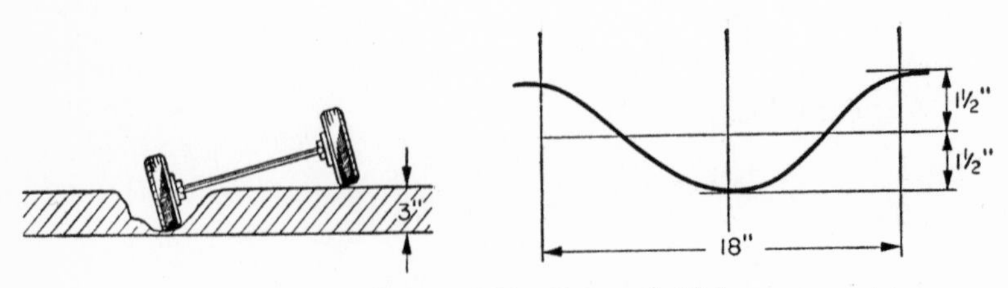

FIG. 10.14. Vehicle of example 10.4

sine wave, 18 in. long, having its mean 1·5 in. below the road level. The polar moment of inertia of the axle with its two wheels, is 60 lb ft^2. Determine the maximum gyroscopic couple that acts on the vehicle and the effects of this on the course of the vehicle. Explain clearly, with the aid of diagrams how you determine the direction of the gyroscopic couple.

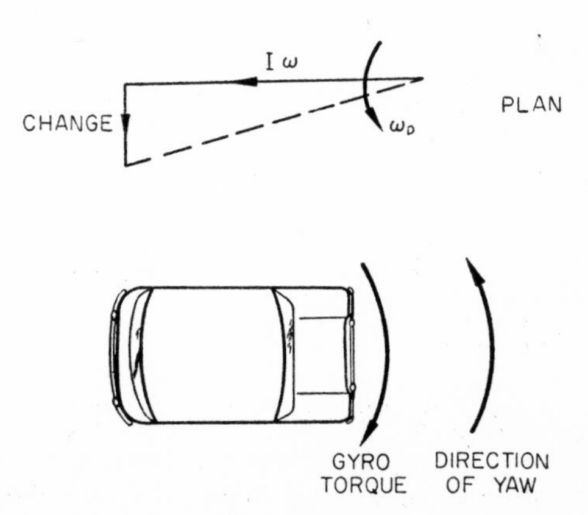

FIG. 10.15. Momentum vectors and gyroscopic effect of example 10.4

Solution

The gyroscopic part of this problem is simple, it is the evaluation of the precession that is more complex than hitherto. The precessional rate when the wheel drops into the hole and rises out of it will vary with simple harmonic motion, having a maximum value $\omega_p(\max)$ = constant × angular amplitude, where constant $= 2\pi/t$ and the time t is approximately the time taken to pass over the 1·5 ft long hole at 100 m.p.h.

$$t = \frac{1{\cdot}5}{100 \times 44/30} = 0{\cdot}012 \text{ sec}$$

and hence constant

$$= \frac{2\pi}{0\cdot0102} = 615.$$

Angular amplitude, as shown in Fig. 10.14, of precessional swing, is half drop divided by track width $= \frac{1\cdot5}{60}$ rad.

Hence

$$\omega_p(\max) = 615 \times \frac{1\cdot5}{60} = 15\cdot4 \text{ rad/sec.}$$

Angular velocity of spin of wheels

$$= 100 \times \frac{44}{30} \times \frac{1}{1} = 146\cdot7 \text{ rad/sec.}$$

Gyroscopic torque

$$= \frac{60}{32\cdot2} \times 146\cdot7 \times 15\cdot4 = 4210 \text{ lb ft.}$$

The momentum vectors drawn in end view are shown in Fig. 10.15 and the gyroscopic torque producing the change of momentum is as shown. The vehicle will yaw in the direction shown under the action of the reaction of the gyroscopic torque.

Examples

10.5. A rear-engined automobile is travelling round a track of 300 ft mean radius. Each of the four wheels has a moment of inertia of 37·5 lb ft^2 and an effective diameter of 24 in. The rotating parts of the engine have a moment of inertia of 20 lb ft^2, the engine axis is parallel to the rear axle, and the crankshaft rotates in the same sense as the road wheels. The gear ratio, engine to back axle is 3 to 1. The vehicle weighs 3000 lb and has its centre of gravity 18 in. above road level. The width of the track of the vehicle is 60 in.

Determine the limiting speed of the vehicle around the curve for all four wheels to maintain contact with the road surface, if this is not cambered.

(U.L.2 Ext., 1953)

Answer: 85 m.p.h.

10.6. A motor cycle with its rider weigh 450 lb, the centre of gravity of the machine and rider combined being 24 in. above ground level when the machine is standing upright. Each road wheel has a moment of inertia of 25 lb ft^2 and a rolling diameter of 24 in. The engine rotates at six times the speed of the road wheels and in the same sense. The moment of inertia of the rotating parts of the engine is 4 lb ft^2. Determine the angle of heel necessary if the unit is travelling at a speed of 40 m.p.h. in a curve of radius 100 ft.

(U.L.2 Ext., 1951)

Answer: 49° 9′.

10.7. (*a*) A motor car takes a bend of 100 ft radius at a speed of 40 m.p.h. Determine the magnitude of the centrifugal and gyroscopic couples acting on the vehicle and state the effect that each has on the road reactions to the road wheels. Assume: each wheel has a moment of inertia of 50 lb ft^2 and an effective radius of 15 in. The rotating parts of the engine and transmission are equivalent to a flywheel weighing 140 lb, with a radius of gyration of 4 in. The engine turns in a clockwise direction when viewed from the front. The back axle ratio is 4 to 1 the drive through the gear box being direct. The gyroscopic effects of the half shafts at the back axle are to be ignored. The car weighs 2500 lb and its centre of gravity is 24 in. above the road level. The turn is in a right hand direction.

(*b*) If the turn had been in a left-hand direction, which answers, if any, need modification. (U.L.2 Ext., 1950)

Answers: (*a*) Centrifugal couple 5340 lb ft. Gyrocouple (wheels) 171 lb ft. Gyrocouple (engine) 53·4 lb ft; (*b*) no change if wheels described as outer and inner.

10.8. The inner wheel of an automobile passes over irregularities in the surface of a proving road which causes the wheel to move vertically with simple harmonic motion. The amplitude of vertical motion is 2 in. and one complete oscillation occupies a forward motion of 2 ft. The wheel weighs 60 lb, has a radius of gyration about the stub axle of 11 in. and a rolling radius of 13·5 in. The forward speed of the vehicle is 30 m.p.h.

Determine the gyroscopic torque on the vehicle due to one wheel when it is in the mean position and moving downwards,

(*a*) if the wheels are mounted on a beam type axle with a track length of 54 in;

(*b*) if the wheel is mounted with its centre of mass at E on the independent suspension shown in Fig. 10.16. Assume centres O and C have no motion in the vertical plane. $AD = BD = 4$ in. $ED = 3$ in. ED and AO are horizontal. Angle $BAO = 80°$. Angle $CBA = 105°$.

(H.N.D. Oxford College of Technology, 1962)

Answers: (*a*) 313 lb ft; (*b*) 190 lb ft.

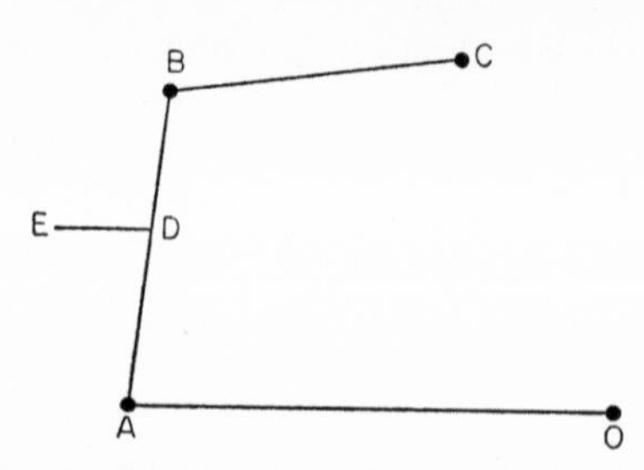

FIG. 10.16. Suspension linkage for example 10.8

10.9. A gyroscope wheel of weight 0·5 lb and with a radius of gyration 0·75 in. is mounted in a pivoted frame *C* as shown in Fig. 10.17. The axis *AB* of the pivot passes through the centre of rotation of the wheel, but the centre of gravity of the frame *C* is at a distance 0·4 in. below the axis. The frame *C*

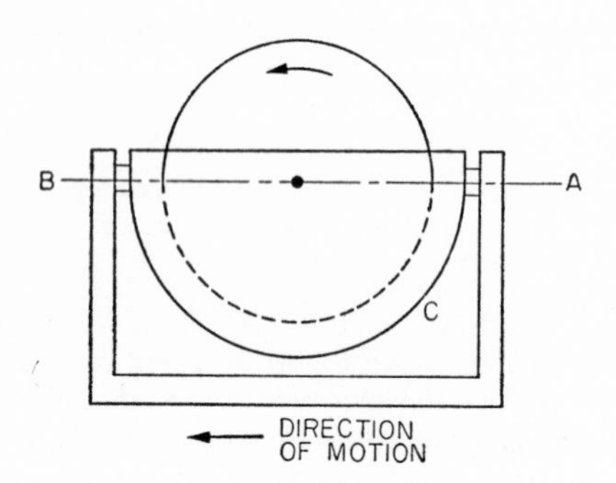

FIG. 10.17. Gyroscopic wheel of example 10.9

weighs 0·3 lb. The speed of rotation of the wheel is 3000 r.p.m. The arrangement is mounted in a vehicle so that the axis *AB* is parallel to the direction of motion of the vehicle. If the vehicle travels at 50 ft/sec in a curve of 160 ft radius, find the angle of inclination of the gyroscope from the vertical, (*a*) when the vehicle moves in the direction shown, and (*b*) when it moves in the opposite direction. (U.L.2 Int., 1948)

Answers: (*a*) 6° 18′, (*b*) 47° 13′.

CHAPTER ELEVEN

VIBRATIONS

VIBRATIONS of a complete automobile, or part of an automobile, may occur in a variety of ways and arise from a variety of sources.

Each part that is capable of motion, linear or angular, relative to another may be made to vibrate with such a motion and is then said to have a certain number of degrees of freedom. The motion of a single rigid body can be specified in terms of component linear motions along three axes mutually at right angles, together with component rotations about the axes and thus has a possible six component motions and thus six degrees of freedom. A system of bodies, such as an automobile, therefore can have a large number of degrees of freedom and, as we shall see later, it is because of this that automobile vibrational considerations can be complex and laborious and generally requiring simplifying assumptions to enable a solution to be made.

A further classification lies in the mode of the disturbance causing the vibration which may be natural as, for example, when the vehicle passes over an isolated irregularity in the road surface, or forced, when the disturbance occurs persistently such as passing over obstructions on a proving road. In the former case, owing to the energy losses of damping, the vibrations die away but in the latter, even with damping present, the forced vibrations persist and under certain circumstances may build up to undesirable levels. Excitation may also arise from the unbalance of the engine, torsional fluctuations in the engine output, cam forces on the valve tappets, whirling of certain transmission parts, etc.

The consideration of vibrational characteristics broadly falls into the categories of: system representation, analysis of the system representation and finally deductions drawn from the analysis. A system is generally represented by a number of vibrating masses, constrained by elastic members and dampers, and acted on by disturbing forces. Whilst for analysis these elements are shown connected individually, they probably exist together. A tyre, for example, has a mass, some elasticity and damping

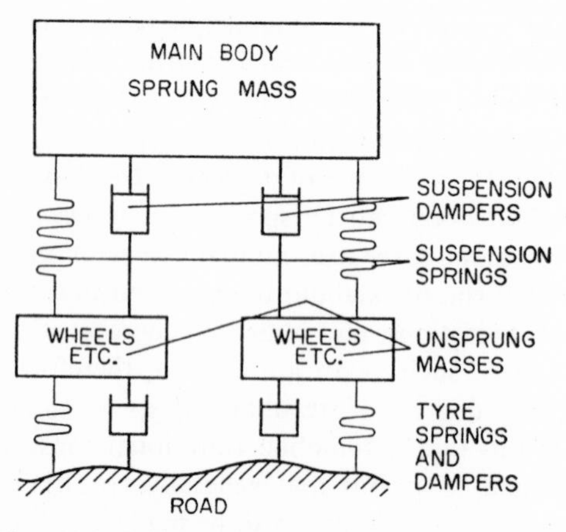

FIG. 11.1. Spring-mass system for ride of a vehicle

capacity. However for analysis it is general to consider masses without elasticity and elastic members without mass. In practice it may be simple to represent a system in this way or, on the other hand, a considerable engineering experience may be needed.

Analysis of the system can be carried out in several ways but often consists in obtaining equations of motion that are symbolic statements of Newton's laws or energy balance. The equations so obtained are solved and this part may be simple or complex. The equation may be of standard form when an answer may be written down with ease, or special mathematical techniques may be needed often with computor assistance, and sometimes a mathematical guess has to be made.

Finally the solution has to be interpreted and this often requires specialized engineering knowledge.

In this chapter we shall start by considering automobile vibrations in a simple manner.

11.1. Vehicle Ride Vibrations with Single Degree of Freedom

The vehicle in complex form is considered to consist of a main body mass suspended on springs so that each wheel is independent and whose motion is damped. The wheels, etc., often referred to as unsprung masses will also have, because of the tyres, some elasticity and damping. Thus the system so far as ride, up and down or pitching is concerned, is represented by the spring-mass system of Fig. 11.1 and there will also be a similar system for the automobile roll.

(a) Simple Natural Vibrations

Consider the vehicle to have a single degree of vertical freedom, i.e., without pitching or rolling and to consist of the simple system shown in Fig. 11.2, in which forcing and damping are absent.

Although it is obvious that so many simplifications have been made that make the system unpracticable, the results will be seen later to have a place in forced vibrations and it serves to illustrate the general approach to vibration problems.

The mass whose weight (W) is carried by a spring of stiffness (S) causes it to deflect STATICALLY by an amount δ. Imagine the mass to be in a state of vibration so that at some instant of time (t) it is in the position, shown in Fig. 11.2, i.e., with a displacement (x) below the static loaded position.

The forces acting on the mass, shown in Fig. 11.2, are the

weight (W) downwards and due to compression of the spring, a force upwards of S (total compression) $= S(x + \delta)$.

The resultant vertical force in the positive (downwards) direction of displacement

$$= W - S(x + \delta) = W - S \,.\, x - S \,.\, \delta.$$

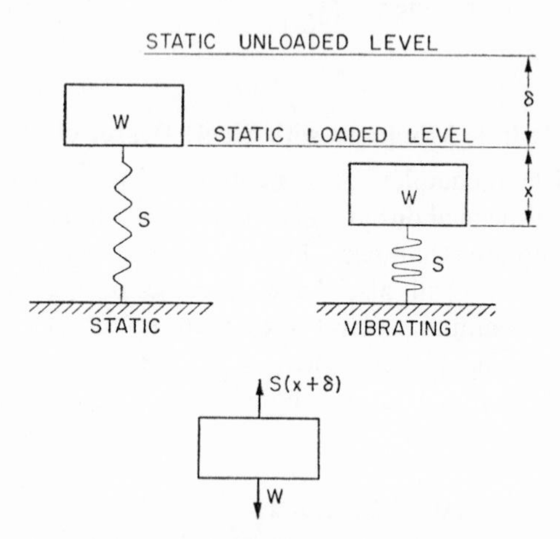

FIG. 11.2. Spring-mass system for natural vibrations of a vehicle

But in the static condition, the spring force $S \,.\, \delta$ is balanced by the weight of mass, and so,

$$W = S \,.\, \delta$$

and hence, the resultant force on the vibrating mass is $-S \,.\, x$ and the acceleration that the mass has will, by Newton's law, be related by the equation

$$\text{Mass} \times \text{Acceleration} = \text{Force},$$

and hence

$$\frac{W}{g} \cdot \frac{d^2x}{dt^2} = -S \,.\, x, \quad \text{or} \quad \frac{W}{g}\frac{d^2x}{dt^2} + S \,.\, x = 0 \qquad (11.1)$$

This is the equation of motion which is valid for all positions of the mass. It may be written,

$$\frac{d^2x}{dt^2} + \frac{S \,.\, g}{W} \,.\, x = 0,$$

or

$$\frac{d^2x}{dt^2} + b \,.\, x = 0,$$

where

$$b = S \,.\, g/W. \tag{11.2}$$

This equation will be recognized as that representing simple harmonic motion for which there is a standard solution of

$$x = A \,.\, \sin \sqrt{b}t + B \,.\, \cos \sqrt{b}t. \tag{11.3}$$

The significance of the constants A and B and of the equation itself can best be seen from the vector diagram of the solution, as shown in Fig. 11.3.

A vector OQ representing B is added at right angles to a vector QP representing A, and giving a resultant vector $OP = \sqrt{A^2 + B^2}$. The vector for B lags behind the resultant at an angle β where $\tan \beta = A/B$. If the system of vectors rotates about O with an angular velocity ω_N then after t secs the angle turned from the position where OQ is horizontal is $\omega_N t$ rad. The vertical displacement of point P from the mean is then

$$x = B \,.\, \cos \omega_N t + A \,.\, \sin \omega_N t = OP \,.\, \sin (\omega_N t + \beta).$$

The amplitude of the motion, i.e., the maximum displacement on either side of the mean, is clearly given by the length of vector OP i.e., amplitude

$$x_o = \sqrt{A^2 + B^2}. \tag{11.4}$$

The periodic time will be the time taken for the vector OP to rotate once round the circle, i.e., $t_N = 2\pi/\omega_N$.

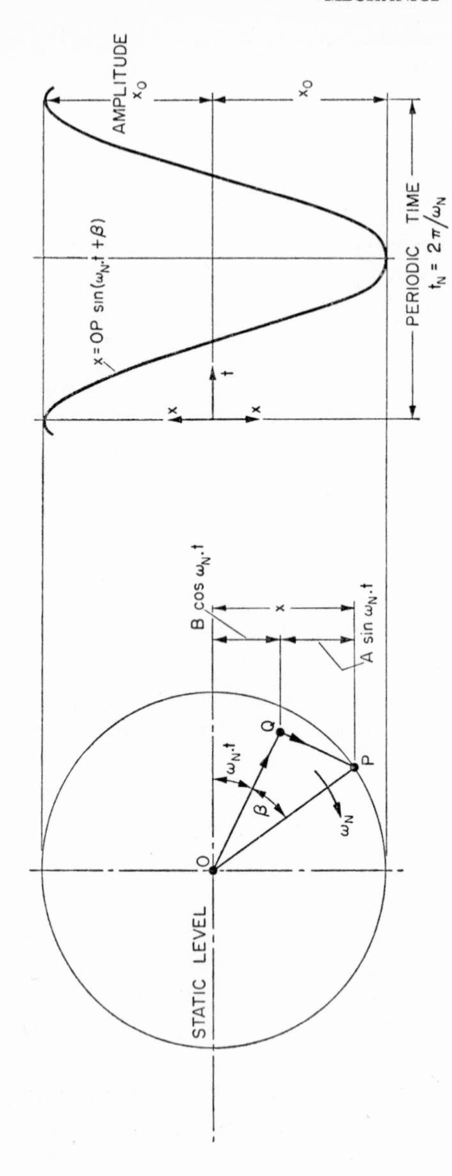

FIG. 11.3. Vector representation of equation 11.3

The frequency of vibration is of more interest, particularly when considering the fatigue of the elastic support.

Frequency of natural vibration

$$f_N = 1/t_N = \omega_N/2\pi = \sqrt{b}/2\pi = \frac{1}{2\pi}\sqrt{\frac{Sg}{W}} = \frac{1}{2\pi}\sqrt{\frac{g}{\delta}}$$

Usually the static deflection is a quantity that can be predicted and so the frequency expressed in terms of δ is of practical value thus with the units correctly substituted,

natural frequency $f_N = \dfrac{187\cdot 8}{\sqrt{\delta}}$ vib/min if δ is expressed in inches. (11.5)

An alternative method of arriving at the equation of motion is to consider the energy of the system. The natural vibration continues owing to the continuous interchange of the kinetic energy of the moving mass and the strain energy stored in the elastic spring. In the absence of any losses of energy, the sum of the kinetic and strain energies (or potential), will remain constant. Thus

$$\underbrace{\frac{W}{2g}\left(\frac{dx}{dt}\right)^2}_{\text{kinetic}} + \underbrace{\frac{1}{2} . S . x^2}_{\text{strain}} = \text{constant}$$

which on differentiation yields

$$\frac{W}{2g} . 2\frac{dx}{dt} \cdot \frac{d^2x}{dt^2} + \frac{S}{2} . 2x . \frac{dx}{dt} = 0,$$

or

$$\frac{W}{g} \cdot \frac{dx^2}{dt^2} + S . x = 0$$

which is the same as equation (11.1).

Note that maximum kinetic energy occurs at mid-position when the strain energy is zero, and that the maximum strain energy is at the extreme displacement when the kinetic energy is zero. Thus if the total energy is constant, the maximum kinetic energy equals the maximum strain energy, although they do not occur at the same time. This principle will be seen later to be of value when dealing with approximate methods for systems with several degrees of freedom.

(b) FORCED UNDAMPED VIBRATIONS

The vehicle is assumed to have a single degree of vertical freedom and a forced disturbance from the road is applied as shown

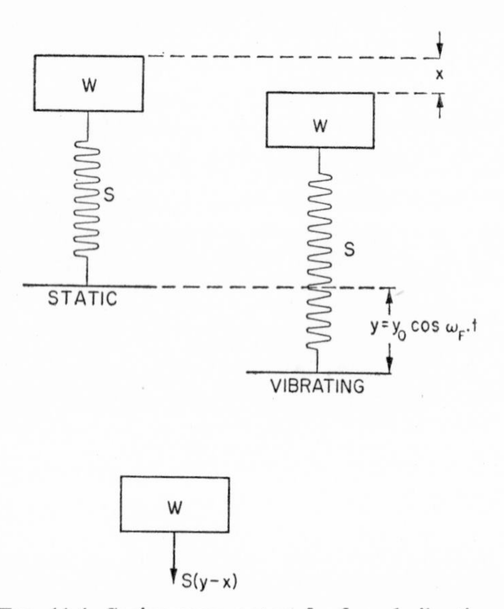

FIG. 11.4. Spring-mass system for forced vibrations

in Fig. 11.4. It is usual to assume that the road disturbance is harmonic since almost any form can be considered the addition of a series of trigonometrical terms. Let the road disturbance be of the form $y = y_o \cos \omega_F t$, the suffix F referring to forced and the suffix N referring to natural vibrations. After t sec, the wheels have moved downwards a distance y whilst the suspended mass has moved down a distance x, both from the static position.

The spring will have been stretched an amount $(y - x)$ and so the spring force acting on the mass is $S(y - x)$ as shown. Since x is measured from the static position, the forces W and $S \,.\, \delta$ which balance will not be shown. Thus,

$$S(y - x) = \frac{W}{g} \cdot \frac{d^2x}{dt^2},$$

or

$$\frac{W}{g} \cdot \frac{d^2x}{dt^2} + S \,.\, x = S \,.\, y,$$

which is rearranged to

$$\frac{d^2x}{dt^2} + \frac{S \,.\, g}{W} \,.\, x = \frac{S \,.\, g \,.\, y}{W}$$

but

$$y = y_o \cos \omega_F t,$$

thus

$$\frac{d^2x}{dt^2} + \frac{S \,.\, g}{W} \,.\, x = \frac{S \,.\, g \,.\, y_o}{W} \,.\, \cos \omega_F t \qquad (11.6)$$

or

$$\frac{d^2x}{dt^2} + b \,.\, x = c \,.\, \cos \omega_F t,$$

where

$$b = \frac{S \,.\, g}{W} = \omega_N^2 \quad \text{and} \quad c = \frac{S \,.\, g \,.\, y_o}{W}.$$

The solution to this standard second order differential equation is

$$x = \underbrace{A \,.\, \sin \sqrt{b}t + B \,.\, \cos \sqrt{b}t}_{\text{transient}} + \underbrace{\frac{c}{b - \omega_F^2} \,.\, \cos \omega_F t}_{\text{steady state}} \qquad (11.7)$$

The first two terms constitute a natural vibration which will usually die away rapidly and called a transient vibration. The other term represents a steady state vibration of simple harmonic form and whose frequency is the same as that of the forcing disturbance. The amplitude of the steady state vibration is

$$x_o = \frac{c}{b - \omega_F^2} = \frac{c/b}{1 - \omega_F^2/b} = \frac{y_o}{1 - \omega_F^2/\omega_N^2}$$

$$= \frac{y_o}{1 - \left(\frac{f_F}{f_N}\right)^2}. \qquad (11.8)$$

It can be seen that the displacement of the mass at one end of the spring does not have to be the same as the other end of the spring but that, for example, when the frequency of the forcing disturbance coincides with the natural frequency of the system, the

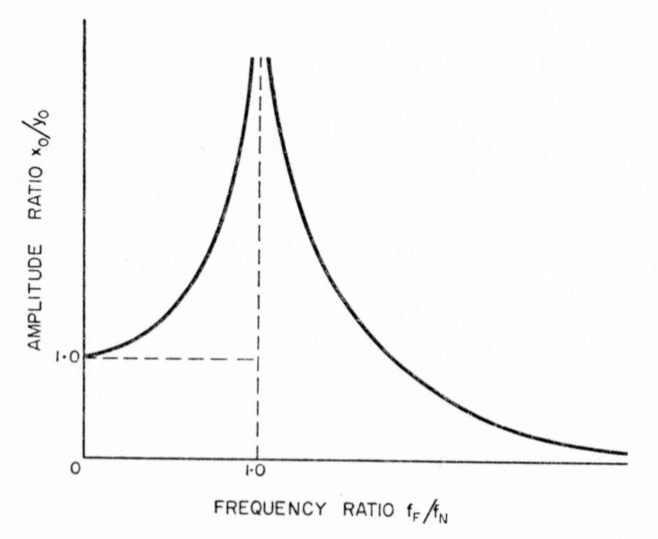

FIG. 11.5. Graph of vehicle response

displacement of the suspended mass theoretically becomes infinite. This condition which is usually to be avoided, is called RESONANCE, and the quantity $1-(f_F/f_N)^2$ is sometimes called the dynamic magnifier. If the amplitude ratio x_o/y_o be plotted against the frequency ratio f_F/f_N, then the curve of Fig. 11.5 is obtained.

It will be seen that with a high frequency disturbance the suspended mass hardly moves more than the wheels do. If the motion of the system be observed by a stroboflash, it will be seen that there is a phase change between the mass and wheels on passing through the resonance condition. In the absence of damping the mass and wheels are either in or out of phase by 180°.

Worked Example

11.1. Determine the response of the vehicle as it moves from the static position shown in Fig. 11.6 at a speed of 20 m.p.h. over the sine-wave road. The vehicle weighs 1500 lb, the total vertical spring stiffness of the suspension is 500 lb/in., the amplitude of the sine wave is 2 in., and the distance between peaks is 210 in. The

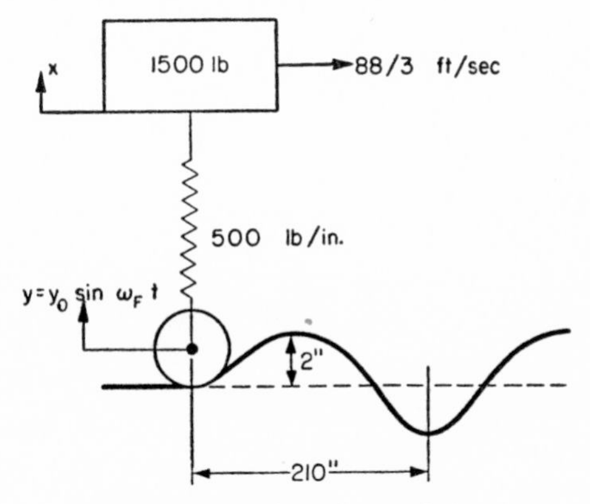

Fig. 11.6. Vehicle of example 11.1

vehicle has zero vertical velocity when in the static position. At what minimum vehicle speed will resonance occur?

Solution

Measuring the displacements x and y upwards as shown, the equation of motion is

$$\frac{W}{g} \cdot \frac{d^2x}{dt^2} + S \,.\, x = S \,.\, y_o \,.\, \sin \omega_F t$$

with t measured from the position when the wheels are at mid-position of the wave.

Thus, $x = A \,.\, \sin \sqrt{b}t + B \,.\, \sqrt{b}t + \dfrac{c}{b - \omega_F^2} \,.\, \sin \omega_F t.$

But, when $t = 0$, $x = 0$ and so

$$x = A \,.\, \sin \sqrt{b}t + \frac{c}{b - \omega_F^2} \,.\, \sin \omega_F t.$$

Also when $t = 0$, $dx/dt = 0$ and so on differentiating

$$0 = A\sqrt{b} + c \,.\, \omega_F/(b - \omega_F^2)$$

giving

$$A = -c \,.\, \omega_F/(b - \omega_F^2)\sqrt{b};$$

$$b = S \,.\, g/W = \frac{500 \times 12 \times 32{\cdot}2}{1500} = 128{\cdot}8 \text{ and } \sqrt{b} = 11{\cdot}3 = \omega_N,$$

$$c = S \,.\, y_o \,.\, g/W = 128{\cdot}8 \times \frac{2}{12} = 21{\cdot}47.$$

Time to pass over a complete wave

$$= \frac{\text{distance}}{\text{velocity}} = \frac{210}{12} \times \frac{3}{88} \text{ sec.}$$

Hence

$$\omega_F = 2\pi/t_F = \frac{2\pi \times 12 \times 88}{210 \times 3} = 10{\cdot}55,$$

$$\frac{c}{b - \omega_F^2} = \frac{21{\cdot}47}{128{\cdot}8 - 111{\cdot}5} = 1{\cdot}25$$

and

$$A = -\frac{1{\cdot}25 \times 10{\cdot}55}{11{\cdot}3} = -1{\cdot}17,$$

and

$$x = -1{\cdot}17 \sin 11{\cdot}7t + 1{\cdot}25 \sin 10{\cdot}55t \text{ feet. (Answer.)}$$

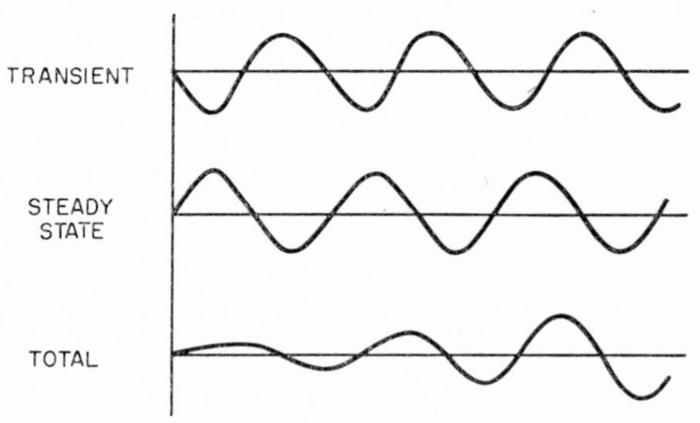

FIG. 11.7. Response of vehicle of example 11.1

The transient, steady state and total responses are shown in Fig. 11.7. Resonance will occur when the forcing frequency corresponds with natural frequency. Thus

$$f_F = f_N \quad \text{or} \quad \omega_F = \omega_N$$

and so

$$\omega_F = 11{\cdot}3$$

and this corresponds to a speed of $20 \times \dfrac{11{\cdot}3}{10{\cdot}55} = 21{\cdot}5$ m.p.h. (Answer.)

(c) FORCED DAMPED VIBRATIONS

There is some damping present in all systems but it may have such a small effect that at certain forcing frequencies the response of the system still becomes very large. To reduce the response, dampers are fitted, and in automobile suspensions these have been of the hydraulic type. Nowadays the rubber–metal bonded types are being extensively used and sometimes both types are used together. It is beyond the scope of the book to analyse with the

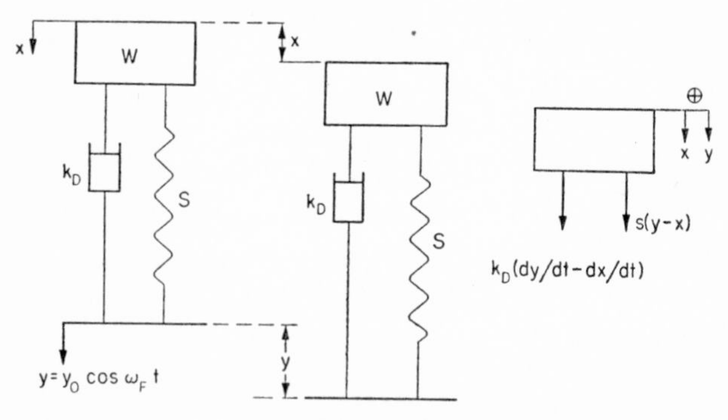

FIG. 11.8. Spring-mass system for forced damped vibrations

rubber type damper because these have non-linear characteristics which cause difficulties in solving the differential equations of motion. Only the viscous type damper will be considered when the damping force F_D (D denotes damped vibrations) is due to the viscous shearing of a fluid and it is assumed that F_D is proportional to the relative velocity of shear giving, $F_D = k_D \cdot \mathrm{d}x/\mathrm{d}t$, where k_D is called the damping coefficient.

Consider the vehicle then to have a single degree of vertical freedom, a forced disturbance from the road of type $y = y_o \cdot \cos \omega_F t$ and a damping force across the ends of the spring. The system is as shown in Fig. 11.8.

After time t, the spring force on the mass $= S(y - x)$ downwards and the damping force on the mass $= k_D \cdot \frac{d}{dt}(y - x)$ downwards. The resulting force on the mass $= S(y - x) + k_D \left(\frac{dy}{dt} - \frac{dx}{dt}\right)$ downwards.

Hence

$$\frac{W}{g} \cdot \frac{d^2x}{dt^2} = S(y - x) + k_D \left(\frac{dy}{dt} - \frac{dx}{dt}\right). \qquad (11.9)$$

But if Y is the motion of x relative to y, then $Y = x - y$ and so

$$\frac{d^2Y}{dt^2} = \frac{d^2x}{dt^2} - \frac{d^2y}{dt^2},$$

giving

$$\frac{W}{g} \cdot \frac{d^2y}{dt^2} + \frac{W}{g} \cdot \frac{d^2Y}{dt^2} = S \cdot Y + k_D \cdot \frac{dY}{dt},$$

or

$$\frac{W}{g} \cdot \frac{d^2Y}{dt^2} + k_D \cdot \frac{dY}{dt} + S \cdot Y = -\frac{W}{g} \cdot \frac{d^2y}{dt^2}, \qquad (11{\cdot}10)$$

and since

$$\frac{d^2y}{dt^2} = -y_o \cdot \omega_F^2 \cdot \cos \omega_F t,$$

then

$$\frac{W}{g} \cdot \frac{d^2Y}{dt^2} + k_D \cdot \frac{dY}{dt} + S \cdot Y = \frac{W}{g} \cdot \omega_F^2 \cdot y_o \cdot \cos \omega_F t$$

which reduces to

$$\frac{d^2y}{dt^2} + a \cdot \frac{dY}{dt} + b \cdot Y = c \cdot \cos \omega_F t, \qquad (11.11)$$

where $a = k_D \cdot g/W$, $b = S \cdot g/W$ and $c = \omega_F^2 \cdot y_o$.

By considering the relative motion across the ends of the spring, the equation of motion becomes of a form similar to that for the undamped system with the exception that there is now a term representative of the damping. A physical interpretation of the solution of this standard second order equation will be given later, but the solution is

$$Y = e^{-\frac{a,t}{2}}\left[A \,.\, \sin\sqrt{b - \left(\frac{a}{2}\right)^2}\, t + B \,.\, \cos\sqrt{b - \left(\frac{a}{2}\right)^2}\, t\right]$$

$$+ \frac{c}{\sqrt{(b - \omega_F^2)^2 + a^2\omega_F^2}} \,.\, \cos(\omega_F \,.\, t - \beta), \quad (11.12)$$

and

$$\tan\beta = \frac{a\omega_F}{b - \omega_F^2},$$

if β = phase angle.

The transient vibrations will die away leaving the steady state vibration of

$$Y = \frac{c}{\sqrt{(b - \omega_F^2)^2 + a^2\omega_F^2}} \,.\, \cos(\omega_F \,.\, t - \beta). \quad (11.13)$$

The amplitude of the relative motion is thus

$$Y_o = \frac{c}{\sqrt{(b - \omega_F^2)^2 + a^2\omega_F^2}}, \quad (11.14)$$

which on substitution of $c = \omega_F^2 \,.\, y_o$ and $b = \omega_N^2$, gives an amplitude ratio

$$\frac{Y_o}{y_o} = \frac{(\omega_F/\omega_N)^2}{\sqrt{[1 - (\omega_F/\omega_N)^2]^2 + \left(\frac{a}{\omega_N}\right)^2 \cdot \left(\frac{\omega_F}{\omega_N}\right)^2}} \quad (11.15)$$

If the values of Y_o/y_o are plotted against the ratio $\omega_F/\omega_N = f_F/f_N$ curves of which those of Fig. 11.9 are typical are obtained. Curves of this kind will be discussed more fully when engine mounting is considered, but it can be seen that damping reduces the relative motion but only to any marked extent near resonance when $f_F/f_N = 1$. It should be noted that the maximum amplitude does not occur at, but near to, the resonance point so defined.

However a better insight of the action of the spring, damping and inertia forces is provided by vector diagrams of the steady

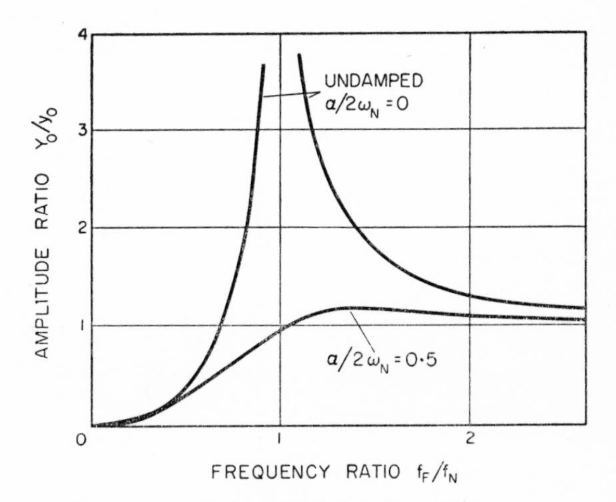

FIG. 11.9. Relative damped motion response to a forced disturbance

state amplitudes. This method is recommended to students as it is relatively simple and does not require the ability to either solve differential equations or to remember standard solutions.

Assuming that the motion of the mass relative to the forcing is of the form $Y = Y_o . \cos(\omega_F . t - \beta)$, and $Y = x - y$, as in the vehicle problem just discussed, then the spring force, damping force and the mass acceleration force (resultant of relative and forcing accelerating forces) will all be either cosine or sine waves of the same frequency. Thus each of these forces can be represented by the vertical projection of a rotating vector. By differentiating the expression for Y and substituting in the expressions for the various forces, the spring force rotating vector is of length representing $S . Y_o$ and drawn at angle $(\omega_F . t - \beta)$ to a datum. The damping force vector $= k_D . \omega_F . Y_o$ at an angle $(90° + \omega_F . t - \beta)$. The resultant of these will equal the accelerating force on the mass, or they will be in dynamic equilibrium with the

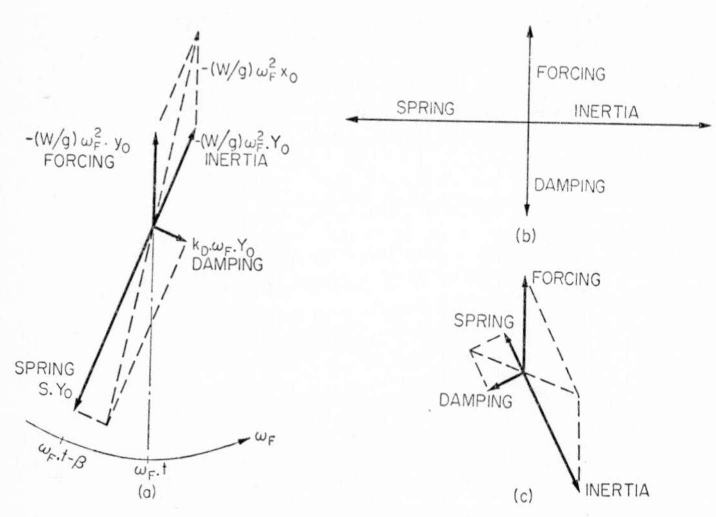

FIG. 11.10. Vector representation of the system of Fig. 11.8

mass inertia force which is represented by a vector $\frac{W}{g} . \omega_F^2 . x_o$ drawn in direction opposite to the accelerating force vector. This mass inertia force vector is split, for convenience, into a relative motion inertia vector $= \frac{W}{g} . \omega_F^2 . Y_o$ at an angle $(\omega_F . t - \beta + 180°)$ together with a forcing inertia vector $= \frac{W}{g} . \omega_F^2 . y_o$ at an angle $(\omega_F . t + 180°)$. These vectors are shown in Fig. 11.10.

These diagrams which rotate at ω_F, show the physical significance of the terms in that at low values of ω_F, when β is small, the damping force plays a minor part and the spring force opposes the inertia and forcing forces as shown in Fig. 11.10a. When $\omega_F = \omega_N$ and $\beta = 90°$, the spring and inertia forces are equal and opposite, and, as shown in Fig. 11.10b, the forcing is opposed only by the damping force which is thus of major importance. At higher values of ω_F and angles of β near 180°, the damping force is again of minor importance and as shown in Fig. 11.10c, the inertia force opposes the forcing and spring forces.

The amplitude at relative motion resonance is thus given when the damping force vector = the forcing vector, or

$$k_D \,.\, \omega_F \,.\, Y_o = \frac{W}{g} \,.\, \omega_F^2 \,.\, y_o$$

and thus giving for the amplitude at resonance (for relative motion)

$$Y_o = \frac{W}{g} \,.\, \omega_F \,.\, \frac{1}{k_D} \,.\, y_o. \tag{11.16}$$

WORKED EXAMPLE

11.2. An automobile having a sprung mass weighing 3000 lb has a static deflection of 10 in. It is mounted on a "bouncing" table that can move up and down sinusoidally with an amplitude of 1 in. Assuming that the four shock absorbers are equivalent to a single viscous action and that they are adjusted to allow a relative amplitude at resonance of 1·5 in., find the viscous friction coefficient per absorber. Neglect the springiness of the tyres and assume vertical motion with a single degree of freedom.

Solution

The vector diagram for relative resonance is as shown in Fig. 11.10b, whence, the forcing and damping forces are equal giving

$$\frac{W}{g} \,.\, \omega_F^2 \,.\, y_o = k_D \,.\, \omega_F \,.\, Y_o,$$

and so,

$$k_D = \frac{W \, . \, \omega_F \, . \, y_o}{g \, . \, Y_o},$$

$$\omega_N = \sqrt{b} = \sqrt{g/\delta} = \sqrt{\frac{32{\cdot}2 \times 12}{10}} = 6{\cdot}22 = \omega_F,$$

therefore

$$k_D = \frac{3000 \times 6{\cdot}22 \times 1}{1{\cdot}5 \times 32{\cdot}2} = 386 \text{ lb/ft/sec}$$

or $= 8$ lb/in./sec per damper.

Alternatively, a solution can be made by substituting in the equation (11.14) (if you can remember it!) the condition $\omega_F = \omega_N$.

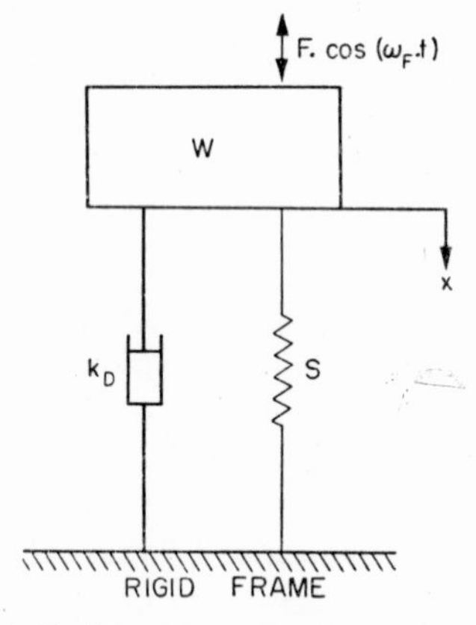

FIG. 11.11. Spring-mass system for engine mounting

11.2. Vibrations Due to Engine Unbalance

It has been seen, in Chapter 7, that the unbalance of an automobile reciprocating engine may be a force, in the line of reciprocation, of the type, $F = F_1 . \cos \theta + F_2 . \cos 2\theta +$ similar terms. The engine is thus subjected to periodic disturbances

$$F = F_1 . \cos \omega_F t + F_2 . \cos 2\omega_F t + \text{etc.},$$

where ω_F is the angular velocity of the engine crankshaft and $\omega_F t = \theta$.

If the engine were mounted "solid" in the automobile, the effect of the unbalanced force on the occupants could be uncomfortable

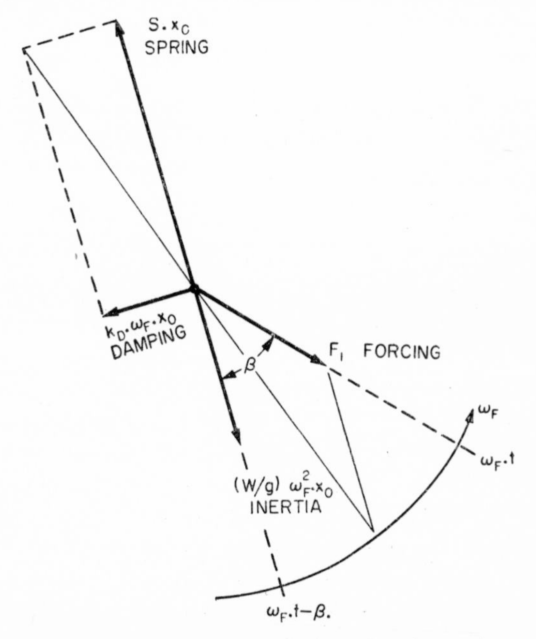

FIG. 11.12. Vector representation of engine motion

and so to minimize the forces transmitted to the engine frame (same as body, chassis, etc.) the engine is normally mounted on rubber-type shock absorbing blocks. Both the elastic and damping characteristics of these blocks are complex, but for an initial analysis, they are usually considered as linear elastic springs having viscous damping. Thus the engine may be considered to have a single degree of vertical freedom as shown in Fig. 11.11, where a forcing disturbance $F_1 \,.\, \cos \omega_F t$, due to primary unbalance, is applied to the vibrating mass. The automobile body is considered to be of large mass and to be fixed.

(a) Forced Damped Motion of Engine Mass

The system is very similar to that considered in section 11.1c and the equation of motion, following the method already outlined, becomes

$$\frac{W}{g} \cdot \frac{d^2x}{dt^2} + k_D \cdot \frac{dx}{dt} + S \,.\, x = F_1 \,.\, \cos \omega_F t$$

and so

$$\frac{d^2x}{dt^2} + a \,.\, \frac{dx}{dt} + b \,.\, x = c \,.\, \cos \omega_F t,$$

where

$$a = \frac{k_D \cdot g}{W}, \quad b = \frac{S \cdot g}{W}, \quad c = \frac{F_1 \cdot g}{W}$$

instead of $\omega_F{}^2 \,.\, y_o$ and x the displacement of the engine in a downwards direction is now absolute and not relative to a moving support as previously. The solution of the equation in terms of a, b, c, will be identical to equation (11.12) and having a steady state solution identical to equation (11.13) and a rotating vector diagram of Fig. 11.12. Note also that the analysis given for single degree systems will apply to statically mounted engines on test beds or in generators. Two worked examples follow, one simple without damping and the other more complex with damping.

Worked Example (U.L.2 Ext., 1952)

A vertical single cylinder engine weighing 1200 lb is carried on elastic beams whose static deflection under the weight of the engine is 0·38 in. Calculate the frequency of free vibration in a vertical plane. The engine is now run at 130 r.p.m. The reciprocating parts weigh 100 lb, the stroke is 7 in. and length of connecting rod 14 in. Calculate from first principles, the vertical movement of the engine due to (a) lack of primary balance, (b) lack of secondary balance.

Solution

The system to be considered will be that of Fig. 11.11 but without the damping.

Frequency of natural vibrations

$$= f_N = \frac{1}{2\pi}\sqrt{\frac{g}{\delta}} = \frac{187{\cdot}8}{\sqrt{\delta}} \text{ vib./min}$$

$$= \frac{187{\cdot}8}{\sqrt{0{\cdot}38}} = 304 \text{ vib./min.}$$

(a) The forcing disturbance due to primary unbalance

$$= F_1 \,.\, \cos \omega_F t \text{ and } F_1 = \frac{W_r}{g} \,.\, r \,.\, \omega_F^2$$

$$= \frac{100}{32{\cdot}2} \times \frac{3{\cdot}5}{12}\left(\frac{130 \times 2\pi}{60}\right)^2 \text{ lb}$$

$$= 167{\cdot}5 \cos \omega_F t \text{ lb and } \omega_F = 13{\cdot}6.$$

Equation of motion is

$$\frac{W}{g} \cdot \frac{d^2x}{dt^2} + S \,.\, x = 167{\cdot}5 \cos \omega_F t$$

and the steady state solution is amplitude

$$x_o = \frac{c}{(b - \omega_F^2)}$$

and

$$c = \frac{F_1 g}{W} = \frac{167{\cdot}5 \times 32{\cdot}2}{1200} = 4{\cdot}5,\ b = \omega_N^2 = \frac{32{\cdot}2 \times 12}{0{\cdot}38} = 1015.$$

Thus

$$x_o = \frac{4\cdot5}{1015-185} = \frac{4\cdot5 \times 12}{830} \text{ in.} = 0\cdot065 \text{ in.}$$

Total movement = twice amplitude = 0·13 in.

(b) Secondary unbalanced force

$$= F_2 \,.\, \cos 2\theta = \frac{F_1}{n} \,.\, \cos 2\omega_F t$$

and since $n = L/r = 14/3\cdot5 = 4$,
unbalanced force $= 41\cdot9 \cos 2\omega_F t$.

The equation of motion is

$$\frac{W}{g} \cdot \frac{d^2x}{dt^2} + S \,.\, x = 41\cdot9 \cos 2\omega_F t$$

giving for the steady state amplitude

$$x_o = \frac{c}{b - (2\omega_F)^2} \text{ and } c = 4\cdot5/4$$

$$= \frac{4\cdot5/4}{1015 - 740} \text{ ft} = \frac{1\cdot125 \times 12}{275} \text{ in.} = 0\cdot049 \text{ in.}$$

Total movement = 2 × 0·049 = 0·098 in.

These deflections are small compared with the static deflection, but when $\omega_F = \omega_N$, i.e., when $\omega_F = 34$ rad/sec, and this at an engine speed of 324 r.p.m. the deflection becomes "infinite". Secondary resonance occurs at half this speed.

WORKED EXAMPLE

11.4. A mass of 20 lb is mounted on helical springs of total stiffness 7·45 lb/in., and is subjected to a periodic force of magnitude 3·72 cos $\omega_F t$ lb acting vertically. Assuming a viscous damping coefficient of amount 1/10 that corresponding to critical damping conditions, determine the frequency of the applied force when the amplitude of the vertical vibrations under steady conditions is a maximum. Find the maximum amplitude in inches and state in degrees the phase difference between the amplitude of the motion and the periodic force.

Solution

The steady state amplitude is given by

$$x_o = \frac{c}{\sqrt{(b - \omega_F^2)^2 + a^2 . \omega_F^2}}$$

and this will be a maximum when the denominator is a minimum thus

$$(b - \omega_F^2)^2 + a^2 . \omega_F^2$$

is a minimum. Differentiation gives

$$2(b - \omega_F^2) \times - 2 . \omega_F + 2a^2 . \omega_F = 0$$

and hence

$$\omega_F^2 = b - \frac{a^2}{2}$$

$$b = Sg/W = \frac{7{\cdot}45 \times 12 \times 32{\cdot}2}{20} = 144,$$

hence

$$\omega_N = \sqrt{b} = 12.$$

The effect of damping on a system depends upon the relative values of a and b. Examination of the transient part of the solution shows that when $b = (a/2)^2$ an exponential function is obtained. When b is greater than $(a/2)^2$ a true damped vibration occurs, whilst if b is less than $(a/2)^2$ the system is so heavily damped that the mass on being displaced slowly moves back to the original position and such motion is not a vibration. The critical value is thus when $b = (a/2)^2$. Hence in this problem, and since $b = \omega_N{}^2 = (a/2)^2$ for critical, so $\dfrac{a}{2\omega_N} = 0{\cdot}1,$

giving

$$a = 0{\cdot}2 \times 12 = 2{\cdot}4, \quad \omega_F^2 = 144 - \frac{2{\cdot}4^2}{2} = 141{\cdot}12$$

and

$$\omega_F = 11{\cdot}85, \; f_F = 1{\cdot}89/\text{sec.}$$

Maximum amplitude

$$= \frac{F \, . \, g/W}{\sqrt{(144 - 11{\cdot}85^2) + 5{\cdot}76 \times 11{\cdot}85^2}} \text{ ft}$$

$$= \frac{3{\cdot}72 \times 32{\cdot}2/20}{28{\cdot}7} = \frac{6 \times 12}{28{\cdot}7} \text{ in.} = 2{\cdot}51 \text{ in.}$$

$$\tan \beta = \frac{2{\cdot}4 \times 11{\cdot}85}{4} = 7{\cdot}12 \quad \text{and} \quad \beta = 82°$$

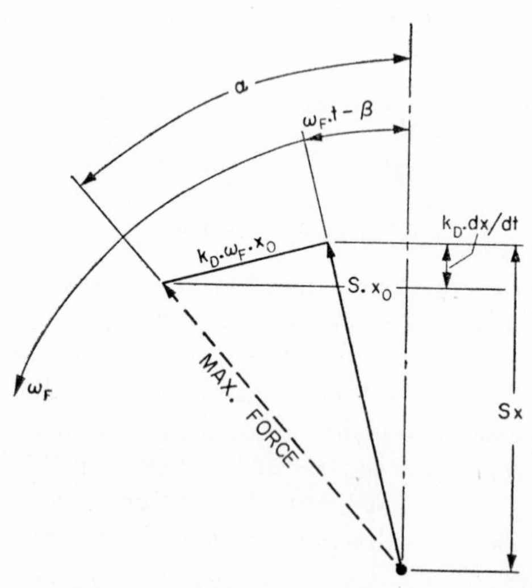

FIG. 11.13. Vector representation of forces transmitted

(b) TRANSMISSIBILITY OF ENGINE MOUNTING

Whilst knowledge of the motion of an engine due to unbalance is desirable, of more significance is the design of the mounting one aspect of which is the minimizing of the forces transmitted to the frame.

Considering the mounting represented in Fig. 11.11. The force transmitted to the frame will be the resultant of the spring and damping forces, as shown in the vector diagram of Fig. 11.13.

The resultant of the rotating vector $S \cdot x_o$ and vector $k_D \cdot \omega_F \cdot x_o$ will be the vector for the resultant force transmitted and so the maximum force transmitted to the frame will be given by the length of the rotating resultant vector itself, thus maximum transmitted force

$$= \sqrt{(k_D \cdot \omega_F \cdot x_o)^2 + (S \cdot x_o)^2}$$

and it will occur when $\alpha = 0°$ or $180°$.

$$\text{Transmissibility is defined as the ratio } \frac{\text{Transmitted Force}}{\text{Impressed Force}}$$

$$= \frac{\sqrt{(k_D \cdot \omega_F \cdot x_o)^2 + (S \cdot x_o)^2}}{F_1}. \qquad (11.17)$$

To investigate the effect of the system characteristics on the transmissibility, curves of transmissibility are plotted against the frequency ratio for values of actual to critical damping ratios, and Fig. 11.14 is typical of the curves obtained. In practice, conclusions drawn from such curves must refer to particular circumstances, but some brief general conclusions are obvious from the curves of Fig. 11.14.

Damping in the mounting is advantageous for frequency ratios less than $\sqrt{2}$, but is detrimental for values greater than $\sqrt{2}$ and the converse is true for stiffness with a "solid" mounting more advantageous for frequency ratios less than $\sqrt{2}$. It is unlikely for operation to be near resonance (ratio $= 1$), and therefore if

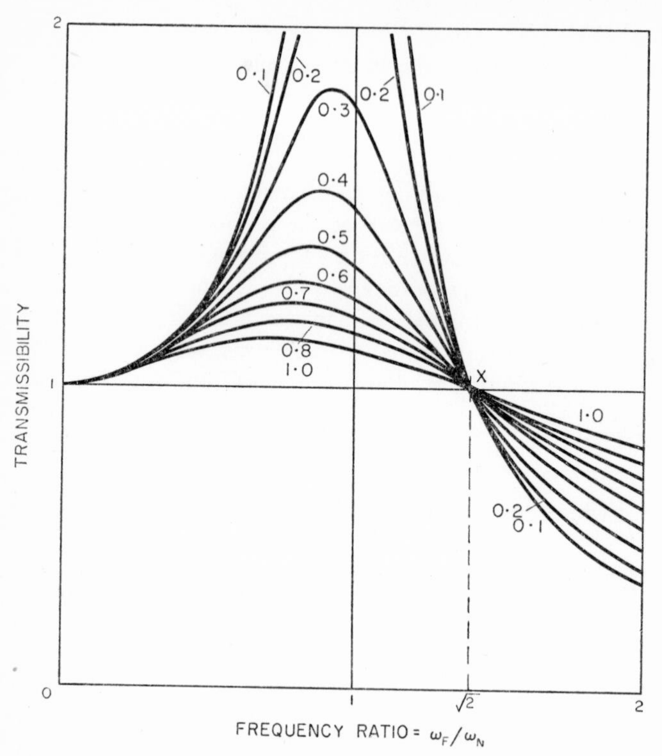

FIG. 11.14. Curves of engine transmissibility

operation is beyond the point X then the small detrimental effect of the damping may be tolerated.

WORKED EXAMPLE (U.L.2 Ext., 1956)

11.5. The Fig. 11.15 shows diagrammatically a single cylinder engine for which the vertical unbalanced force is $80 \sin \frac{40}{3} . t$ lb. The engine weighs 200 lb and is supported by a spring system of stiffness 300 lb/in. A dash-pot is fitted between the engine and the frame which give a force of $48v$ lb for a vertical velocity of v ft/sec. Calculate the maximum force transmitted to the frame (a) through the springs, (b) through the dash-pot and (c) through the springs and dash-pot together.

Solution

(a) Maximum force $= S \,.\, x_o$ lb

$$x_o = \frac{c}{\sqrt{(b - \omega_F^2)^2 + a^2\omega_F^2}}$$

and $a = \dfrac{48 \times 32{\cdot}2}{200} = 7{\cdot}73$; $b = S \,.\, g/W = 300 \times 12 \times 32{\cdot}2/200 = 580$; $\omega_F = 41{\cdot}3$; $c = 80 \times 32{\cdot}2/200 = 12$, thus

$$x_o = \frac{12{\cdot}9}{\sqrt{(580 - 41{\cdot}3^2)^2 + (7{\cdot}73 \times 41{\cdot}3)^2}} = 0{\cdot}01055 \text{ ft.}$$

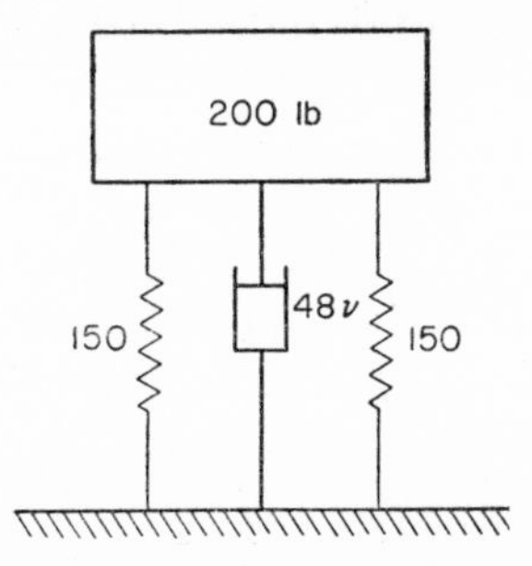

FIG. 11.15. Mounting of the engine of example 11.5

Maximum force $= 3600 \times 0{\cdot}01055 = 38$ lb giving with dead weight a total of 238 lb on the frame.

(b) Maximum force $= k_D \,.\, \omega_F \,.\, x_o = 48 \times 41{\cdot}3 \times 0{\cdot}01055 = 21{\cdot}2$ lb or a total of 221·2 lb on frame.

(c) Maximum force

$$= \sqrt{(k_D \cdot \omega_F \cdot x_o)^2 + (S \cdot x_o)^2} = \sqrt{(38^2 + 21{\cdot}2^2)} = 43{\cdot}4 \text{ lb}$$

or a total of 243·4 lb.

11.3. Vehicle Ride Vibrations with Two Degree of Natural Freedom

The vehicle represented by Fig. 11.16 has degrees of freedom in bounce and pitch. Interest is in the frequency and mode of natural vibration when the system has been disturbed. It is obvious that if a vertical upwards force is applied, the vehicle will move upwards, but unless the force is applied at some specific place the vehicle may rotate as well. Similarly if a couple were applied to cause the vehicle to pitch, it could also cause the vehicle to bounce. When motion in one degree of freedom can excite motion in another, the two degrees of freedom are said to be coupled.

(a) Frequency and Amplitude of Natural Undamped Vibration

Consider the vehicle to be in a state of natural vibration such that its position is defined, as shown in Fig. 11.16, by an upward displacement, x, of the centre of mass, G, together with a small rotation, θ, about G. Both x and θ are measured from the static position and direction. Then, as a result of the motion, spring extensions are: $x_1 = x - L_1 \cdot \theta$ and $x_2 = x + L_2 \cdot \theta$. The equation of motion for bounce is force = mass × acceleration and for pitch is torque = moment of inertia × angular acceleration, giving

$$-S_1(x - L_1\theta) - S_2(x + L_2\theta) = \frac{W}{g} \cdot \frac{d^2x}{dt^2},$$

or

$$\frac{W}{g} \cdot \frac{d^2x}{dt^2} + x(S_1 + S_2) + \theta(S_2L_2 - S_1L_1) = 0 \qquad (11.18)$$

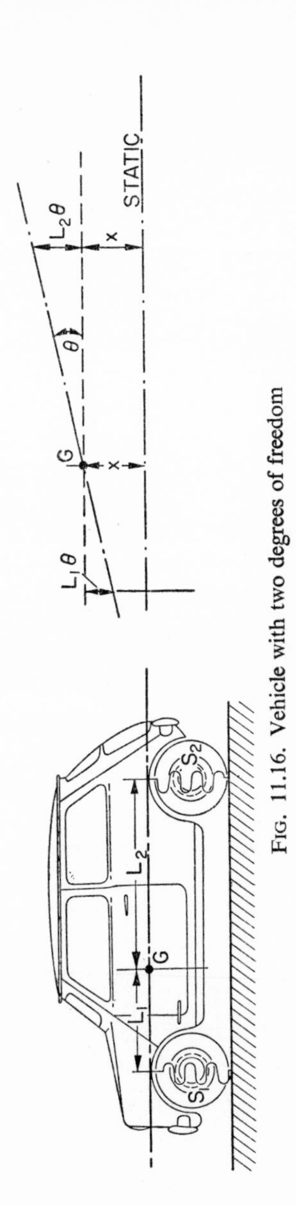

FIG. 11.16. Vehicle with two degrees of freedom

and

$$-S_2(x + L_2\theta)L_2 + S_1(x - L_1\theta)L_1 = I \, . \, \frac{d^2\theta}{dt^2},$$

or

$$I \, . \, \frac{d^2\theta}{dt^2} + \theta(S_1L_1^2 + S_2L_2^2) + x(S_2L_2 - S_1L_1) \qquad (11.19)$$

where I is the moment of inertia of the vehicle body in pitch about an axis through G.

To determine the frequency of the coupled vibrations it is assumed that

$$x = x_o \cos \omega_N t \quad \text{and} \quad \theta = \theta_o \cos \omega_N t, \qquad (11.20)$$

i.e., that the bounce and pitch motion of the system has the same coupled frequency. However, it should be noted that there are two modes of vibration, up whilst rotating clockwise or anticlockwise, and thus there will be two natural coupled frequencies, one for each mode. Substitution of the values of x, θ, and derivatives, of equation (11.20) in (11.18) and (11.19), give, when $\cos \omega_N t$ has been cancelled,

$$-\frac{W}{g} \, . \, x_o \, . \, \omega_N^2 + (S_1 + S_2)x_o + \theta_o(S_2L_2 - S_1L_1) = 0, \quad (11.21)$$

$$-I \, . \, \theta_o \, . \, \omega_N^2 + \theta_o(S_1L_1^2 + S_2L_2^2) + x_o(S_2L_2 - S_1L_1) = 0 \qquad (11.22)$$

Elimination of either x_o or θ_o between these two equations yields a characteristic frequency equation which is a quadratic in ω_N^2, the two roots of which give the two coupled natural frequencies with their corresponding amplitude ratios of x_o/θ_o. The frequency equation is

$$\omega_N^4 - \omega_N^2 \left\{ \frac{S_1 g}{W} + \frac{S_2 g}{W} + \frac{S_2 L_2^2}{I} + \frac{S_1 L_1^2}{I} \right\} + \frac{g}{W \, . \, I}\{(S_1 + S_2)(S_2L_2^2 + S_1L_1^2) - (S_2L_2 - S_1L_1)^2\} = 0 \qquad (11.23)$$

(b) COUPLING OF NATURAL VIBRATIONS

Equations (11.21) to (11.23) are not in a form suitable for the study of the effects of the system parameters of stiffness, mass, etc., on the coupling between bounce and pitch motions. There are several other ways of specifying the coordinates of the vehicle motion and the forces and couples arising from the suspension springs. Two typical arrangements only are considered.

Firstly, consider the vehicle body motion supplied by a single spring of stiffness, S, acting at G, together with a torsion spring of stiffness, q, for the rotational motion about G. The system is shown in Fig. 11.17.

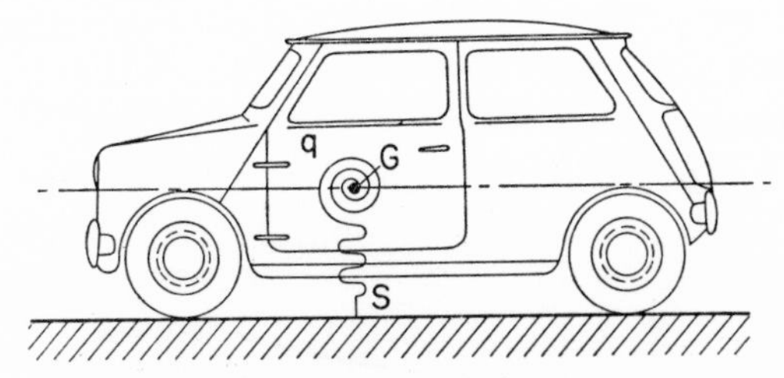

FIG. 11.17. Spring system for the vehicle of Fig. 11.16

Then the following equations represent the required conditions

$$S = S_1 + S_2;$$

and

$$q\theta = S_1L_1\theta \cdot L_1 + S_2L_2\theta \cdot L_2,$$

or

$$q = S_1L_1^2 + S_2L_2^2.$$

Examination of equations (11.21) and (11.22) show that the coupling between them is $(S_2L_2 - S_1L_1)$. Let this coupling $= C$.

The equations of motion then become

$$-\frac{W}{g} \cdot x_o \cdot \omega_N^2 + S \cdot x_o + C \cdot \theta_o = 0; \tag{11.24}$$

$$-I \cdot \theta_o \cdot \omega_N^2 + q \cdot \theta_o + C \cdot x_o = 0, \tag{11.25}$$

which by the substitutions of equation (11.20) give the frequency equation

$$\omega_N^4 - \omega_N^2\left(\frac{Sg}{W} + \frac{q}{I}\right) + \frac{S\,.\,g\,.\,q}{W\,.\,I} - \frac{C^2\,.\,g}{W\,.\,I} = 0.$$

But if the vertical motion were uncoupled, its circular frequency would be $\omega_x^2 = \dfrac{S\,.\,g}{W}$ and similarly for the pitch motion $\omega_\theta^2 = \dfrac{q}{I}$, thus the frequency equation may be written in terms of the uncoupled frequencies giving

$$\omega_N^4 - \omega_N^2(\omega_x^2 + \omega_\theta^2) + \omega_x^2\,.\,\omega_\theta^2 - \frac{C^2\,.\,g}{W\,.\,I} = 0 \qquad (11.26)$$

and so

$$\omega_N^2 = \frac{1}{2}\left\{(\omega_x^2 + \omega_\theta^2) \pm \sqrt{(\omega_x^2 - \omega_\theta^2)^2 + \frac{4\,.\,C^2\,.\,g}{W\,.\,I}}\right\}. \qquad (11.27)$$

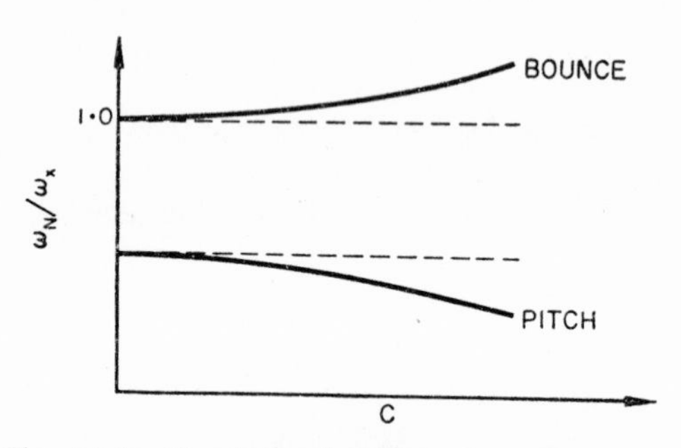

FIG. 11.18. Graph showing effect of coupling on the frequency response

If the coupling is zero, by a suitable choice of spring stiffnesses and position, then $C = 0$ and $\omega_N^2 = \omega_x^2$ or ω_θ^2, but if the coupling C has some value then the term $\dfrac{4C^2g}{W\,.I}$ has an influence on the value of the natural coupled frequencies which become greater and less than their range of values with zero coupling. This is illustrated in the graphs of Fig. 11.18, for the case when ω_x and ω_θ are not equal.

Since the vertical force provided by the spring acting at G can be replaced, for analysis, by an equal force at some other position together with an additional couple, there are several other possible systems, consisting of a force and couple, which enable the coupling to be expressed in different ways. If, for example, a force were applied to the sprung vehicle so that it did not pitch, but only bounced, such a force would have to be positioned at some distance, Z, from G as shown in Fig. 11.19. Thus $S_1Z_1 = S_2Z_2$, and, if the vertical force were provided by a spring, its stiffness, S, would be given by $S = S_1 + S_2$, the torsional spring stiffness (total) q_1 would be given by

$$q_1 = S_1Z_1^2 + S_2Z_2^2,$$

and the equations of motion then become

$$\frac{W}{g} \cdot \frac{d^2x}{dt^2} + S(x + Z \,.\, \theta) = 0$$

$$I \,.\, \frac{d^2\theta}{dt^2} + q_1 \,.\, \theta + S(x + Z \,.\, \theta)Z = 0,$$

or

$$\frac{W}{g} \cdot \frac{d^2x}{dt^2} + S \,.\, x + S \,.\, Z \,.\, \theta = 0 \tag{11.28}$$

$$I \,.\, \frac{d^2\theta}{dt^2} + \theta(q_1 + S \,.\, Z^2) + S \,.\, Z \,.\, x = 0. \tag{11.29}$$

The coupling factor is now Z, which, if zero, removes all the coupling effect. The characteristic equation now becomes

$$\omega_N^4 - \omega_N^2 \left(\frac{S \,.\, g}{W} + \frac{(q_1 + S \,.\, Z^2)}{I} \right) + \frac{S \,.\, g}{W} \cdot \frac{q_1}{I} = 0 \tag{11.30}$$

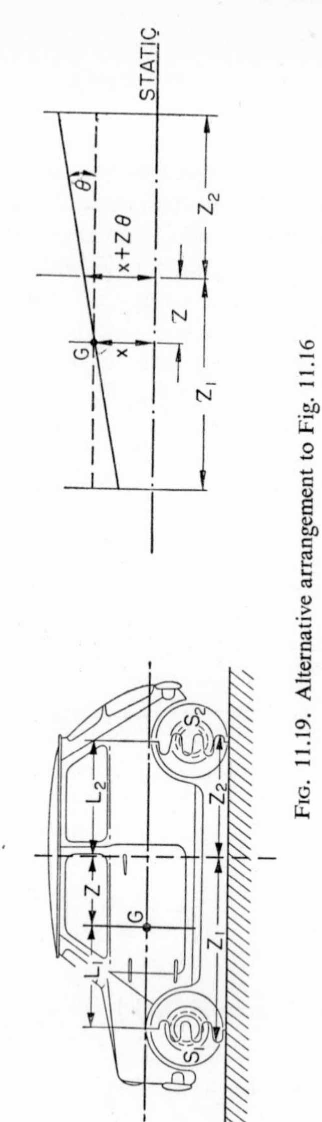

FIG. 11.19. Alternative arrangement to Fig. 11.16

But $S \,.\, g/W = \omega_x^2$ and $I = W \,.\, k^2/g$, thus

$$\left(\frac{\omega_N}{\omega_x}\right)^4 - \left(\frac{\omega_N}{\omega_x}\right)^2\left[1 + \frac{q_1}{Sk^2} + \frac{Z^2}{k^2}\right] + \frac{q_1}{S \,.\, k^2} = 0. \quad (11.31)$$

If values of ω_N/ω_x are plotted against values of $q_1/S \,.\, k^2$, for values of Z/k, the effect of the coupling Z is as shown in Fig. 11.20. The curves below the uncoupled line are for one value of ω_N and those above, for the other value of ω_N.

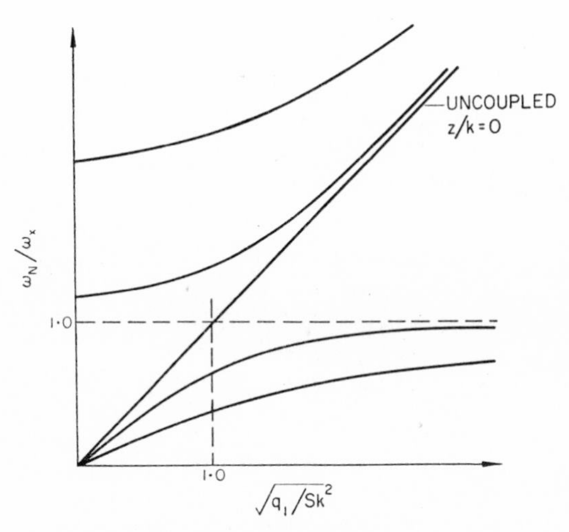

FIG. 11.20. Graph showing effect of coupling

(c) INSTANTANEOUS CENTRES FOR NATURAL VIBRATIONS

The combined motion of bounce and pitch is equivalent to a rotation about the instantaneous centres shown in Fig. 11.21. For one value of the amplitude ratio $x_o/\theta_o = d_1$ the ends of the vehicle move out of phase, whilst for the other value of the amplitude ratio $x_o/\theta_o = d_2$ the ends move in phase. In the absence of damping the phase difference is 180°.

Considerations of the centres show that:

(i) If one centre is at G the vehicle has pitch only and if the other centre is at an infinite distance from G, the body has bounce only. With centres at these places the motion is uncoupled and can be brought about by a force at G and a couple about G. ($S_1L_1 = S_2L_2 = S_1Z_1 = S_2Z_2$ and $Z = 0$).

(ii) Since the road profile causes displacements of the wheels, it is of interest to consider the effect of movement of the points of

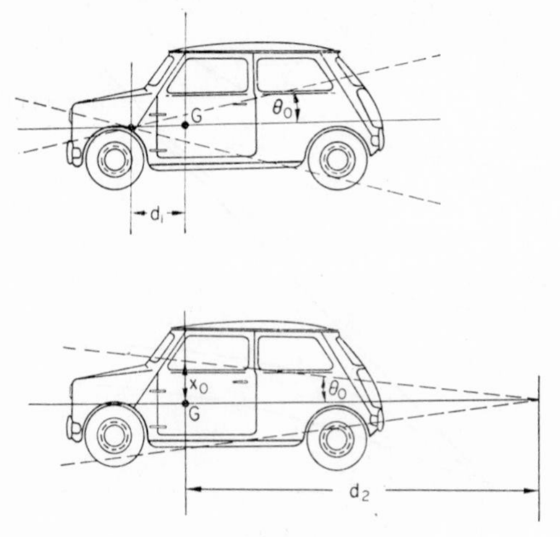

FIG. 11.21. Centres of vibration

attachment of the springs and body. If the body pitches about the front point, then $d_1 = L_1 = x_o/\theta_o$, and substitution of this value in equations (11.21) and (11.22) gives

$$\frac{W}{g} \cdot \omega_N^2 = S_2(1 + L_2/L_1) \text{ and } I \cdot \omega_N^2 = S_2L_2^2(1 + L_1/L_2).$$

A similar result obtains for motion of pitch about the rear point. If these motions are uncoupled, then $S_1L_1 = S_2L_2$ and then

$$\omega_N^2 = \frac{g}{W}(S_1 + S_2) = \omega_x^2 \text{ and } \omega_N^2 = q/I = \omega_\theta^2$$

Thus the front and rear attachment points are also centres for uncoupled vibrations.

(iii) If in addition the uncoupled frequencies are the same, then

$$\omega_x^2 = \omega_\theta^2 \text{ and } \frac{S \cdot g}{W} = \frac{q}{I}.$$

This gives

$$\frac{(S_1 + S_2)g}{W} = \frac{g(S_1 L_1^2 + S_2 L_2^2)}{W \cdot k^2},$$

and then

$$k^2 = L_1 \cdot L_2. \qquad (11.32)$$

Note that this is one condition required for the inertia of the body to be equivalent to two concentrated masses, each at the attachment points of the body and springs. The coupling is then due to the dispersed inertia.

An automobile suspension obviously has to cope with various disturbances which give rise to both transient and steady state damped response. The methods so far used for analysis would, with the inclusion of forcing and damping or even with more degrees of natural freedom, soon become cumbersome and other methods would be required. One such method, usually called the Impedance Method, is described in the following section.

11.4. Impedance Method

For the steady state solution of many vibrating systems an assumed solution of the form $x = x_o \cos \omega_F t$ is made. Provided the motion arises from forces that are proportional to displacement or acceleration, the dynamic equilibrium relates these forces to x_o, with a common factor $\cos \omega_F t$ cancelling throughout. However the inclusion of viscous damping results in all forces not being completely in or out of phase with each other and so $\sin \omega_F t$ terms will appear in the equations. If in addition there are several degrees of freedom and therefore several simultaneous equations, solution of these can be laborious. The amount of

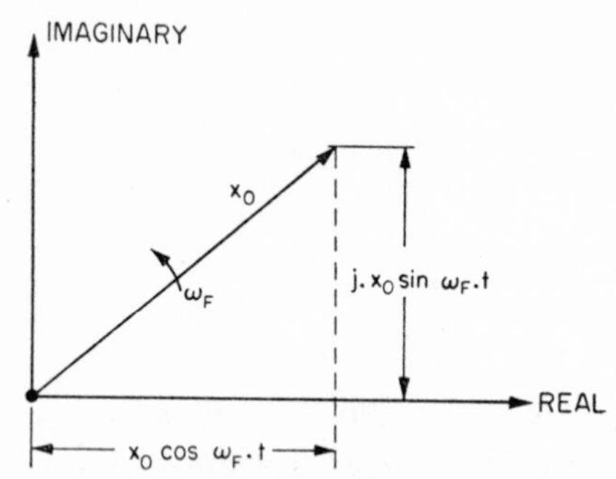

FIG. 11.22. Complex number amplitude vectors

labour involved is reduced in the impedance method by representing the vector $x = x_o \cos \omega_F t$ in a complex number form as follows.

The rotating vector for the amplitude, x_o, as shown in Fig. 11.22, can be resolved into the complex number vectors of $x_o \cos \omega_F t$ and $j \,.\, x_o \sin \omega_F t$ and thus $x = x_o \cos \omega_F t$ is the real part of the complex vector.

But in exponential form, $x_o \cos \omega_F t + j \,.\, x_o \sin \omega_F t = e^{j \,.\, \omega_F \,.}$ and so

$$x = x_o \,.\, e^{j \,.\, \omega_F \,.\, t}. \tag{11.33}$$

Differentiation gives

$$\frac{dx}{t} = j \,.\, \omega_F \,.\, x_o \,.\, e^{j \,.\, \omega_F \,.\, t} \quad \text{and} \quad \frac{d^2x}{dt^2} = -\omega_F^2 \,.\, x_o \,.\, e^{j \,.\, \omega_F \,.\, t}.$$

Thus a second order differential equation of the form

$$\frac{W}{g}\cdot\frac{d^2x}{dt^2} + k_D\,.\,\frac{dx}{dt} + S\,.\,x = F = F_o \cos \omega_F t = F_o\,.\,e^{j\,.\,\omega_F\,.\,t}$$

becomes

$$\frac{-W}{g}\,.\,\omega_F^2\,.\,x_o + j\,.\,k_D\,.\,\omega_F\,.\,x_o + S\,.\,x_o = F_o,$$

or

$$\left(\frac{-W}{g}\,.\,\omega_F^2 + j\,.\,k_D\,.\,\omega_F + S\right) = \frac{F_o}{x_o} \qquad (11.34)$$

The ratio $\frac{\text{Force } (F_o)}{\text{Displacement } (x_o)}$ is called the mechanical impedance although it should be noted that a similar result for Force/Velocity can be obtained and this is sometimes called the impedance. However, the name impedance is given because the analogous electrical quantities of resistance, inductance and capacitance can be added in complex number manner to give a voltage/current ratio termed impedance.

It can be seen that equation (11.34) corresponds to the frequency equations of section (11.3) and that the damping quantity, as well as those of inertia and spring force, may be easily written in the equation by inspection of the given system. Although rules may be written for the application of the method, this will not be done since the method will be used several times in the remainder of this chapter.

11.5. Torsional Vibrations of Engine and Transmission

A reciprocating engine crankshaft is subjected to torques, at each crank, that have been developed during the combustion process and transmitted by the reciprocating mechanism. The torque on each crank will vary considerably during a cycle and the system, which has elasticity in torsion, is essentially an example of a forced vibration having, as we shall see later, several degrees of freedom. Of interest to a designer is therefore the representation of the system, the natural frequencies and modes of vibration, the nature of the forcing, resonant conditions and the suppression of the amplitude of undesirable vibrations.

(a) THE VIBRATING SYSTEM

Since the system is one of torsional vibration the necessary elements consist of oscillating masses of some pre-determined

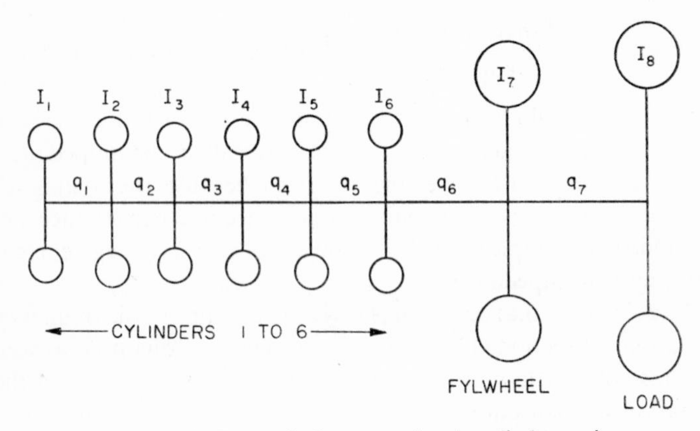

FIG. 11.23. Rotor-shaft system of a six-cylinder engine

inertia connected together by elastic members in torsion. It is convenient to represent each cylinder and a portion of the crankshaft by a rotor of inertia (I) placed at the crank position and the crankshaft elasticity by portions of shaft of stiffness (q) connecting the rotors. The flywheel can be represented by a single rotor connected to the engine by a shaft of some stiffness. The transmission and load may be similarly represented. The full system for a six-cylinder engine is shown in Fig. 11.23.

It should be noted that this is a simplified system for analysis and although it is beyond the scope of this book to show how to determine, for example, the rotor inertias or shaft stiffnesses the process is complex and lengthy.

To understand the method of determination of the natural frequencies of the system of Fig. 11.23, it is advisable to study the simpler systems consisting of two and three rotors.

(b) Torsional Vibrations of Two-rotor System

The system shown in Fig. 11.24 consists of a rotor of inertia I_1 representing a single cylinder engine, connected by a shaft of

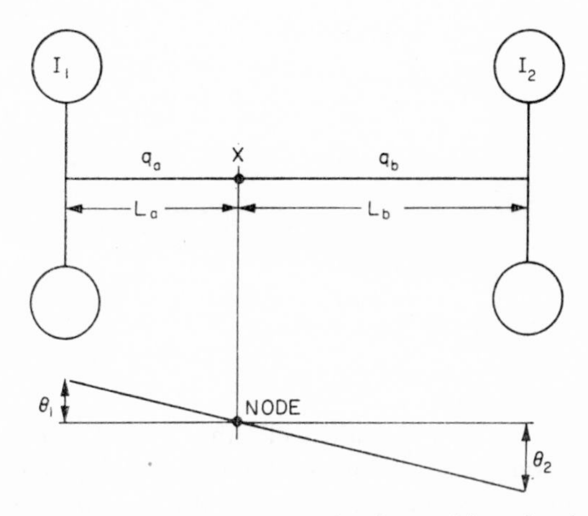

Fig. 11.24. Two-rotor system showing position of node

torsional stiffness q_1 to a load represented by a rotor of inertia I_2. Let the two rotors be twisted angularly in opposite directions and released. The system now performs natural vibrations each rotor having angular motion about the mean position. The ends of the shaft will be twisted to the same extent as the rotors connected to them and as a result the shaft provides a torsional elastic "spring."

It should be noted that the shaft ends have to move in opposite directions for the motion to continue periodically. At some point along the shaft there will be no relative twisting and this point X, in Fig. 11.24, is called a node. The shaft could be imagined "fixed" at the node with portions on either side vibrating freely. Let the node divide the shaft of diameter d into lengths L_a and L_b, giving stiffnesses q_a and q_b. Then on either side of the node are single degree of freedom systems having the same natural frequency given by

$$f_N = \frac{1}{2\pi}\sqrt{\frac{q_a}{I_1}} = \frac{1}{2\pi}\sqrt{\frac{q_b}{I_2}}$$

but, for a shaft of circular section,

$$q_a = T/\theta = \frac{G\,.\,J}{L_a} \quad \text{and} \quad q_b = \frac{G\,.\,J}{L_b},$$

and so

$$f_N = \frac{1}{2\pi}\sqrt{\frac{G\,.\,J}{I_1 L_a}} = \frac{1}{2\pi}\sqrt{\frac{G\,.\,J}{I_2 L_b}}, \tag{11.35}$$

and the node position is given by

$$I_1 L_a = I_2 L_b. \tag{11.36}$$

For a given system the values of either L_a or L_b are calculated using equation (11.36) knowing that $L_a + L_b$ = length of shaft. The position of the node is thus established and then the frequency is calculated using either of the parts of equation (11.35). Care must be taken with the units since J = 2nd moment of area $= \pi d^4/32$ for a circular shaft, G is the modulus of rigidity of the shaft and I is the moment of inertia.

The amplitude of the ends of the shaft vary linearly from θ_1 at one end to zero at the node X and then from zero to θ_2 in the opposite sense as shown in Fig. 11.24. The straight line is often called the elastic line for the shaft.

An alternative method using impedances, whilst for this simple case is no shorter, is however of value in that a forcing term can be included and an important principle is demonstrated. Imagine the system of Fig. 11.24 having a torque harmonic $T = T_o \cos \omega_F t$ applied to the rotor representing the engine whilst the complete system is rotating. This is more realistic than the previous case of natural vibration. If θ_1 and θ_2 are the amplitudes of the two rotors relative to the mean angular position, then by impedance method

$$-I_1\omega_F^2\theta_1 + q_1(\theta_1 - \theta_2) = F_o \quad \text{for rotor 1,}$$
$$-I_2\omega_F^2\theta_2 + q_1(\theta_2 - \theta_1) = 0 \quad \text{for rotor 2.}$$

Note that for the stiffness term, it is always given by qx the near end amplitude – the far end amplitude. This will apply to springs as well. The impedance equations can now be written as

$$(q_1 - I_1\omega_F^2)\theta_1 - q_1\theta_2 = F_o \qquad (11.37)$$
$$-q_1 0_1 + (q_1 - I_2\omega_F^2)\theta_2 = 0 \qquad (11.38)$$

Values of θ_1 and θ_2 could best be evaluated using determinants thus

$$\theta_1 = \frac{\begin{vmatrix} F_o & -q_1 \\ 0 & q_1 - I_2\omega_F^2 \end{vmatrix}}{\begin{vmatrix} q_1 - I_1\omega_F^2 & -q_1 \\ -q_1 & q_1 - I_2\omega_F^2 \end{vmatrix}}$$

and similarly for θ_2

However resonance is such that $\omega_F = \omega_N$ and then the amplitude θ_1 is infinite. For this the denominator determinant has to be zero

$$\begin{vmatrix} q_1 - I_1\omega_N^2 & -q_1 \\ q_1 & q_1 - I_2\omega_N^2 \end{vmatrix} = 0$$

and this gives the natural frequency equation

$$I_1 I_2 \,.\, \omega_N^4 - q_1(I_1 + I_2)\omega_N^2 = 0 \text{ or, } \omega_N = \sqrt{\frac{q_1(I_1 + I_2)}{I_1 I_2}}. \qquad (11.39)$$

WORKED EXAMPLE (U.L.2 Ext., 1950 Modified)

11.6. A single cylinder engine has rotating masses (including an allowance for reciprocating masses) equivalent to 225 lb at 1 ft radius. The torque produced by the engine includes a harmonic term of maximum value $\pm$ 100 lb ft and frequency 150 cycles/min. The engine is coupled by a shaft 2 in. diameter and 4 ft long to a flywheel of moment of inertia 500 lb ft^2. Find the maximum displacements of the engine crank and flywheel from their mean running positions. Assume $G = 12 \times 10^6$ lb/in^2.

Solution

The system is as shown in Fig. 11.24 with a force applied to the rotor representing the engine.

Moment of inertia of engine

$$= \frac{225}{32{\cdot}2} \times 1^2 = 7 \text{ slugs ft}^2.$$

Moment of inertia of flywheel

$$= \frac{500}{32{\cdot}2} = 15{\cdot}5 \text{ slugs ft}^2$$

$$\omega_F = 2\pi f_F = 5\pi$$

$$q = \frac{GJ}{L} = 12 \times 10^6 \times 144 \times \frac{\pi \times 2^4}{32 \times 144 \times 144} \times \frac{1}{4},$$

$$q = 32{,}700 \text{ lb ft/rad.}$$

Thus, the impedance equations are

$$-7 \times 25\pi^2 \,.\, \theta_1 + 32{,}700(\theta_1 - \theta_2) = 100$$

$$-15{\cdot}5 \times 25^2\theta_2 + 32{,}700(\theta_2 - \theta_1) = 0,$$

giving

$$\theta_1 = \frac{\begin{vmatrix} 100 & -32700 \\ 0 & 32700 - 3830 \end{vmatrix}}{\begin{vmatrix} 32700 - 1730 & -32700 \\ -32700 & 32700 - 3830 \end{vmatrix}}$$

$$= \frac{100 \times 28870}{(30970 \times 28870) - (32700 \times 32700)}$$

$\theta_1 = -0{\cdot}0162$ rad, or $0{\cdot}093^\circ$

$$\theta_2 = \frac{32700 \times \theta_1}{32700 - 3830} = -0{\cdot}0184 \text{ rad, or } 1{\cdot}06^\circ.$$

(c) Torsional Vibrations of the Three-rotor System

The impedance method may be applied to the three-rotor system shown in Fig. 11.25.

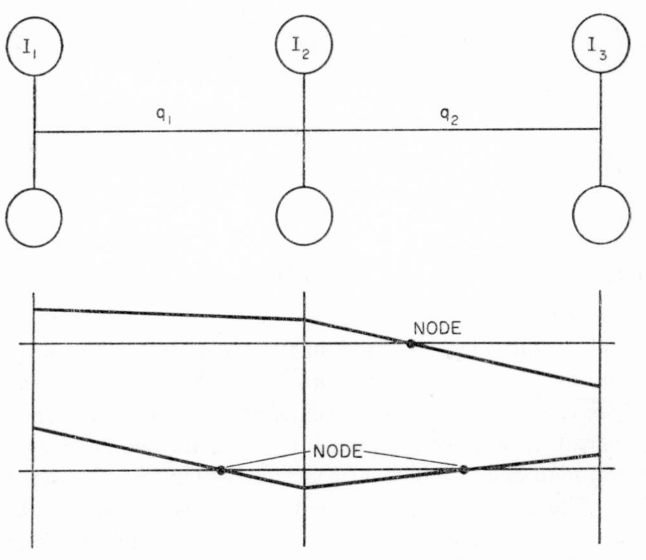

Fig. 11.25. Three-rotor system showing positions of nodes

With the notation of section 11.5(b), the impedance equations are

$$-I_1\omega_N^2\theta_1 + q_1(\theta_1 - \theta_2) = 0,$$
$$-I_2\omega_N^2\theta_2 + q_1(\theta_2 - \theta_1) + q_2(\theta_2 - \theta_3) = 0,$$
$$-I_3\omega_N^2\theta_3 + q_2(\theta_3 - \theta_2) = 0. \qquad (11.40)$$

These are for natural vibrations, but if forcing is applied to a rotor the equation for that rotor would have a forcing amplitude F_o on the right hand side instead of zero. However, the determinant for the natural frequency becomes

$$\begin{vmatrix} q_1 - I_1\omega_N^2 & -q_1 & 0 \\ -q_1 & q_1 + q_2 - I_2\omega_N^2 & -q_2 \\ 0 & q-_2 & q_2 - I_3\omega_N^2 \end{vmatrix} = 0$$

and evaluation of the determinant gives the frequency equation

$$I_1I_2I_3\omega_N^4 - (q_1I_2I_3 + q_1I_1I_3 + q_2I_1I_3 + q_2I_1I_2)\omega_N^2$$
$$+ q_1q_2(I_1 + I_2 + I_3) = 0. \qquad (11.41)$$

The elastic line shows that the two frequencies given by equation (11.41) correpond to a one node or two node shape as shown in Fig. 11.25.

WORKED EXAMPLE (U.L.2 Ext., 1944)

11.7. As a first approximation in the determination of the natural frequencies of torsional oscillation, a four-cylinder engine, flywheel and rigidly connected generator are equivalent to three rotors mounted on a shaft of diameter 6 in. The engine is equivalent to a rotor of moment of inertia 840 lb ft^2 and the generator to one of moment of inertia 1000 lb ft^2 at a distance of 75 in. The flywheel has a moment of inertia of 7000 lb ft^2 and is between the engine and generator at a distance of 35 in. from the engine rotor. Find the two frequencies of natural torsional oscillation, the modulus of rigidity of the shaft materials being 12×10^6 lb/in².

Solution

The system is represented by Fig. 11.25

$$I_1 = \frac{840}{32 \cdot 2} = 26 \cdot 1 \text{ slug ft}^2 \qquad I_2 = \frac{7000}{32 \cdot 2} = 217 \cdot 7 \text{ slug ft}^2$$

$$I_3 = \frac{1000}{32 \cdot 2} = 31 \cdot 1 \text{ slug ft}^2 \qquad q_1 = \frac{GJ}{L_1} = 12 \times 10^6 \times 144 \times \frac{\pi}{32 \times 16} \times \frac{12}{35}$$

$$= 3 \cdot 63 \times 10^6 \text{ lb ft/rad.}$$

$$q_2 = 3 \cdot 63 \times 10^6 \times \frac{35}{40} = 3 \cdot 18 \text{ lb ft/rad.}$$

Examination candidates are advised to express the impedances and determinants in symbols as it is simpler to evaluate with them rather than with numerical values. Following the procedure of the previous section, and dividing equation (11.41) by $I_1 I_2 I_3$,

$$\omega_N^4 - \left(\frac{q_1}{I_1} + \frac{q_1}{I_2} + \frac{q_2}{I_2} + \frac{q_2}{I_3}\right)\omega_N^2 + \left(\frac{q_1 q_2}{I_1 I_2} + \frac{q_1 q_2}{I_1 I_3} + \frac{q_1 q_2}{I_2 I_3}\right) = 0.$$

Substitution of the above values in this equation gives

$$\omega_N^4 - (0 \cdot 273 \times 10^6)\omega_N^2 + 11 \cdot 55 \times 10^{12}\left(\frac{1}{5670} + \frac{1}{812} + \frac{1}{6760}\right) = 0,$$

$$\omega_N^4 - 2 \cdot 73 \times 10^5 \omega_N^2 + 1 \cdot 8 \times 10^{10} = 0,$$

giving

$$\omega_N^2 = 1 \cdot 62 \times 10^5 \text{ or } 1 \cdot 11 \times 10^5$$

and

$$\omega_N = 403 \text{ or } 333$$

or

$$f_N = 64{\cdot}2 \text{ or } 53 \text{ vib/sec.}$$

(d) Holtzer Tabulation Method for Torsional Vibrations

Considering the multi-rotor system of Fig. 11.23, and writing the impedance equations for the rotors:
for the first rotor,

$$-I_1\omega_N^2\theta_1 + q_1(\theta_1 - \theta_2) = 0,$$

giving

$$\theta_2 = \theta_1 - \frac{I_1\omega_N^2\theta_1}{q_1}$$

and for the second rotor,

$$-I_2\omega_N^2\theta_2 + q_1(\theta_2 - \theta_1) + q_2(\theta_2 - \theta_3) = 0$$

and

$$\theta_3 = \theta_2 - \left(\frac{I_1\theta_1 + I_2\theta_2}{q_2}\right)\omega_N^2$$

Hence

$$\theta_n = \theta_{n-1} - \frac{\omega_N^2}{q_{n-1}}(I_1\theta_1 + I_2\theta_2 + \ldots I_{n-1}\theta_{n-1}).$$

However for natural vibrations the sum of the inertia torques is zero and so, $T = 0 = (I_1\theta_1 + I_2\theta_2 + \ldots I_n\theta_n)\omega_N{}^2$. Using the values shown above for θ_2, θ_3 etc., the quantity in the brackets can be evaluated for some assumed value of θ_1 and a trial value of ω_N. If the correct value of ω_N has been selected then, $\Sigma I \,.\, \theta \,.\, \omega_N^2 = 0$. The process is thus one of trial and error and as such can be best carried out in a tabular form known as Holtzer's Tabular Method. Since the amplitude does not affect the natural frequency it is convenient to let the initial amplitude, say for θ_1, be unity. To obtain a trial value for ω_N for a given system, such system may be simplified to a two- or three-rotor system and a value calculated as shown in the previous sections. The various stages and form of tabulation can be best shown by the following worked example.

WORKED EXAMPLE (H.N.D. Year 4 Oxford College of Technology, 1962)

11.8. Figure 11.26 shows a rotor system equivalent for torsional vibrations to a four-cylinder engine with flywheel and

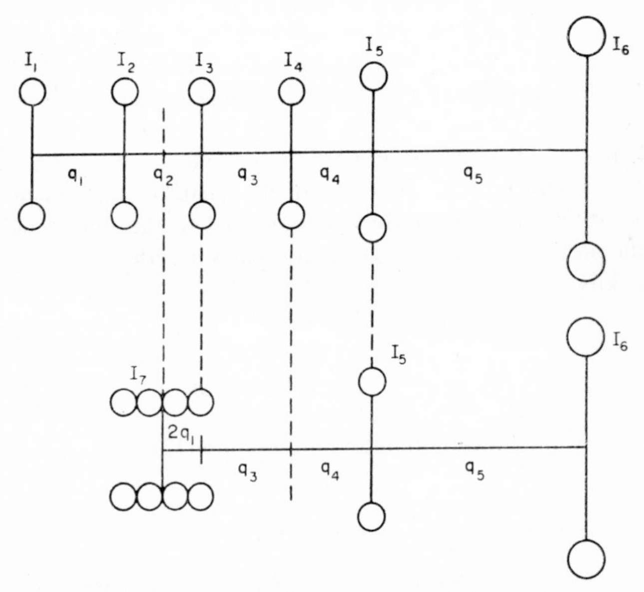

FIG. 11.26. Rotor-shaft system and equivalent system of example 11.8

transmission. The moments of inertia of the rotors are $I_1 = I_2 = I_3 = I_4 = 0{\cdot}64$ lb ft^2 $I_5 = 9{\cdot}6$ lb ft^2 and $I_6 = 130$ lb ft^2. The The stiffness of the shaft portions are $q_1 = q_2 = q_3 = q_4 = 8{\cdot}3 \times 10_4$ lb ft/rad, and $q_5 = 4{\cdot}2 \times 10^2$ lb ft/rad.

(i) Give the values of shaft stiffnesses and rotor inertias of a simplified system from which an approximate frequency of natural torsional vibrations may be calculated.

(ii) Assuming that the frequency given by (i) is 355 vib/min, verify this value using a Holtzer tabulation.

Solution

(i) There are many systems that may be assumed to represent the given one but to illustrate the method, it will be assumed that the four cylinder rotors are combined into a single rotor of inertia $I_7 = I_1 + I_2 + I_3 + I_4 = 2{\cdot}56$ lb ft^2 and that this rotor is placed at the centre of the cylinder rotors. This is shown in Fig. 11.26. The stiffness of the shaft connecting I_7 and I_5 is now required.

This portion consists of portions q_4 and q_3 of the original system together with a part of half the length of that giving q_2. Since stiffnesses are inversely proportional to the shaft lengths, so the portion of stiffness q_6 will have parts in series of $2q_2$, q_3, q_4, and thus

$$1/q_6 = 1/2q_2 + 1/q_3 + 1/q_4$$

and hence

$$q_6 = 3{\cdot}32 \times 10^4 \text{ lb ft/rad.}$$

(ii) For the tabulation, $\omega_N^2 = \dfrac{335 \times 2^2}{60} = 1225.$

TABLE 11.1

(1)	(2) I slug ft^2	(3) $I.\omega_N^2$	(4) θ_o	(5) $I.\omega_N^2\theta_o$	(6) $\Sigma I.\omega_N^2\theta_o$	(7) q lb ft/rad	(8) $\frac{\Sigma I.\omega_N^2\theta_o}{q}$
Cylinder 1	0·02	24·5	1·0000	24·5	24·5	8·3 × 10^4	0·000295
Cylinder 2	0·02	24·5	0·9997	24·45	48·95	8·3 × 10^4	0·000590
Cylinder 3	0·02	24·5	0·9991	24·4	73·35	8·3 × 10^4	0·000883
Cylinder 4	0·02	24·5	0·9982	24·35	97·7	8·3 × 10^4	0·00117
Flywheel	0·298	363	0·9970	362	459·7	4·2 × 10^2	1·09
Transmission	4·04	4930	−0·0930	−457	2·7	—	

Column 1 lists the rotors of the system. Column 2 gives the moments of inertia in slug ft² of the rotors. Column 3 gives the values of $I \, . \, \omega_N^2$ for each of the rotors using the trial value of ω_N. Column 7 lists the stiffnesses of the shaft portions in lb ft/rad. The columns so far mentioned can be completed using the given data.

Column 4 shows the angular amplitude and a value of 1·0000 is inserted on the first line for cylinder 1. Column 5 then is given by column 3 multiplied by column 4, and, in the first line, this is also the value for column 6. Finally on the first line column 8 is given by column 6 divided by column 7.

Column 4, second line, is now the value of column 4, first line, minus the value in column 8, first line. The remainder of the second line is completed as outlined and in this way the full table is completed. The last figure to be entered is in column 6 and if a correct value for ω_N has been selected the torque residue of column 6 should be zero. In this problem it can be seen that whilst the final value of column 6 is not zero, it is very small compared to other values in the column. The first natural frequency is therefore 335 vib/min.

Note that this procedure can be carried out for other modes of vibration. Also that the values of column 4 if plotted give the elastic line, and that in this problem the node is close to the rotor representing the transmission.

(e) Critical Speeds and Phase Diagrams

Each harmonic of the forcing torque on the crankshaft, as shown in Fig. 11.27, will induce a forced torsional vibration of its own frequency. Many of these are far removed from any of the natural frequencies so that the amplitude of forced vibration is small and in any case, there will be some damping present. However, resonance will occur whenever the frequency of any order coincides with a natural frequency.

In the case of a two stroke engine where the cycle of events, induction, compression, etc., occupy one revolution of the crank, the frequency of torque harmonics will be multiples, 1, 2, 3 etc., of the engine speed. With a four-stroke engine the cycle of events occupies two revolutions of the crankshaft and the frequency of forced torque harmonics is therefore, 1/2, 1, $1\frac{1}{2}$, 2, etc., times the

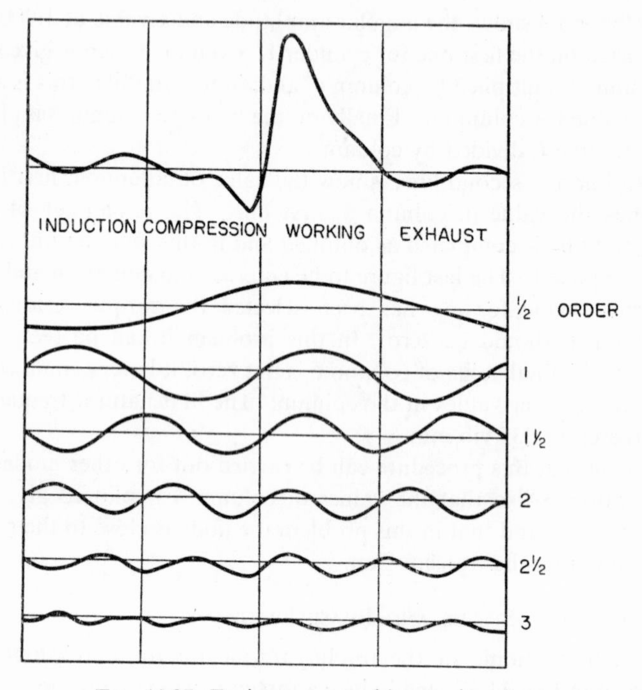

FIG. 11.27. Engine torque and harmonic orders

engine speed. There are therefore many engine speeds at which resonance can occur and these are called either Major or Minor Critical Speeds.

Major critical speeds are those in which not only is there resonance, but harmonic components of ALL the cylinders are in phase, i.e., all cylinders added. All other resonant speeds are called minor critical speeds, i.e., the harmonics are not in phase. In considering the magnitude of the effect of forced engine vibrations it is of interest to determine the major speeds and for this purpose phase diagrams are usually drawn. Some of these are now considered starting with a single cylinder engine. For a single cylinder, two-stroke, engine the torque harmonics will be multiples of engine speed and therefore can be represented by rotating vectors as shown in Fig. 11.28a. The vectors have been drawn having the same amplitude and in an initial examination this is customary although the torque orders have different amplitudes. Clearly all orders are major critical speeds.

Next, a two-cylinder, two-stroke engine with cranks at 180° give the phase diagrams of Fig. 11.28b. For the first order, the vector for cylinder 1 points say, at 0° and that for cylinder 2, points at 180°. For the second order, cylinder 1 is again at 0° whilst cylinder 2, is at twice 180°, i.e., 360° and points in the same direction as that for cylinder 1. The second order is at twice engine speed is therefore a major speed. Similar reasoning shows that the fourth order at four times engine speed is also critical and similarly for the sixth, eighth, etc.

A two-cylinder, two-stroke engine with cranks at 90° gives the phase diagrams of Fig. 11.28c, and 4th, 8th, 12th are major critical.

A four-cylinder, four-stroke engine with cranks at 0°, 180°, 180° 0°, give the phase diagrams of Fig. 11.28d, and even orders are major critical.

It is beyond the scope of this book to deal with the actual magnitude, i.e., length of the phase vectors, but it is obvious that the application of torques of the same magnitude at the various cylinders does not produce the same angle of twist. The angle of twist and thus the input of energy will depend upon the elastic properties of the system which is related to the elastic line mentioned in previous work on torsional vibrations.

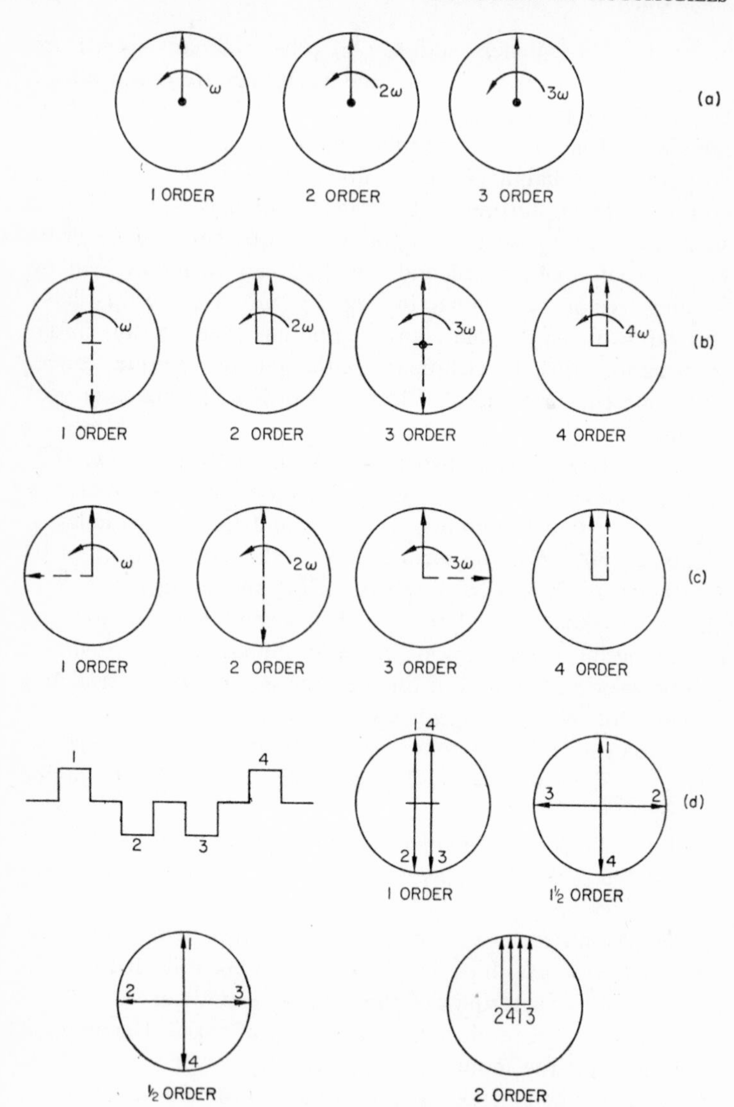

FIG. 11.28. Phase diagrams for various engines

(f) Torsional Dampers and Absorbers

Large torsional vibrations that can occur at various critical engine speeds may be reduced by the fitting of dampers or by attaching an additional system called an absorber.

(i) *Viscous Torsional Damper*

These dampers which can be very effective, are represented by the system shown in Fig. 11.29. The interaction between the damper and the engine crankshaft is due only to viscous shear

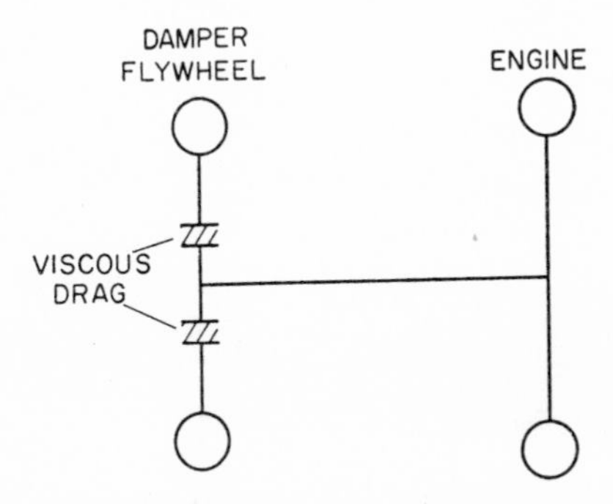

Fig. 11.29. Viscous torsional damper system

since the damper flywheel would otherwise rotate freely on the engine crankshaft. If I_D is the moment of inertia of the damper flywheel, k_D the damping coefficient and θ_D and θ_C the steady state angular amplitudes of the damper and crankshaft, then, for the damper flywheel acted on by an inertia and damping torques

$$T_D, \qquad -I_D \, . \, \omega_F^2 \, . \, \theta_D + j \, . \, k_D \, . \, \omega_F(\theta_D - \theta_C) = 0. \tag{11.35}$$

Equation (11.35) rearranged gives

$$\theta_D = \theta_C \left[\frac{1}{1 + \dfrac{j \, . \, I_D \, . \, \omega_F}{k_D}} \right],$$

or

$$\theta_D = \theta_C \frac{1}{\sqrt{1 + \left(\frac{I_D \,.\, \omega_F}{k_D}\right)^2}}$$

and the phase difference between θ_D and the relative angle $(\theta_D - \theta_C)$ is β, where $\tan \beta = I_D \,.\, \omega_F / k_D$ as shown in Fig. 11.30.

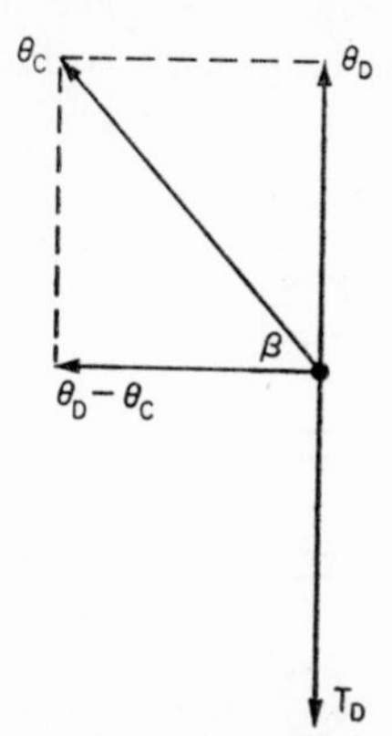

FIG. 11.30. Vector amplitude diagram for system of Fig. 11.29

Damping is due to energy dissipated in shear and will be most effective when it is a maximum. This is commonly called "optimum damping."

Energy dissipated

$$E = \int_0^{2\pi} T \,.\, d\theta$$

for one first order cycle giving

$$E = \pi \,.\, T_D(\theta_D - \theta_C) = \pi \,.\, I_D \,.\, \omega_F^2 \,.\, \theta_D(\theta_D - \theta_C)$$

and from Fig. 11.30,

$$E = \pi \,.\, I_D \,.\, \omega_F^2 \,.\, \theta_C \,.\, \cos \beta \,.\, \theta_C \,.\, \sin \beta$$

and E is thus a maximum when $\beta = 45°$, giving

$$E_{max} = \frac{\pi \,.\, I_D \,.\, \omega_F^2 \,.\, \theta_C^2}{2}. \qquad (11.36)$$

Calculations of natural frequencies when a multirotor system has a damper would be involved, but an approximation may be made by assuming that the damper is equivalent to a rotor of some inertia I_e, having the amplitude of the crankshaft, then for the same energy

$$I_e \,.\, \theta_C^2 = I_D \,.\, \theta_D^2,$$

or

$$I_e = I_D \,.\, \left(\frac{\theta_D}{\theta_C}\right)^2 = I_D \left[\frac{1}{1 + \dfrac{I_D \,.\, \omega_F}{k_D}}\right]$$

and for optimum damping $I_D \,.\, \omega_F = k_D$, and hence

$$I_e = \frac{I_D}{2}. \qquad (11.37)$$

Note that the damper is only at the optimum value for a particular value of ω_F, and is therefore not necessarily fully effective at other critical speeds.

(ii) *Undamped Vibration Absorber*

In many instances bonded rubber torsional vibration limiters are used and since these have elasticity as well as some damping capacity, they operate as absorbers as distinct from dampers. Analysis of a damped absorber with non-linear damping is lengthy and cannot therefore be included here, but the analysis of an undamped absorber is basically similar and will serve to illustrate the basic principles.

Consider the engine system to consist, as shown in Fig. 11.31, of a main rotor of inertia I_E with elastic constraint of torsional stiffness q_E. The absorber attached to the crankshaft has a torsional stiffness q_A and a moment of inertia I_A. For convenience it will be assumed that the angle of twist of the engine shaft shown in Fig. 11.31 is the same as the amplitude θ_E of the engine rotor, and that a periodic torque $T = T_o \cos \omega_F t$ is applied to the engine rotor.

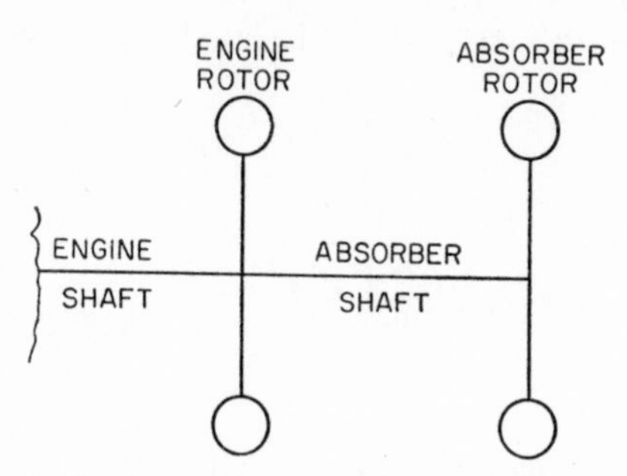

FIG. 11.31. Undamped torsional vibration absorber system

Impedance equations for the main and absorber rotors are

$$-I_E \,.\, \omega_F^2 \,.\, \theta_E + q_E \,.\, \theta_E + q_A(\theta_E - \theta_A) = T_o, \quad (11.38)$$

$$-I_A \,.\, \omega_F^2 \,.\, \theta_A + q_A(\theta_A - \theta_E) = 0.$$

The determinant for θ_E is

$$\theta_E = \frac{\begin{vmatrix} T_o & -q_A \\ 0 & -I_A \,.\, \omega_F^2 \end{vmatrix}}{\begin{vmatrix} -I_E \,.\, \omega_F^2 + q_E + q_A & -q_A \\ -q_A & -I_A \,.\, \omega_F^2 + q_A \end{vmatrix}}$$

whence

$$\theta_E = \frac{-T_o \,.\, I_A \,.\, \omega_F^2 + T_o \,.\, q_A}{I_E I_A \,.\, \omega_F^4 + \omega_F^2(-I_A q_E - I_A q_A - I_E q_A) + q_A q_E}$$

To make the expression dimensionless, let

$$\omega_A^2 = \frac{q_A}{I_A}; \quad \omega_E^2 = \frac{q_E}{I_E} \quad \text{and} \quad \theta_S = \frac{T_o}{q_E}$$

where θ_S is the angular deflection of the main (engine) system due to a "static" torque of magnitude T_o. Substitution and simplification then gives

$$\frac{\theta_E}{\theta_S} = \frac{1 - \dfrac{\omega_F^2}{\omega_A^2}}{\left(1 - \dfrac{\omega_F^2}{\omega_A^2}\right)\left(1 + \dfrac{q_A}{q_E} - \dfrac{\omega_F^2}{\omega_E^2}\right) - \dfrac{q_A}{q_E}}, \tag{11.39}$$

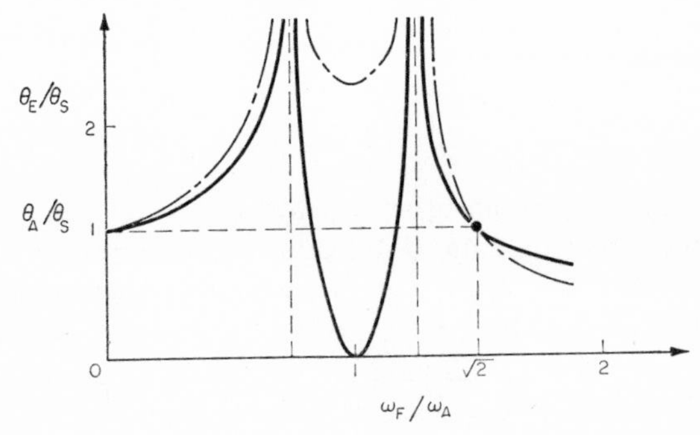

FIG. 11.32. Frequency response of main and absorber rotors

and, similarly

$$\frac{\theta_A}{\theta_S} = \frac{1}{\left(1 - \dfrac{\omega_F^2}{\omega_A^2}\right)\left(1 + \dfrac{q_A}{q_E} - \dfrac{\omega_F^2}{\omega_E^2}\right) - \dfrac{q_A}{q_E}}, \tag{11.40}$$

where in both cases, the right-hand side of the equations is the dynamic magnifier. The relationships of equations (11.39) and (11.40) are shown in the curves of Fig. 11.32, the full line for the engine and dotted line for the absorber.

Examination of equations (11.39) and (11.40) or Fig. 11.32, shows that

(i) there are two values of ω_F (engine speed) at which resonance of the engine system can occur;

(ii) when $\omega_F = \omega_A$, the engine amplitude is zero whilst that of the absorber may be considerable. Thus by a suitable selection of the moment of inertia and torsional stiffness of the absorber unit, the amplitude of the main system can be reduced. This process of selection is called tuning;

(iii) the absorber is intended for use when the main system amplitude would otherwise be very large, i.e., at resonance and so $\omega_F = \omega_E$. Then tuning gives

$$\omega_F = \omega_A = \omega_E,$$

or

$$\frac{q_E}{I_E} = \frac{q_A}{I_A}; \qquad (11.41)$$

(iv) the undamped absorber is fully useful at one engine speed only and clearly would not be adequate for an automobile engine since absorption at one speed gives resonances at two other speeds. Damping present in the rubber however adequately improves the absorption. Although not used to any marked extent in automobile engines, replacement of the torsional "springs" by a pendulum type absorber has been effective in aero engines.

(g) Torsional Vibrations of a Simple Gear Train

The engine and transmission of an automobile, for the purposes of torsional vibration calculations, can in its simplest form consist of an engine rotor connected by a shaft and simple gear train to a driven shaft carrying a rotor representative of the rear axle and load, etc. Unless the gear ratio engine to back axle is unity, then there are two separate rotor shaft systems rotating at different speeds. It is convenient to replace, for calculations, the two-speed system by an equivalent system consisting, if the gear wheel and shaft inertias can be neglected, of a two-rotor system connected by a shaft all of which rotates at constant speed. The given system and its equivalent are shown in Fig. 11.33.

Considering natural vibrations, which continue as a result of the interchange of kinetic energy of the rotors and torsional strain energy of the shafts, then for equivalence, both systems must have the same kinetic and strain energies. Thus if rotor I_1 at A and shaft AB of stiffness q_1 is kept the same as in the original

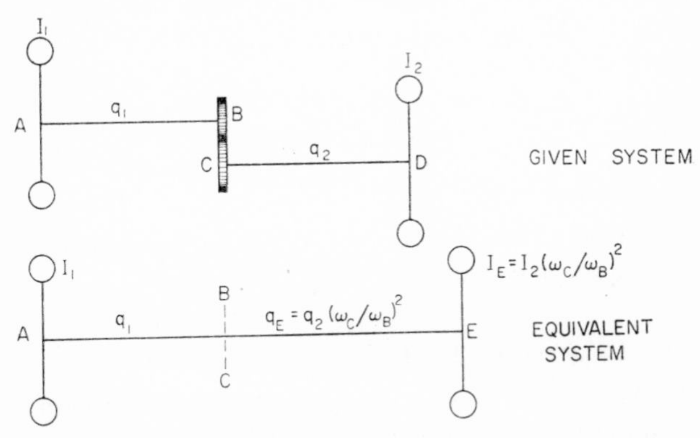

FIG. 11.33. Simple gear system and its torsional vibration equivalent

system and to it is attached a shaft CE of stiffness q_E carrying a rotor at E of inertia I_E, then the value of q_E must satisfy the strain energy requirement and I_E the kinetic energy requirement.

For the same kinetic energy

$$\tfrac{1}{2}I_1\omega_A^2 + \tfrac{1}{2}I_2\omega_D^2 = \tfrac{1}{2}I_1\omega_A^2 + \tfrac{1}{2}I_E\omega_E^2$$

and since $\omega_A = \omega_E$ then

$$I_E = I_2 \cdot \frac{\omega_D^2}{\omega_A^2} = I_2 \cdot \frac{\omega_C^2}{\omega_B^2} \tag{11.41}$$

To find the equivalent stiffness q_E, let D and E be fixed and some gradually increasing torque T be applied to A, giving angles of twist θ_1, θ_2, θ_E over portions AB, CD and CE. The strain energy is given by $\frac{1}{2}$ stiffness times twist in rad² and so for the original and equivalent systems

$$\tfrac{1}{2}q_1\theta_1^2 + \tfrac{1}{2}q_2\theta_2^2 = \tfrac{1}{2}q_1\theta_1^2 + \tfrac{1}{2}q_E\theta_E^2,$$

giving

$$q_E = q_2\left(\frac{\theta_2}{\theta_E}\right)^2.$$

But θ_2/θ_E owing to the gearing $= \theta_C/\theta_B = \omega_C/\omega_B$, and so

$$q_E = q_2\left(\frac{\omega_C}{\omega_B}\right)^2. \quad (11.42)$$

Determination of frequencies, etc., now follow the method given for the two rotor system in section 11.5b.

WORKED EXAMPLE (U.L.2 Ext., 1952)

11.9. An electric motor running at 2250 r.p.m. drives a centrifugal pump running at 650 r.p.m. through a single stage reduction gear. The motor armature has a moment of inertia of 750 lb ft² and the pump impeller one of 2000 lb ft². The shaft from the pump to the gears is 3·5 in. diameter and 12 ft long, and that from the motor to the gears is 2 ft long. What should be the diameter of the shaft from the motor to the gears to ensure that the node for natural torsional vibrations is at the gears? Determine the frequency of these vibrations and the amplitude of the impeller vibrations for an amplitude of one degree at the motor. $G = 12 \times 10^6$ lb/in².

Solution

Using the equivalent system,
Equivalent inertia of impeller

$$I_E = 2000 \times \left(\frac{650}{2250}\right)^2 = 166 \text{ lb ft}^2.$$

Stiffness of original impeller shaft $= GJ/L$.

$$= \frac{12 \times 10^6 \times 144 \times \pi \times 3{\cdot}5^4}{32 \times 144 \times 144 \times 12} = 102{,}000 \text{ lb ft/rad}.$$

Equivalent stiffness of impeller shaft

$$= 102{,}000 \left(\frac{650}{2250}\right)^2 = 8500 \text{ lb ft/rad}.$$

If the node is to be at the gear position, then the frequencies of equivalent shaft portions on either side of the node must be thc same and so

$$q_1/I_M = q_E/I_E,$$

giving

$$q_1 = \frac{8500 \times 750}{166} = 38{,}400 \text{ lb ft/rad}.$$

Hence

$$J_1 = \frac{38{,}400 \times 2}{12 \times 10^6 \times 144} = 44{\cdot}5/10^6 \text{ ft}^4 = \pi d_1^4/32,$$

$$d_1^4 = \frac{44{\cdot}5 \times 32}{10^6 \times \pi} \text{ ft}^4,$$

giving

$$d_1 = 1{\cdot}75 \text{ in}.$$

Frequency

$$f_N = \frac{1}{2\pi}\sqrt{\frac{q_1}{I_M}} = \frac{1}{2\pi}\sqrt{\frac{38{,}400}{750/32{\cdot}2}} = 388 \text{ vib/min}.$$

Since angles of twist are inversely proportional to the stiffness,

$$\theta_E/\theta_1 = q_1/q_E = 4{\cdot}5$$

and hence if $\theta_1 = 1°$ then $\theta_E = 4{\cdot}5°$.
But

$$\theta_D = \theta_E \times \frac{650}{2250} = 1{\cdot}3°.$$

Examples

11.10. The springs of a motor vehicle carry a total load of 2500 lb and with equal springing front and rear the combined spring rate is 500 lb/in. Calculate the frequency of vertical natural vibrations with the dampers removed. If the dampers are adjusted to give a total damping force of 300 lb/ft/sec, calculate the frequency of damped vibrations and the ratio of the second downward movement to the first downward movement.

(A.M.I.Mech.E., 1959)

Answers: 84 vib/min.; 81·7 vib/min; 0·242.

11.11. An engine weighing 400 lb is to be supported on four helical springs. When the engine speed is 900 r.p.m. there is a primary vertical disturbing force of maximum value 70 lb due to the unbalanced reciprocating weights. Assuming that the engine vibrates in the vertical direction with no horizontal nor angular movement, find the stiffness of each spring in lb/in. of deflection to limit the maximum total periodic force on the foundations to 5 lb. What will be the amplitude of vibration of the engine when its speed is 600 r.p.m.?

(U.L.2 Int., 1950)

Answers: 153 lb/in.; 0·00895 in.

11.12. An instrument is mounted on a table, the table being suspended from the roof of a building by a set of springs. The effective weight of the table with instrument is 240 lb and the effective stiffness of the set of springs is 60 lb/in. Motion of the table is damped by a fractional resistance proportional to the velocity, the resistance being equal to 15 lb at a velocity of 1 ft/sec. If the roof vibrates vertically $\pm 0{\cdot}1$ in. about a mean position with a frequency of 20 cycles/sec., find from first principles, the amplitude of the table,

(*a*) taking account of the damping force,
(*b*) neglecting the damping force.
Comment on the difference between these values.

(U.L.2 Ext., 1953)

Answers: (*a*) 0·00062 in.; (*b*) 0·00062 in.

11.13. A car has a natural frequency of single degree of freedom in a vertical direction of 80 vib/min., and is driven over a road at a forward speed of 35 m.p.h. The road surface consists of sine waves whose distance apart is 100 ft and whose amplitude is 2 in. Determine the amplitude of the car if the shock absorbers give a viscous damping that is 0·32 of the critical value. At what car speed will resonance occur?

Answers: 2·3 in.; 91 m.p.h.

11.14. An engine weighing 1500 lb is mounted on blocks whose total vertical stiffness is 1500 lb/in., and which provide a viscous damping force coefficient of 15·2 lb/in./sec. The engine has a primary unbalanced periodic force of 500 . sin 10π . t lb. Determine the maximum steady state force transmitted to the vehicle frame.

Answer: 1830 lb including dead weight of engine.

11.15. Figure 11.34, shows a body suspended at its ends on springs so that it may have vibrations in the plane of the springs. Determine the two natural

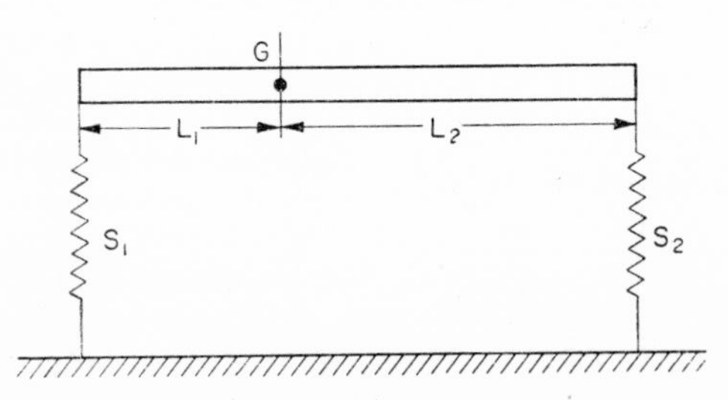

FIG. 11.34. Spring-mass system of example 11.15

frequencies of vibration and the position of the node corresponding to each frequency. The body weighs 3220 lb and has a radius of gyration about the centre of gravity G of 4 ft. $S_1 = 2400$ lb/ft, $S_2 = 2600$ lb/ft, $L_1 = 4{\cdot}5$ ft, $L_2 = 5{\cdot}5$ ft.

Answers: 1·44 and 1·10 vib/sec, 14·6 ft and 1·09 ft from G.

11.16. The flywheel of an engine driving a dynamometer weighs 300 lb and has a radius of gyration of 10 in.; the armature weighs 220 lb and has a radius of gyration of 8 in. The driving shaft has an effective length of 18 in. and is 2 in. in diameter, and a spring coupling is incorporated at one end, having a stiffness of $0{\cdot}25 \times 10^6$ lb/in./radian. Neglecting the inertia of the coupling and shaft, calculate the natural frequency of torsional vibration of the system. What would be the natural frequency if the spring coupling were omitted? Take $C = 11{\cdot}9 \times 10^6$ lb/in^2. (U.L.2 Ext., 1941)

Answers: 860 vib/min; 1920 vib/min.

11.17. Two parallel shafts AB and CD are connected together by toothed gear wheels at B and C and carry rotors at A and D whose moments of inertia are 1250 lb in^2 and 25,000 lb in^2 respectively; shaft AB is of length 40 in. and diameter 2·5 in. and CD is of length 26 in. and diameter 3·25 in.; the speed of AB is 2·5 times that of CD. Find, from first principles, the natural frequency of vibration of the system neglecting the masses of the gears at C and B. Explain concisely how to allow for the moments of inertia of the gear wheels if these were given. (U.L.2 Ext., 1954)

Answer: 4200 vib/min.

11.18. Figure 11.35 shows a system of rotors which are dynamically equivalent for torsional oscillations to a four-cylinder reciprocating engine and flywheel directly coupled to a rotor. The moments of inertia of the mass at each crank (C_1 to C_4) is 0·6 ton ft^2, that of the flywheel (F) is 20 ton ft^2 and that of

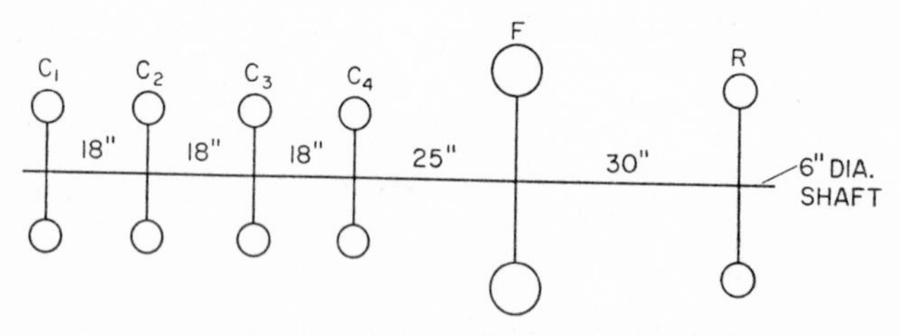

FIG. 11.35. Rotor-shaft system of example 11.18

the rotor (R) is 8 ton ft^2. The equivalent diameter of the shaft is 6 in. Show that the first frequency of natural torsional vibration is approximately 957 vib/min. and draw the elastic line for the shaft giving the distance of the node from the flywheel. $C = 12 \times 10^6$ lb/in^2.

(U.L.2 Ext., 1952)

Answer: 7.68 in.

11.19. A four-cylinder in-line reciprocating engine is represented by a four-rotor system, each rotor having a moment of inertia of 8·3 slug. ft^2 and connected by a shaft of stiffness between rotors of 8300 lb ft/rad. The engine drives a flywheel of moment of inertia 167 slug ft^2 through a shaft of stiffness 830 lb ft/rad. Find the first and second natural frequencies of torsional vibration.

Answers: 50 vib/min; 240 vib/min.